MEAT GOATS

Their History, Management and Diseases

Stephanie Mitcham and Allison Mitcham

Sumner, Iowa, USA

ISBN 0-9664476-2-X
Published 2000, Crane Creek Publications
First Edition, Second Printing

CONTENTS

Foreword   7

1. Introduction: An Historical Perspective   9

2. The Contemporary Shortage of Goat Meat: A Problem in Asia and
America Too   15

3. Meat Goats in the United States: The American Quest for the Ideal
Meat Goat   20

4. Management   45
    A) Forages: An Economic Necessity   45
    B) Is Bigger Better? In Many Environments, Not Necessarily!50
    C) Stress   51
    D) Marketing   52

5. Getting Started in the Goat Business   56

6. Goat Selection and Record Keeping   60

7. Facilities, Feeders and Fencing   67

8. Handling Systems   81

9. Nutrition   89

10. Grazing Management   97

11. Routine Procedures   102

12. Kid Production   109

13. Diseases   119
    I. Parasites   119
        Internal Parasites   119

Coccidia 120
Cryptosporidia 123
Liver Flukes 124
    Fasciola species 124
    Fascioloides magna 127
    Dicrocoelium dendriticum 128
Lungworms 129
    Dictyocaulus filaria 129
    Protostrongylid lungworms 130
Meningeal Worm (Parelaphostronglylosis) 130
Oestrus ovis (Nasal Bots) 133
Stomach Worms (Nematode Gastroenteritis) 133
Tapeworms (Cestodes) 139
External Parasites 140
    Lice 140
    Maggots/Fly Strike 142
    Mange 142
        Chorioptic Mange 142
        Sarcoptic Mange (Scabies) 143
        Psoroptic mange (Goat Ear Mite) 143
    Ticks 144
II. Nutritionally Related Diseases 144
    Bloat 144
    Goiter/Iodine Deficiency 147
    Grain Overload/Lactic Acidosis 147
    Hypomagnesemia (GrassTetany, Grass Staggers) 149
    Laminitis (Founder) 150
    Listeriosis (Circling Disease) 150
    Overeating Disease or Enterotoxemia 152
    Plant Toxicities 154
    Polioencephalomalacia (Cerebrocortical Necrosis) 155
    Secondary Nutritional Problems 156
    Undernutrition/Pecking Order 157
    Urinary Calculi (Obstructive Urolithiasis) 157
    White Muscle Disease (Selenium - Vitamin E Deficiency) 159
    Zinc Deficiency 161
III. Reproductive Problems 161

Abortions 161
Congenital and Inherited Defects 166
Hypocalcemia (Milk Fever) 166
Ketosis (Pregnancy Toxemia and Lactational Ketosis)
 167
Kidding Problems (Dystocias) 168
Retained Dead Fetus 170
Retained Placenta (Retained Afterbirth) 171
Udder Problems 171
   Enlarged (balloon) teats 171
   Mastitis 171
   Trauma 173
Uterine Prolapse 173
Vaginal Prolapse 173
IV. Miscellaneous Diseases 174
Bacterial Skin Disease 174
   Dermatophilosis (Streptothricosis) 174
   Staphylococcal Dermatitis 175
Bluetongue 175
Broken Horns 176
Caprine Arthritis-Encephalitis (CAE) 176
Caseous Lymphadenitis (Contagious Abscesses) 177
Diarrhea 178
Floppy Kid Syndrome 179
Foot Abscess 180
Foot Rot 180
Footscald (Interdigital Dermatitis or Benign Foot Rot)
 182
Johne's Disease (Paratuberculosis) 182
Joint Ill (Bacterial Polyarthritis) 183
Pinkeye (Infectious Keratoconjunctivitis) 184
Pneumonia, Bacterial 184
Posthitis, Ulcerative (Pizzle Rot) 185
Rabies 186
Ringworm 187
Scrapie 188
Soremouth (Contagious Ecthyma) 188
Tetanus 189
Umbilical Hernia 190

5

Umbilical Abscess   **191**

14. Artificial Insemination   **192**

15. Embryo Transfer   **194**

16. Showing Meat Goats   **201**

17. Guard Animals   **207**

18. Herding Dogs: The Border Collie   **217**

19. Healthy and Delicious Meat   **223**

Appendix I. Meat Goat Calendar   **236**

Appendix II. Normal Goat Temperature, Pulse and Respiratory Ranges
and Goat Aging   **240**

Appendix III. Medication Administration   **241**

Appendix IV. Drug Dosages   **243**

Appendix V. Induction of Abortion or Parturition in the Doe   **245**

Appendix VI. Evaluating the Gestational Age of Aborted Goat Fetuses
                                                                     246

Appendix VII. Tattooing   **247**

Appendix VIII. Fecal Examination for Gastrointestinal Parasites   **248**

Appendix IX. Meat Goat Nutrition and Ration Balancing   **250**

References   **258**

FOREWORD

We have written this book because of the new and increasingly widespread interest in North America in meat goats, animals whose great potential has by and large long been overlooked in this part of the world. There is, we have found, a dearth of books on this subject.

Recently, however, there have been a number of helpful and interesting articles published in magazines as well as several very worthwhile commentaries in books. Consequently, we have set our sights on not only providing readers with our personal findings and observations about meat goats but with giving an overview of other opinions we consider significant as well.

In contrast to its Asian and African forebears, the meat goat in the United States and Canada does not have a long and illustrious history. Here, it has *not* been man's mainstay and companion down through countless centuries as it has on these faraway continents.

The meat goat is an immigrant to North America. Though the first meat goats were introduced into the Americas just over 400 years ago, they were soon abandoned and largely ignored by their importers.

Only quite recently (in the 90s), after taking a closer look at the attributes of these quite exceptional animals, have the descendents of these early immigrants been reevaluated and new breeds of meat goats brought to this continent. Egged on by physicians, scientists and farmers/ranchers, touting the benefits of eating what many maintain is the leanest, healthiest, and often the tastiest of all red meat (when the goats are young and properly looked after and the meat well prepared) - as well as being cheaper to produce (under the right foraging conditions) because they can survive and thrive on land which would not support other livestock - consumers, who a decade ago would never have considered buying chevon (goat meat), have begun to respond enthusiastically. So positive, indeed, has this response been that supply cannot keep up with demand.

The authors have had a long association with goats - and books. A goat and sheep breeder and a veterinary pathologist, Stephanie has raised Angoras for the past 13 years. Several years ago she added Boer goats to her herd and, more recently, Savanna goats. She has also experimented with Boer/Angora crosses. Apart from giving many tips on care and management, Stephanie has written an extensive chapter on the diseases to which goats can be subject - and provided much useful information on their treatments. The authors of this work are also the authors of a very successful book on Angoras as well as many published articles.

We wish to thank a number of people for their help in producing this work: Dr. Dan Morrical, for his chapter on meat goat nutrition, rations and ration balancing; the staff of Print Atlantic, especially Roy Dawson; the staff of Mount Allison University Library, particularly Anne Ward (interlibrary loans), Hannah and Brian McNally and Emma Cross; and Dr. Peter Mitcham for his careful and charming illustrations.

1. INTRODUCTION: AN HISTORICAL PERSPECTIVE

"When man began his first farming operations in the dawn of history, the goat was the kingpin of the pastoral life, making possible the conquest of desert and mountain and the occupation of the fertile land that lay beyond. The first of man's domestic animals to colonize the wilderness, the goat is the last to abandon the deserts that man leaves behind him."
- David Mackenzie, *Goat Husbandry* (London: Faber and Faber, 1980).

Goats are considered to be the hardiest and most ubiquitous of animals. They thrive and proliferate on land which cannot support other species and they crop up all over the globe. As well, in small numbers, goats can be managed easily by someone who has learned to think like a goat, so to speak, and has, it would seem, been accepted as companionable - almost like one of the herd.[1]

Like other herd animals, however, single animals kept on their own tend to languish and fail. On the other hand, like all animals, goats do poorly when overcrowded.

Traditionally, where goats were first domesticated, they were kept in small numbers by individual owners for both milk and meat. Frequently the survival of a family depended on these few goats per household.

Wild or domesticated goats exist worldwide except in the Arctic and Antarctic and they have many varied appearances, sizes and capabilities depending on where they come from and why they are raised. There are milk goats and meat goats - as well as goats which serve both these purposes.[2] Other breeds, like the Angora and Cashmere have special fleeces which have added to their value. Worldwide, scores of breeds have been adapted over centuries to various locations, particularly in Asia where the first wild goats [Genus *capra*] are said to have originated some 7,000,000 years ago, early in the Pliocene Epoch. More than 200 breeds of goats have been recorded.

Down through the ages goats have been valued for their delectable flesh, especially digestible milk, pliable skins[3] and, particularly in the case of Angora and Cashmere goats, luxurious fibres. Early on, their worth was

9

most apparent in dry and infertile parts of Asia, and, somewhat later, in arid regions of Mediterranean countries such as Greece and Spain, as well as near-desert areas of North Africa where other animals would not thrive - or perhaps not even survive. However, wherever they live "... most goats are exploited only for meat production," Maurice Shelton, well-known goat authority from Texas A & M University Agricultural Research Extension Service, has succinctly observed.[4]

Goats are domesticated more easily than most other animals, doubtless the reason they are reckoned to be the first wild animals tamed for domestic purposes (apart from the dog) - some 9,000 to 12,000 years ago, according to educated guesses. Interestingly enough, goats are also quicker to revert to a wild state than other domesticated animals. Likely this is because, in the dry and rocky regions where they prefer to browse contentedly on scrub brush and sparse pockets of grass, they need little or no help from human beings to survive. These feral goats are now hunted enthusiastically as game animals in many parts of the world.

Although goats have long been of huge economic importance in Asia, parts of Africa, as well as in some Mediterranean countries such as Greece and Spain, they have not, until quite recent times, been a significant economic resource in North America. In fact, the genus *capra* did not exist in America until the Spanish imported some of their goats for meat in the 16th century. These were (and are) extremely hardy animals, well adapted to survive unattended. Many wild and domesticated goats are descended from these Spanish imports.

North America's indigenous so-called wild goat - the Rocky Mountain goat [*Oreamnos americanus*] - is not a true goat. It is, in fact, a different species, often described as a 'goat antelope'. In any case, this wild 'goat' exists in such remote and unapproachable habitats that it is out of reach of most human beings. In the past, only a few aboriginal peoples, such as the Tlingits of southern Alaska and northwestern British Columbia, were able to climb onto the high, rocky outcroppings which these incredibly agile animals frequent, to harvest meat for their larders and hair for their famous Chilcat ceremonial blankets.

The Myotonic (also nicknamed "Stiff Leg", "Wooden Leg", or "Fainting") goat - which appeared somewhat mysteriously in Tennessee about 1880 - has sometimes also been termed an indigenous North American goat, though our present ignorance of its distant antecedents does not necessarily make this so. This unusual - and recently much touted - meat goat is discussed in Chapter 3.

Aside from the early (16th century) importation of 'Spanish' goats, it was not until well on in the 19th century that goats with special capabilities were introduced into North America. Among these were the mohair-producing Angoras from Turkey and milk goats, mostly from Switzerland and the French Alps.[5] Only very recently, late in the twentieth century, have special breeds of meat goats - such as Boer goats from South Africa - been brought to North America. Their introduction has coincided with an increase in population of human beings who have traditionally depended on goat meat. As well, long-established North Americans, many of whose forebears declined such delicacies, have begun to consider eating goat (and sheep) meat for some of the reasons Asians long ago subscribed to.

A good many people too have begun to realize that North America no longer has the seemingly limitless free - or almost free - grasslands their ancestors once counted on for pasturing herds of large and less efficient ruminants like cattle. Moreover, considerable numbers of discriminating contemporary consumers seeking leaner meat with high nutritional value - meat tasting at least as good as the beef they have generally favored - have begun to supplement their usual fare with dishes made from chevon (goat meat) or lamb (from breeds of sheep such as the Dorper, which produce meat almost as lean as that of the Boer goat[6]). They have not been disappointed. Proof of the increasingly widespread nature of this change in North American eating habits is that the supply of goat meat cannot at present keep up with the demand.

This book deals primarily with meat goats in North America - their history, care, maintenance, the diseases to which they are subject (as well as how to prevent and treat these maladies), and suggestions (and recipes) for preparing chevon - though there are also many references to meat goats in other parts of the world where they have been central to life for thousands of years.

Notes: Chapter 1

1. David Mackenzie in his excellent book, *Goat Husbandry* (London: Faber and Faber, 1980) in the chapter entitled "The Control of Goats," provides some fascinating insights into the goat's instinctive - and distinctive - behavior with one another and with man.

Also in *Goatwalking* (New York: Viking Penguin, 1991) p. 28, Jim Corbett - from personal experience in the Sonora desert and elsewhere - substantiates Mackenzie's findings: "Because goats will readily admit hu-

11

man beings into herd membership, they can be managed and moved without fences, corrals, hobbles, tethers, or any of the other mechanical devices used to control other livestock. From the Alps to the Empty Quarter, Java to Baja, with the goat as a partner, human beings can support themselves in most wildland environments.... The herder must therefore cultivate and maintain a bond with the herd that is so strong they will come down [from the heights they love], against instinct, when he calls."

Burt Smith, Extension Specialist in Pasture and Livestock Management at the University of Hawaii, is especially notable for his practical studies of behavior and management of domestic animals. See his book, *Moving 'em - A Guide to Low Sress Animal Handling* (The Graziers Hui, Kamuela, Hawaii, 1998). He has remarked that: "One of the great things I've always found about hand raised, intensively grazed animals is that, due to their interactions with humans, and their greater decision-making ability than confinement animals, they tend to be smarter as well." Smith gets plenty of mail from farmers substantiating his claims.

2. Among the breeds used for both meat and milk are: the Bhuj Goat, originating from the Kutchi breed of India, and found in northeastern Brazil; the Benadir Goat, found in the Webi Shibeli region of southern Somalia; the Beetal Goat, found in Punjab, Pakistan and India; the Irish Goat, a long-haired goat found, as one would expect from its name, in Ireland; the Norwegian goat (also long-haired) and, not surprisingly, found in Norway; the Peacock Goat, an ancient mountain breed, found in Switzerland; the Nubian, also called the Anglo-Nubian, developed in England from Egyptian, Ethiopian and European breeds of milk goats and imported into the United States in 1909; the Pyrenean Goat, usually long-haired, found in the French and Spanish Pyrenees and the Cantabrian Mountains of Spain; the Itawah, originating from a cross between local Indonesian goats and Jamunapari goats imported from India between 1918 and 1931, found in Indonesia; and a very considerable number of additional dual purpose (meat and milk) breeds found in south and west India and in China.

3. Skins have long been an important by-product of meat goat production. They have been - and still are - of more economic significance in Asia, Africa and even Europe than in North America. From early times goat skins were fashioned into tents, fine leather goods and water carriers. Later on, in fashionable circles, special purses, shoes, luggage and gloves of kid

skins were much in demand by those who could afford them. Today, goat skins are still valuable. Even in the United States, specialty shops sell goat skins as scatter rugs and chaps (from Angoras - though Angora skins are generally considered unsuitable for leather goods because they have insufficient connective tissue).

For all these products and others, however, the condition of the skin is important. It must be free of blemishes. Thus even for this reason, goat producers would do well to avoid infestations with external parasites which may ruin their goats' skins. (See section on external parasites in the diseases chapter of this book.) Other factors which can cause hide damage are: bruising during transport to market, tattooing and injections. Good nutrition throughout the goat's life improves the strength of the hide.

The goat's skin is reckoned to be worth 15% of its slaughter price.

4. Maurice Shelton, "Goat Production," *Encyclopedia of Agricultural Science, Volume 2* (San Diego, New York, Boston, London, Sydney, Tokyo, Toronto: Academic Press, 1994), p. 459.

5. Angoras were introduced into the United States in 1849. For a detailed account of Angoras see *The Angora Goat: its History, Management and Diseases* (2nd edition, 1999) by Stephanie and Allison Mitcham (Crane Creek Publications, 3061 160th Street, Sumner, IA 50674).

A publication of the Canadian Department of Agriculture, Ottawa, entitled simply *Goats* (Publication 1704, [no author given], printed 1980, and revised in 1981), states: "The meat of the Angora is also regarded as the best chevon." (p. 10) However, since Angoras are raised primarily for their mohair, relatively few people have had the opportunity to eat their meat.

According to the *Encyclopedia Americana* (1997), the most common breeds of dairy goats found in the United States are Toggenburg, Saanen, French Alpine, Nubian and Rock Alpine - all of which are registered with the American Goat Society, De Leon, Texas. The Toggenburg and Saanen both hail from Switzerland, the former having been brought to the United States in the late nineteenth century and the latter in 1904. The French Alpine, as one would imagine, comes from the French Alps and was introduced into the United States in 1922. The Nubian, native to Egypt and Ethiopia, was imported to the U.S., through Mexico, in 1909. Nubians are the most numerous of these primarily dairy breeds in the United States. Only the Rock Alpine was developed in the U.S. In 1910 Mary E. Rock produced this breed by crossing Saanens and Toggenburgs. A first-rate book, which deals primarily with dairy goats is David Mackenzie's *Goat Husbandry*. Though this book's focus is on Great Britain, many of his observations are also useful to those who raise goats in small flocks in North America.

6. In N.H. Casey and W.A. Van Niekerk's article, "The Boer Goat II: Growth, Nutrient Requirements, Carcass and Meat Quality," p. 6, these South African researchers noted that Boer goats were only marginally leaner than Dorper sheep (18.2% vs 19.3%) in terms of total carcass fat but fatter than SAMM [South African Mutton Merino](14.1%). However, it should be pointed out here that Boer goats tend not to be so lean as many other breeds of goats.

2. THE CONTEMPORARY SHORTAGE OF GOAT MEAT: A PROBLEM IN ASIA AND AMERICA TOO

"Goat meat accounts for approximately 63% of the total volume of the meat produced in the world, and the per caput (per adult) supply of goat meat is on the decline in Asia. This clearly suggests that the contribution by goats has failed to keep pace with the increasing demand for [goat] meat by humans and projected national targets."
- C. Devendra, International Development Research Centre, Singapore, on *Goat meat production in Asia* at a conference/workshop held in Tando Jam, Pakistan, March 1988, to try to determine how to increase Asia's production of goat meat.

"The demand for goat meat [in the U.S.] has continued to increase over the last decade and a half. In 1977, the first year that USDA began keeping statistics of goat slaughter at federally inspected plants, approximately 35,000 goats were slaughtered nationwide (NASS, 1994). By 1994, that number had risen to nearly 350,000, essentially a 1000% increase over that period....Even with this significant increase in domestic slaughter, the United States continues to be a net importer of goat meat. In 1989, the United States imported 1,200 metric tons of frozen or chilled goat meat valued at $1.7 million (FAS, 1994)."
- Terry A. Gipson, "Marketing: Kids," *Proceedings of the Virginia State Dairy Goat Association*, April 1, 1995, Blacksburg, VA.

"The last count I heard was that we [in the United States] have about 700,000 [meat] goats[1], not even enough to meet the expanding ethnic market pounding at our doors...."
- Sylvia Tomlinson, "Oats and Fetlocks," *Meat Goat News* (San Angelo, Texas), Vol. 6, No.2, March 1999.

When Dr. Devendra, one of the world's most recognized and referred to authorities on meat goats, made the above pronouncement in 1988

15

about the shortage in Asia of goat meat, and pointed out that developing countries - where goat meat has traditionally been "highly relished and sought after" - produced and consumed 93% of the world's goat meat, his statement came as no great surprise. Asia and Africa had by then been short of goat meat for several decades[2] : it was just that by 1988 the lack of this staple was approaching a crisis situation in these parts of the world.

What may come as something of a surprise, though, to people not close to North America's burgeoning meat goat industry, are Terry Gipson's and Sylvia Tomlinson's comments about the shortage of chevon here - a phenomenon which has occurred over the last decade, accelerating rapidly in the last 5 or 6 years, as Gipson so clearly shows. And, as both Gipson and Tomlinson indicate, correction of this shortage is not likely to take place any time soon. Tomlinson's projection that the 4 million or so meat goats necessary to fill current American demands is "several decades away" - despite the best efforts of a good many goat ranchers - indicates that the troublesome question of how to up production of chevon enough to approximate demand is a North American as well as an Asian problem.

Although this is a relatively new situation in North America, it is scarcely so recent or obscure a concern as such a prestigious book of knowledge as the *Encyclopedia Americana* (1997) would indicate in its cursory dismissal of the American meat goat industry: "In China, India, and parts of Africa, goats are regularly slaughtered for meat. In the United States, 'slaughter' prices are so low that there is little incentive to raise meat goats." That this has not been the case for much of this decade is evinced by the increasing amount of information on meat goats and their significance, circulated in such enthusiastically subscribed to publications as *The Meat Goat News*[3] and the *Meat Goat Production and Marketing Handbook* (1996).

The analogy between the shortage of chevon throughout Asia and Africa and that in a Western country like the United States cannot, however, be pushed - any more than the production methods in these very dissimilar environments can be closely compared. Above all, the immense disparity in numbers of goats raised in these divergent cultures underlines a very basic difference between the Asian/African and the American situation. Whereas the world's three largest producers of goat meat[4] - India, China and Pakistan - count their goats in the many millions [more than 200 million, in fact, if grouped together], the United States still has only about 4 1/2 million goats all told, about 1 million of which are specifically referred to as 'meat goats'. The major American goat breed is the Angora (of which there are some 2 million), an animal rarely, in this part of the world, raised or praised for its meat. (Accurate numbers of goats everywhere are, however, hard to come by - according to authorities worldwide - since many owners of small herds do not give out - or even keep - inventories of births, slaughter and sales of their animals.)

While the Asian shortage has been a long-term and growing problem, Western concerns in this department have only recently surfaced, and they are not extreme. Countries such as the United States have not yet, either, been plagued with the current and wide-ranging Asian/African abuses within the production and distribution system: the slaughtering of breeding animals for meat as a short-term solution to the scarcity of chevon; rocketing chevon prices as the number of meat goats raised cannot keep up with burgeoning human populations; the substitution by unscrupulous dealers of mutton from poor-quality sheep for chevon;[5] and the fact that in many third world countries urban sprawl has now engulfed land on which goats were once pastured.

Hannah McNally, who grew up in urban Malawi, witnessed the disappearance of goat pastures adjacent to Blantyre, the city in which she and her family lived - and the corresponding decline in the availability of goat meat.

"When I was growing up," Hannah explained, "my grandmother kept goats. Every morning the goat boy would come and collect them, take them out to the country to the pasture, and bring them back again to her yard in the city before dark. There, they were penned up till the next day. This all worked very well, and from time to time, on special occasions, we had meat from these goats. Mind you, in Malawi we do not eat so much meat as people do here in North America. We eat more fish.*

"Gradually, though, we saw buildings cover the goat pastures, and, since there was nowhere nearby to let the animals loose, my grandmother gave up keeping them - and we rarely had goat meat. It had become very scarce in the markets.

"Of course, in the villages things stayed much the same as they'd always been. There, the goats still roam freely and the villagers use the meat as they want it. Surprisingly, they never seem to get their goats mixed up with their neighbors'."

North American problems in goat meat production and marketing, though generally unlike those encountered in Africa or India, are nevertheless real enough. Frank Pinkerton, with his usual straightforward and

*This is not a surprising fact considering the size of Lake Malawi.

commonsensical approach, pinpoints some of these in his Introduction to "Recommendations for Goat Industry Development" in the *Meat Goat Production and Marketing Handbook*: "The present status of both goat production and marketing is rather haphazard with substantive variation in animal availability, body weight and condition at slaughter, variable carcass characteristics, lack of standardized processing techniques and inadequately developed market distribution."[6]

Finally, while Asian and African farmers have produced a tremendous variety[7] of excellent meat goat breeds, adapted over many generations to suit specific environments and tastes, North Americans, with only a few breeds - most of which have only recently been imported - are still in search of the ideal meat goat.

Notes: Chapter 2

1. According to Ulrich Jaudas in the *New Goat Handbook*, there were (in 1989) 3 to 4 million goats of all sorts in the United States, and about 480 million domestic goats, worldwide, some 95% of these in the developing world. (p. 82) At the time Jaudas made this statement, the majority of the goats in the United States were Angoras.

However, Frank Pinkerton and Lynn Harwell, quoting the 1987 Census of Agriculture, cite the U.S. goat total as 437,228 and goats raised specifically for meat as 100,103.

2. "The per caput supplies of goat meat over the last 20 years are decreasing consistently in all regions of the developing world." C. Devendra on "The nutritional value of goat meat," published in the proceedings of the Tando Jam workshop held in Pakistan in March, 1988, p. 76.

3. A publication which has grown from an initial 4 page weekly newsletter (in 1995) to a tabloid-size magazine (in 1997) - a format which it still holds to.

4. There is some disagreement over whether India or China has the largest number of goats. Abdus Salam Akhtar, Member (Animal Sciences) of Pakistan Agricultural Research Council and keynote speaker at the abovementioned Tando Jam workshop, cites India as the largest producer (with 95 million goats in 1982, according to N.K. Bhattacharyya and B.U. Khan in the recorded proceedings of this same workshop, p. 125) and China as

second (p. 7), whereas Huang Wenxiu, speaking on "Goat meat production in China," says that "China now has the largest goat population in the world" (as of 1985). However, his 1984 figure, 78.5×10^6, (see p. 119 ff. of proceedings of the Tando Jam workshop/conference) would indicate that China is a strong second in goat production. Third-ranking producer (in 1988), Pakistan, had 31 million goats, according to Akhtar. A certain discrepancy in numbers is not surprising because in Asia small numbers of goats are owned by so many individual families that keeping accurate tabs on them is virtually impossible. The other 7 leading goat-producing countries (ranked according to descending numbers) are: Nigeria, Ethiopia, Somalia, Iran, Sudan, Turkey and Indonesia.

5. Although Westerners often think of goat meat as a poor man's fare, chevon has become the most expensive meat in many third world countries. This is the case in India, for instance, partly because chevon is thought to be the tastiest and most delicate meat, and partly because it is considered acceptable to people of all castes and religions. "About 35 million goats (43%) are slaughtered annually to produce 0.32×10^6 t of total meat production; FAO 1985." See "Goat meat production in India," by N.K Bhattacharyya and B.U. Khan, Central Institute for Research on Goats, Mathura, Uttar Pradesh, India, published in the proceedings of the 1988 Tando Jam workshop.

As well, C. Devendra notes, on p. 76 of the same publication, that "A widening gap between production and consumption has resulted in increased prices."

6. Frank Pinkerton, "Recommendations for Goat Industry Development," *Meat Goat Production and Marketing Handbook*, p. 11. Also see Pinkerton's "Meat Goat Marketing in Greater New York City."

7. For instance, Huang Wenxiu, in his article "Goat meat production in China," in the proceedings of the 1988 Tando Jam workshop, notes that of the 25 distinct goat breeds in his country, 11 are meat breeds well suited to specific regions.

19

3. MEAT GOATS IN THE UNITED STATES: THE AMERICAN QUEST FOR THE IDEAL MEAT GOAT

"Several U.S. goat breeds exist that could contribute to efficient goat production.... No single goat breed [in the U.S.] has all the desirable traits needed for efficient meat goat production.... The meat goat industry [in the U.S.] is hampered by the lack of an efficient goat breed for meat production on a low-input system."
- Terry A. Gipson, "Genetic Resources for Meat Goat Production," Virginia State University, 1997.

"... four key traits amenable to genetic improvement in goats used primarily for meat production have been identified (Shelton, 1990). These are: 1) adaptability to environmental and production conditions, 2) productive rate, 3) growth rate and 4) carcass value. To date, no single U.S. breed or type possesses an acceptable array of these traits."
- Frank Pinkerton and Lynn Harwell, "Marketing Channels for Meat Goats," *Meat Goat Production and Marketing Handbook*, 1996.

Spanish, Boer, Myotonic (Tennessee Wooden-leg), and Kiko goats are all breeds which come to mind in connection with the burgeoning American meat goat industry. Each of these breeds has been judged to have advantages and disadvantages for contemporary North American conditions and markets. As well, there are several so-called dual purpose goats - the Nubian, sometimes called the Anglo-Nubian (milk and meat), the Kinder and the Angora (mohair and meat) - about whose potential in the goat meat industry in this part of the world, opinions are, again, divided. Finally, there is the very small goat, the Pygmy, West Africa's favorite meat goat which, however, qualifies here (in the United States) - with reservations - as a meat goat.

THE SPANISH GOAT
The so-called 'Spanish' goats have been here longest. They arrived in the Americas with the early Spanish explorers - conquistadores such as

20

Cortes, Desoto and Coronado - who frequently provisioned their sailing ships with these robust, manageable and quite small creatures. Of a size convenient for the large crews of such vessels to butcher and eat at one or two sittings in an age long before refrigeration, Spanish goats provided tasty and nourishing fresh meat for the long-drawn-out early voyages to the New World.

Once arrived in America, however, the sailors soon discovered wild meat sources aplenty. Abandoning to their own devices the goats which had survived the passage, the delighted mariners hunted the abundant indigenous game birds and animals, feasting enthusiastically on this seemingly inexhaustible resource.

Many of the goats - of no specific ancestral breed - which the Spanish sailors had let loose in the New World wilderness apparently fended for themselves quite satisfactorily. Governed by the Darwinian principles of natural selection and survival of the fittest, those best suited to their new environment lived, multiplied and evolved. Survivors were the smaller, especially agile goats, and, among the females, those with small udders which wouldn't be lacerated by underbrush, rocks and thorns.

For over 400 years pockets of these feral goats survived without most Americans - people either resident or itinerant in what is now the United States - paying much attention to them. Although some of these goats (chiefly kids) were hunted by Spanish-speaking Americans for the tasty barbecued cabrito, there were too many other readily available, inexpensive and preferred meats - both domestic and wild - for 'Spanish' goat meat to loom large on menus of the majority of well-to-do Americans.

Early settlers nevertheless tolerated - and even to some extent valued - these 'Spanish' goats because of their brush-clearing abilities, which spared the newcomers a good deal of backbreaking labor. In this role, 'Spanish' goats were frequently referred to as 'brush' goats. Most of the descendents of these goats live in Texas, where, in 1990, they were reckoned to number about 300,000, and, by 1996, roughly half a million in the entire United States. From time to time over the years there have been unplanned infusions of dairy and Angora blood into these herds of Spanish goats.

Only quite recently, due to the surging demand for chevon, have farmers and ranchers begun to take a closer look at the 'Spanish' or 'brush' goat with a view to increasing the size and meat quality of these animals. The final verdict on their contemporary potential as meat goats has still not been delivered.

More research is needed to determine how valuable they will be in this role. According to some experts, there are a number of positive attributes as well as unknowns associated with the Spanish goat's performance. Terry G. Gipson of Virginia State University has stated cautiously: "The Spanish goat of Texas is considered to be well adapted to an extensive management system and has moderate reproductive and growth rates, although it may be a seasonal breeder, which would limit accelerated kidding."[1] If the Spanish goat is indeed a seasonal breeder in Texas, it is said to have such an extended breeding season that some of the ranchers on whose land these goats live declare that they are aseasonal (year round) breeders.

Frank Pinkerton, retired Extension goat specialist at Langston University and himself an experienced goat farmer, in his very interesting article in *Meat Goat Production and Marketing Handbook* (1996) on "Procurement of Foundation Stock," says that Spanish goats are the first-time meat goat buyer's "only realistic source of seed stock" (in the United States). He justifies this conclusion by stating: "Theoretically, there are alternatives - Tennessee Woodenlegs, meat-type Nubians and/or their crosses and, eventually, Boer and Boer crosses. However, inadequate numbers and high prices (relative to meat kid prices) preclude any but small, localized purchases of these animals, for now anyway."[2]

The 'Spanish' or 'brush' goat generally has horns and can occur in many colors - white, black, red, tan and many combinations of these colors. Mature females tend to weigh about 100 lbs (45 kg) and bucks about 150 lbs (68 kg).

THE BOER GOAT

Like the Spanish goat, the Boer goat in its native environment is a 'brush' goat par excellence, strong and well adapted to coping with rough terrain in its homeland. In its native South Africa - where it is said this sturdy goat was called "boer" (meaning farm) by Afrikaners to differentiate it from the then more valuable Angoras - it was put out in brush-covered wild lands to eat the otherwise useless and troublesome ground cover, thus preparing the area for veld (grassland) on which sheep and Angoras could eventually be pastured. Under these rugged conditions, the Boer goat in South Africa, like the Spanish goat in America, survived pretty much on its own for a good many generations despite the often intense heat, the biting and stinging insects and almost impenetrable bush.

The Boer goat's survival under such trying conditions was chiefly due to several natural adaptations to this environment. Its thick skin, covered by short, sleek hair, made it all but impervious to superficial wounds from the thorns and prickly bushes it routinely encountered, and also prevented penetration by biting insects and external parasites carrying tick-, fly- and mosquito-borne diseases. As well, the Boer goat's heavy skin pigmentation was instrumental, in a sun-drenched land, in preventing cancers in such vulnerable spots as the udder, belly, eyes and reproductive organs.

It was not until early in this century that some perspicacious South African farmers, admiring the Boer goat's strength and ability to cope under such harsh conditions, began to wonder how, under an intensive breeding program, this animal could be a profitable meat goat. In 1959 a registry of Boer goats was set up in South Africa to establish breed standards, and, since 1970 especially, the Boer goat's performance has been closely monitored in performance and progeny tests for meat production - more so, it is said, than that of any other meat goat.[3]

In the United States, the greatest number of Boer goats, like their 'Spanish' cousins, reside in Texas, a state proven well suited (particularly in its more arid regions) to the well-being of goats in general - a fact to which the century-long proliferation and enhancement of Angoras bears testimony. All told, though, to date the population of Boer goats, not only in Texas but in the entire United States, is only a small fraction of the Spanish or Angora goat population (about 1 to 30 of the Spanish), and they are too recently arrived (in 1993) in this country for anyone to be absolutely sure of their ultimate potential here.

When compared with the Spanish goat, the Boer goat appears at first glance to come out ahead. It is larger in size (generally more than double) with a much faster growth rate, has a more uniform carcass (doubtless in large measure attributable to the more than 40 years of breeding and selection - chiefly in South Africa - as a meat animal), possesses better mothering abilities (mainly because Boer goat does have a very abundant supply of milk for their kids), is an even better 'brush' goat (because of its voracious appetite, larger size and its preference for 82% brush to 16% grass, versus the Spanish goat's choice of a 50/50% brush to grass diet),[4] and, finally, the Boer goat carcass dresses out at a slightly higher percentage (just over 50%, versus less than 50% for the Spanish goat).[5]

The Boer goat at its best is eye-catching. It is large [with mature bucks weighing at least 240 to 300 lbs (110 to 135 kg) and does between 200 and 225 lbs (90 to 100 kg)] and is a spectacularly beautiful animal. With its striking reddish brown head and sleek, firmly-muscled and well-proportioned body, it looks like a million dollars. That's just as well, since a first-rate Boer goat can fetch more than $5,000 U.S. When first imported some sold for $50,000 and more (U.S).

The Boer goat has received much favorable attention on account of its exceptionally rapid growth rate (under intensive, performance-tested conditions, males averaging 60 lbs at 3 months, 140 lbs at 8 months, 202 lbs at 12 months, 237 lbs at 18 months, 253 lbs at 25 months; and females averaging 53 lbs at 3 months, 99 lbs at 12 months, 140 lbs at 18 months and 185 lbs at 24 months)[6], high fertility and prolific kid crop. (A kidding rate of 200% is said to be common.)[7] To underline these goats' potential as a meat animal, South African researchers, N.H. Casey and W.A. Van Niekerk have noted that "their [Boer goats'] highly prolific, polyestrous nature means a higher meat yield per doe than per cow."[8]

Despite such impressive statistics, some doubts have been cast on the overall performance of the Boer goat in commercial circumstances in this country. For instance, Goatex Genetics Breeders, a specialized research group focused on Boer and Kiko goats, have stated: "As a consequence of high retail prices and a single-minded pursuit of purebred status [in the U.S.] in order to satisfy the undoubted breeders' market that then existed, few animals have yet been offered for slaughter in commercial circumstances. In fact, virtually no purebred Boer or Kiko goats are currently being run in truly commercial conditions with the result that performance figures are significantly skewed by excessively intense management and a predilection for pen feeding. Both factors have combined in the case of the Boer to ensure that it is almost impossible to determine what the purebred Boer is capable of in the commercial Texas situation."[9]

Like the Spanish doe, the Boer doe in North America is considered to be a seasonal breeder (although the Boer's breeding season, in South Africa, is an extended one and some American breeders contend that this is also the case here). Nonetheless, this seasonal breeding pattern, especially when considered in conjunction with several less satisfactory attributes of this goat - particularly when raised in confinement or semiconfinement, as it often is in this part of the world - gives some prospective North American breeders/ranchers pause.

The Boer goat has a voracious appetite. This is all very well when it devours unwanted brush at a spectacular rate - which it does happily when it can (in South Africa and Australia, for instance) - but a grave financial concern when the farmer has to buy or raise feed, as often seems to be the case in the United States. Here, by most accounts, the Boer goat is considered at present to be a high-input animal.

Whereas in South Africa, Boer goats have traditionally been able to feast on their preferred browse for most of their nutritional needs - a fact which seems partially to control internal parasite infestation as well - by and large, this is not the case at present in the United States.

In confinement or semiconfinement in North America (as in New Zealand), the Boer goat is said to be highly susceptible to internal parasites.[10] This is apparently not the case under range conditions in South Africa[11] - and, one would conjecture, in arid regions of Australia as well.

Several other problems pertaining to the Boer goat have to do with their meat. These are not specifically American concerns, but universal ones. They have been raised by such meticulous South African researchers as N.H. Casey and W.A. Van Niekerk, Department of Livestock Science, University of Pretoria.

These scientists have stated that "Eating quality of Boer goat meat, as judged for toughness and flavor, has been regarded as inferior to lamb and mutton."[12] They explain that marketing older animals may be partly responsible for this toughness. Some studies, they state, have indicated that the meat's toughness may also be related to a quite high collagen level (compared to several breeds of sheep which had tenderer meat). While suggesting that improved breeding "probably holds the key to improving the tenderness of Boer goat meat,"[13] Casey and Van Niekerk also point out that South Africans of Dutch descent (Afrikaners) share the general and long-standing Western European (i.e. British, German, Scandinavian ...) preference for lamb and mutton over goat meat - a fact which in South Africa is understandable if one compares the young, tender meat of the South African Dorper with meat from an older, tougher Boer goat. (To appreciate Boer goat meat at its best, the animal should, some say, be slaughtered at between 5 and 10 months.)

Besides reacting unfavorably to the toughness of Boer goat meat (from older goats), Casey and Van Niekerk state that many white South Africans have also complained about its taste - objections, the researchers note, "which are currently [1988] being investigated." However, on a more upbeat note, they do say that, when ground into sausage meat and mixed with pork fat, trained panels rated the sausages "highly acceptable."[14]

Still, for the considerable numbers of people ready to switch to chevon for its much touted leanness when compared to other red meat, the Boer goat sausage with added pork fat is not acceptable. And although most chevon is considerably leaner than other red meat, including lamb [See table at beginning of Chapter 19] - because the fat is deposited internally, rather than in the muscle - Boer goat chevon, without additives, has a higher fat content than that of other meat goats. (Its fat content is, researchers state, comparable to meat from sheep.)[15]

Given the pros and cons of the purebred Boer goat as a meat producer, cross breeding, many believe, may be the answer to utilizing the Boer goat's most valuable qualities and minimizing its less satisfactory ones. In several countries, including the United States and Canada, trials of Boer crosses are underway, with satisfying results. The earliest of these studies have, understandably, been conducted in South Africa, some of the more recent in New Zealand and the United States. [The Boer/Kiko cross - resulting in a new breed called the 'Genemaster' will be discussed in connection with the Kiko goat.]

In South Africa, "Angenye and Cartwright (1987) concluded from cross breeding studies with east African, Galla and Boer goats, that the Boer was a logical sire breed, contributing significantly directly additive effects to body weights at 4 to 12 months of age, and to preweaning absolute growth rates." An interesting subsidiary result of this study, however, was that "Boer goat maternal additive effects were mostly negative."[16]

THE MYOTONIC GOAT (ALSO KNOWN AS THE WOODEN LEG, STIFF-LEG, FAINTING GOAT OR TENNESSEE MEAT GOAT)

The name of the Myotonic - (sometimes nicknamed "wooden leg," or even "fainting" as well as "stiff-leg") - goat comes from its bizarre propensity to stiffen, and sometimes even fall over, when startled, frightened or jostled by its peers at the feeding trough. These brief (10 to 20 second) episodes, which some people call "fainting" spells - (somewhat incorrectly, because during these episodes the goat does not lose consciousness, its respiration remains normal, and, if it has been chowing down at the trough, it continues eating) - occur frequently. Some people conjecture that such episodes build up the goat's muscles, making it a meat goat of exceptional quality.

Researcher, Dr. Terry Gipson, neither supports nor denies a relation between myotonia and muscularity. He simply states: "The degree to which myotonia and muscularity are related is not known. Therefore, it is not known if selecting against myotonia will affect muscularity."[17] His findings, however, state that the Myotonic goat has a muscular and meaty conformation and that it is prolific.[18]

Dr. Philip Sponenberg, a geneticist at the Virginia-Maryland Regional College of Veterinary Medicine and the owner of more than 100 Myotonic goats, is clear and succinct about the advantage of the Tennessee meat goats' (the Myotonics') musculature. He says: "The significance of this [thick muscling and thick conformation throughout] for meat production is that these goats simply have more muscle for their weight than do other goats."

And he goes on to state: "... folks who have tried [eating] Tennessee goats as well as other [goats] tend to rank the Tennessee at the top of meat quality. The meat is consistently praised for tenderness, which at first thought might seem at variance with the stiffness encountered while the goat is alive. It is important to realize that the stiffness in no way results in tough meat, but rather just the opposite!"[19] As for the Tennessee meat goats' prolificacy, Sponenberg is specific. Assessing his own herd, he notes: "My results indicate a kidding rate of 200% for does over one year old."[20]

As well, by all accounts, these goats kid easily and are excellent mothers. Many producers say they are aseasonal; others simply that they have an extended breeding season.

The origins of the Myotonic goat are obscure and the story explaining its first appearance in the United States is unusual. A man by the name of John Tinsley turned up one day in 1880 - or thereabouts - at the Tennessee farm of Dr. H. Mayberry with 4 myotonic goats - 3 nannies and 1 billy - in tow. Tinsley said that he had brought the animals from Nova Scotia.

Dr. Mayberry, apparently fascinated by the goats' unusual behavior when stressed, bought all four. Tinsley, it is said, disappeared soon after making the sale. These original goats were small, but adjusted well to their new surroundings in Tennessee.

It has been stated that the Myotonic goats' "spells" are a neurological disorder, caused by a genetic irregularity which occasionally crops up in other species - pigeons, dogs, horses, and even man.

As with other goat breeds, there is a wide discrepancy between Myotonic individuals - between, for instance, the original small Myotonic goats and the much larger, "improved", contemporary animals which some breeders have produced - particularly in Texas since they were introduced to that state in the 1950s. Sponenberg states that weights at maturity vary from 60 pounds to more than 175 pounds.[21]

Tennessee meat goats have other advantages, Sponenberg notes. They are good foragers, though their myotonic condition limits their climbing activities to some extent. Even this limitation has the advantage of their being less dedicated escape artists than most other goats. As well, these goats appear to be somewhat parasite resistant.[22]

Sponenberg concludes that "The Tennessee goat has much to offer meat goat producers interested in a well-adapted goat for a low-input forage-based system."[23]

Nevertheless, despite all these wonderful qualities, the Myotonic is not a perfect meat goat in some situations. These goats' bad feature is that they take 3 to 4 years to mature - many times the maturation rate of most other meat goats, the Boer in particular. Therefore, crossing Myotonic with Boer goats for faster growth at an earlier age would seem like a good idea, provided the resultant offspring retain the excellent meat quality of the Myotonic.

The estimated population of Myotonic goats in the United States is between 3,000 and 5,000. Most of these are in Texas and Tennessee.

THE KIKO GOAT

Like the Boer goat and the Spanish goat, the ancestors of the contemporary Kiko* goat of New Zealand spent several centuries coping on their own in the wild until astute ranchers, impressed by this creature's ability to survive bad weather, parasites, disease and kidding - and thrive - without human intervention, decided that it would be a good idea to use this feral stock in a breeding program aimed at developing a superior meat goat.

*"Kiko", by the way, is the aboriginal [Maori] New Zealand word for "meat".

As they were, these wild goats were not marketable. They produced little meat and milk. As well, they were small; mature does weighing about 55 pounds and mature bucks about 88 pounds.

However, the ranchers reckoned that by breeding feral does to pure-bred domestic bucks they might come up with a first-rate breed. And indeed they did.

In 1970*, with the capture of several thousand randomly-chosen feral goats, this breeding program was launched. Selection for superior traits then ensued, after which the chosen does were bred to purebred domestic (dairy) bucks (Anglo-Nubian, British Toggenburg and Saanen) in hopes of increasing frame size, muscling and milk in the offspring.

The Kiko goat is descended from escaped milk goats introduced into New Zealand by European colonists in the latter part of the 18th century, supplemented by a variety of domestic goats turned loose in the Depressions of the 1890s and 1930s, and Angoras released after a failed attempt to establish a mohair industry during World War I. Unlike its ancestor, the newly-developed [from about 1970] Kiko - infused with superior domestic goat genetics - is a larger, meatier animal. Mature bucks weigh up to 300 pounds, or more, and does up to 200 pounds, or more. They are not heavily boned, and are reputed to have a "lean and succulent carcass."

Since the ranchers - aided by geneticists in the Ministries of Agriculture and Fisheries - were determined to preserve the inherent hardiness of the feral goats, their new breed had to survive under range conditions in the steep New Zealand hill country. No shelter, no assistance during kidding, no supplemental feeding and no hoof-trimming were provided. Only minimal parasite control was administered.

Animals which performed exceptionally well - judged by survivability and weight gain under these rigorous conditions - were kept in the program. After 4 generations of breeding, a dramatic improvement in live weight was recorded.

By 1986, the herd was closed to outside bucks, though small numbers of outside does which met the selection criteria, were introduced gradually. By this time, the Kiko breed was well established.

*1970 was a significant year in the meat goat breeding world. Not only was the Kiko breeding program begun in New Zealand, but that was the year Afrikaners began to monitor their Boer goats closely and upgrade them.

The contemporary Kiko is a large-framed and early-maturing goat, reportedly producing lean and tender meat. Consequently, this new breed is in demand in a good many parts of the world.

The United States is one of the countries to which Kiko goats have been exported. Because Kiko goats have been in the United States such a relatively short time, there are still not enough of these goats to supply a regular commercial market in this country.

The Kiko developers - now known as the Goatex Group Ltd. - keep close tabs on their registered stock. They have founded a New Zealand Kiko registry in which purebred Kikos are enrolled. Shipments of Kiko goats abroad are closely watched and these animals' superior qualities regularly recorded.

As a Goatex Group publication points out: "The primary characteristic of the Kiko goat is its hardiness and ability to achieve substantial weight gains when run under natural conditions without supplementary feeding. In New Zealand it is known as the 'go anywhere, eat anything' goat. The Kiko is not affected by broad variations in climate and is equally at home in subalpine mountain country and arid brushland."[24]

In 1994 and 1995, the Goatex Group experimented by crossing Kikos with Boer goats which had been imported into New Zealand several years earlier. The venture seems to have been a success. The cross has produced a new breed of meat goat, dubbed the "Genemaster", and in the United States, the "Texas Genemaster".

THE TEXAS GENEMASTER

The New Zealand based Goatex Group has pioneered the crossing of Kiko with Boer goats in both New Zealand and the United States. The group's original rationale was that, since the Boer goat in both countries failed to thrive sufficiently under commercial conditions for it to become a commercial producer of goat meat, breeding Boer females to enhanced Kiko males might increase the hardiness of the resultant offspring, while maintaining the animals' meat-producing ability.

In short order the cross the group fixed on as most successful was a three-eights Kiko/five-eights Boer - producing an animal which, Graham Culliford explains, "would exhibit the vigor of the Kiko (and maintain much of the elevated cutting percentages of that breed) while retaining the carcass conformation of the Boer."[25] This cross - the Genemaster or Texas Genemaster - is now considered a new breed.

Culliford states that: "The carcasses tend to the lighter bone structure of the Kiko while retaining the heavier muscling of the Boers, yet display the leaner fat configuration of the Kiko."[26]

DUAL PURPOSE GOATS
THE NUBIAN GOAT

Among this country's dual purpose goat breeds with significant meat-producing capabilities, the Anglo-Nubian (usually simply called the Nubian in the U.S.) - and its offspring, the Kinder - cannot be overlooked. Although, as a number of authorities worldwide have remarked, all goats are potentially meat goats - in the sense that most eventually end up at sale barns and are slaughtered for meat - some which are not raised for meat first and foremost are nevertheless, like the Nubian, Kinder and Angora, important in this capacity under certain circumstances.

The Nubian, known primarily as a high-yielding milk producer and a significant progenitor of new breeds such as the Kiko and Kinder, should not then be overlooked as a meat goat in its own right. In this capacity, it is, at maturity, only slightly less efficient than the ordinary Spanish goat - though well below the Boer, the Kiko and the improved Spanish. [See Figure 1]

Figure 1: Production and index score estimates of potential meat goat breeds.

	Boer	Kiko	Nubian	Pygmy	Spanish	Selected Spanish	Tennessee Wooden-leg	"Ideal"
Litter size (kids/doe)	2.0	2.0	1.6	1.8	1.5	1.3	2.0	2.0
Kidding interval (days)	365	365	365	240	365	240	365	240
Birth weight (kg)	4.2	2.5	2.3	1.6	2.5	2.5	2.3	3.0
Pre-weaning average daily gain (g/d)	200	160	140	80	115	140	125	170
Productivity index[a] (kg kid weaned/doe/yr)	32.1	24.8	18.7	17.8	14.2	23.1	19.9	40.9
Mature doe body weight (kg)	65	50	60	30	35	45	45	65
Efficiency index[b]	1.40	1.32	0.87	1.39	0.99	1.33	1.15	1.79

[a]Productivity index = conception rate * litter size * (1 - mortality rate to weaning/100) * 365/kidding interval * (birth weight + preweaning average daily gain/1000 * age at weaning). Assumptions: conception rate = 90%; mortality rate = 10%; age at weaning = 80 d
[b]productivity index/(doe body weight)[75]

Source: Gipson, T.A., Meat Goat Breeds and Breeding Plans, Meat Goat Production and Marketing Handbook, Sponsored by Rural Economic Development Center Raleigh, North Carolina and Mid-Carolina Council of Governments, Fayetteville, North Carolina, EC 683, Rep. October 1996

The purebred Nubian ranks first numerically among milk goats in registrations in the United States. According to current estimates, there are about 100,000 registered breeding stock in this country. Such numbers make this breed hard to overlook.

The Nubian is descended from goats herded for centuries by nomadic desert people. Human beings generally find their association with Nubians pleasant. These goats are tractable, easily-restrained and timid - so timid, indeed, owners report that a kid of another breed can bully an adult female.

The Nubian has distinctive looks: long, hanging ears (useful for flapping away insects), a Roman nose and almond eyes. Moreover, as Alan Mowlem in the chapter entitled "Goat Meat," in his book, *Goat Farming* (1988), remarks, the Nubian and the Boer goat look quite alike: "These impressive animals [Boers] look like extremely muscular Anglo-Nubians."[27]

Several prominent British goat experts recommend kid meat from improved dairy breeds - particularly the Anglo-Nubian.

Alan Mowlem states that "... most of the improved dairy breeds found in Britain produce kids that, with a favourable rearing regime, can show quite impressive weight gains and will yield a high percentage of usable lean meat when slaughtered. Of the important dairy breeds, the Anglo-Nubian shows the most promise for meat production. Some can grow to impressive mature weights...."[28]

Such notable British goat authorities as David Mackenzie, Lois Hetherington and Alan Mowlem, when discussing goat meat, all focus primarily on the care and marketing of young male offspring of dairy goats, contending that most of these kids are otherwise expendable in the dairy goat industry. All three writers advocate castrating* these male kids early to avoid running the risk of the meat being tainted by male hormones.

Both Mackenzie and Hetherington underscore the leanness of kid meat. Hetherington states categorically: "Kid meat has no fat...."[29]

THE KINDER GOAT

Kinder goats are a new and dual purpose (milk and meat) goat whose origin is due chiefly to happenstance.

In the fall of 1985 at the Showalter's farm in Snohomish, Washington, the old Nubian buck had died, leaving the two Nubian does without a mate. Since the Showalters had several Pygmy goats, they bred their Nubian does to a Pygmy male. In the spring, 3 doe kids were born - the first Kinders. Since these offspring were good-natured, efficient milkers and able to produce 3 to 6 kids every year, making additional crosses seemed like a good idea.

* Castration, however, according to world goat authority, C. Devendra, "tends to increase the fat content of the [goat] meat." [See p. 76 of "The Nutritional Value of goat meat," *Goat Meat Production in Asia* ....]

A woman by the name of Teresa Hill, seeing the potential in producing more of these moderately-sized goats with highly efficient feed conversion, rich milk and desirable flesh, joined forces with two other Snohomish women, Daralyn Hollenbeck and Kathy Gilmore, to register, develop and promote this new breed. According to available information: "It is easily possible for a Kinder doe weighing about 115 pounds to produce five kids who in 14 months can weigh 80 pounds, thereby producing 250 pounds of meat each year."[30]

The Pygmy genetics should be an important factor in supporting the Kinder's originators' claims about the excellent quality of this goat's meat.

THE PYGMY GOAT

In Africa, where Pygmy goats - formerly called Cameroon Dwarf goats because they were indigenous to that former West African colony - originate, their meat is considered choice; indeed, the best. As well, in their native environment, the Pygmy is more resistant than most goats to parasites and is an aseasonal breeder. It is also, unlike many other goat breeds - most of which perform best in arid environments - said to be well adapted to humid climates.

In Africa, the small size of the Pygmy goat has long been considered advantageous because the animal could be slaughtered, cooked and eaten in its entirety by a family unit within a short space of time, thus avoiding the spoilage and waste inevitable with larger animal carcasses in hot countries lacking widespread refrigeration - particularly in rural areas. In contemporary America, however, where refrigeration is almost universal and where a large carcass is generally favored over a small one, the Pygmy has, to date, not been a major contender for top place among meat goats.

Indeed, in the years following its 1959 importation into the United States,[31] the Pygmy goat tended to be thought of as a curiosity - an exotic animal, chiefly confined to zoos or kept as a pet. Today, though, when there are reckoned to be more than 30,000 Pygmys in this country and goat meat is in high demand compared to times past, some farmers are beginning to take a new look at this robust and productive little goat - both on its own and for the genetics it can infuse into new breeds like the Kinder.

The Pygmy goat is full-barreled and well muscled. Mature animals measure between 16 and 23 inches at the withers (shoulder blades to ground). Pygmies are usually grey agouti. Coat length and density vary with environmental differences - a fact which underlines the Pygmy goat's adaptability.

THE ANGORA GOAT

Americans do not, by and large, consider the Angora goat to be a prime meat goat, although in other countries its flesh is much touted.

In Britain, for instance, David Mackenzie, perhaps that country's most famous goat expert of long-standing, in his "bible" of goat books, *Goat Husbandry*, states categorically: "The flesh [of the Angora] is superior to all other goat meat, and at least as acceptable as prime mutton to the fat-abhorrent housewife."[32] Elsewhere in the same book, Mackenzie qualifies this statement somewhat by saying that the Angora goat "supplies the tastiest of all goat meat in cooler regions."[33]

Canadian government, Department of Agriculture publication, *Goats*, also endorses Angora meat: "The meat of the Angora is also regarded as the best chevon."[34]

Foremost Asian goat authority, C. Devendra, pontificating on goat meat at an international conference on the subject, remarked on the superb juiciness and tenderness of chops and roasts from young Angoras: "Yearling (12-20 month) Angora goats produced chops and roasts that were juicier and more tender than those from 3- to 5-month-old kids."[35]

From personal experience, the authors of this book subscribe to these favorable opinions. For us, Angora goat meat has been a treat.

However, it is not surprising that Angora meat has generally not been thought much of in the United States. Few people have tried it. After all, the chief value of the 2 million or so Angoras in the United States has lain in their wonderful fleece, the luxurious mohair they produce. Consequently, prime young Angoras - and even middle-aged ones - were rarely butchered in the past. Only the culls - mostly the halt, the lame and very old - went to the sale barns and were subsequently slaughtered, turned into sausage meat, and usually shipped abroad. Only in the last few years - due to the removal of the government subsidy on mohair and a decrease in demand for this luxurious fleece - have more Angoras found their way to meat markets in this country.

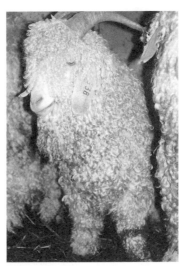

But, despite the superb quality of their flesh, keeping Angoras strictly as meat goats does not, in terms of management, make sense. They need to be shorn twice yearly - whether or not the mohair sells profitably. As well, Angoras are quite susceptible to internal parasitism, so, in some regions, labor and cost of deworming decrease their profitability.

Crossing Angoras with Boer goats to increase size and early maturity has been suggested - and tried - but again, despite the worthwhile input of both valuable gene pools, the resultant animals (in the first generation) may still need shearing, which some consider too great an expense and inconvenience to justify raising this cross as a viable meat goat.

BOER/ANGORA CROSS

This cross is not without its defenders. Fred Homeyer, a Texas rancher who has experimented for more than three years with crossing does of a good many breeds [Spanish, Nubian, Alpine, Toggenberg, Angora, 3/4 Persian Ibex x Spanish, Spangoras (Spanish x Angoras), la Mancha, and Angora x Nubian] with a full blood Boer buck has stated that "the best cross and most consistent cross, in my opinion, is the full blood Boer buck crossed on an Angora doe.... My Angora does will weigh as much as 150 pounds and the 3/4 Boer-1/4 Angora doe will weigh as much as 180."[36] Certainly our own 1/2 Boer-1/2 Angora kids grow at a rapid rate and are delicious eating (see photograph below).

While the Boer genetics contribute superior heft and fast growth to the union, the Angora contribution is a "considerably milder tasting [meat] than the meat of some other breeds such as the straight Spanish goat in Texas or the brush goat of the Southeastern United States."[37] For Homeyer this cross is "the diamond meat."

1/2 Boer-1/2 Angora kids (Crane Creek Enterprises).

And so it is that, after looking at and laying out characteristics of various meat goats now in North America - all of which have much potential in disparate contexts - we have come full circle, back to the opinions of the two authorities cited at the beginning of this chapter: that, despite the promise of each of these various breeds and some of their crosses, the ideal meat goat for this part of the world has not yet evolved - or at least is not present in sufficient numbers to adequately and consistently supply the commercial market. Perhaps, we will find that, as in India, China and Africa, we will have to be content with a good many different breeds adapted over time to various regions. Environment is bound to be a dominant force to be reckoned with, and breeds which do wonderfully in Texas will not necessarily adapt so well to Maine, Oregon, Massachusetts, Michigan or New York.

Notes: Chapter 3

1. Terry A. Gipson, "Genetic Resources for Meat Goat Production," *Proceedings Southeast Regional Meat Production Symposium,* Feb. 24, 1996, Tallahassee, FL. Gipson also notes that most of these Spanish goats live in the vicinity of the Edwards Plateau of central Texas; and, apropos of the Spanish goat's breeding season, he states: "More information on seasonality is available for the Spanish goat than for other breeds. Research under Texas range conditions and with continuous exposure to the male indicated that the breeding season for Spanish does extended from August to January. The months of February to early March and May to July are transitional periods with deep anestrus occurring March through April. The majority of the parturitions occurred between November and February and a second peak was observed in May. The average kidding interval was 326 days but followed a bimodal distribution. A small group of does that kidded in October to December rebred before the anestrus period and had a kidding interval of approximately 200 days. The vast majority of does had a kidding interval of 355 days."

2. Frank Pinkerton, "Procurement of Foundation Stock," *Meat Goat Production and Marketing Handbook*, Rural Economic Development Center, Raleigh, North Carolina and Mid-Carolina Council of Governments, Fayetteville, North Carolina, 1996, p. 2.

3. Thian Hor Teh and Terry Gipson, "Establishing a Chevon Industry: The Boer Goat (Part I)," E. (Kika) de la Garza Institute for Goat Research, Langston University, Langston, Oklahoma, (1993), pgs. 2 and 7, and Gipson, "Genetic Resources for Meat Goat Production," p. 2.

4. N. H. Casey and W.A. Van Niekerk, "The Boer Goat I: Origin, Adaptability, Performance Testing, Reproduction and Milk Production," http://www.boergoats.com/niekerk1.html, May 1988, p. 3.

5. Teh and Gipson, "Establishing a Chevon Industry: The Boer Goat (Part I)," p. 3.

6. Ibid.

7. Thian Hor Teh, "Establishing a Goat Meat Industry: Using the Boer Germ Plasm (Part II)," E. (Kika) de la Garza Institute for Goat Research, Langston University, Langston, Oklahoma, 1993, p. 1; and also see the excellent and extensive section on growth of the Boer goat by Casey and Van Niekerk, Department of Livestock Science, Faculty of Agriculture, University of Pretoria, Pretoria, South Africa (May 1988) entitled, "The Boer Goat II, Growth, Nutrient Requirements, Carcass and Meat Quality," http://www.boergoats.com/niekerk2.html; and Gipson, "Genetic Resources for Meat Goat Production," p. 5.

8. Casey and Van Niekerk, "The Boer Goat II," p. 10.

9. Goatex Genetics LLC (Breeders and Developers of Genemaster Goats), "Maximizing Production by Harnessing Hybrid Vigor: Alternative Breeding Strategies for Boer and Kiko Goats," P.O. Box 34-021, Fendalton, Christchurch, New Zealand 8030, Telephone/Facsimile 64 3 3296 255; e-mail tasman@xtra.co.nz, promotional literature, p. 1.

10. Gipson, "Genetic Resources for Meat Goat Production," p. 4: "Anecdotal producer evidence suggests that the Boer is as 'susceptible' to internal parasites as is the Angora, which is itself notoriously 'susceptible' to internal parasites (Thedford, 1993)". According to Goatex research recorded in "Maximizing Production by Harnessing Hybrid Vigor: Alternative Breeding Strategies for Boer and Kiko Goats," "... management inputs (for Boers) have been substantially greater than anticipated.... All

animals (and more particularly juveniles and kids) appear to display a susceptibility to internal parasites (especially *Haemonchus contortus*) on a par with Angora goats. In New Zealand, during periods of parasite prevalence, both Angoras and Boers may require drenching every three weeks. This is generally considered to create management costs which mitigate against economic commercial production." (p.2)

11. Casey and Van Niekerk, "The Boer Goat I," p. 1.

12. "The Boer Goat II," p. 9.

13. Ibid., p. 10.

14. Ibid.

15. The and Gipson, "Establishing a Chevon Industry: The Boer Goat (Part I)," p. 3

16. Casey and Van Niekerk, "The Boer Goat II," p. 6. In Alberta, Canada, where Boer goats were introduced on a large scale about three years before they were brought to the United States, studies have also been undertaken with Boer crosses. In one such study, researchers charting the results of Boer bucks bred to Spanish, Alpine and Saanen does, noted that: "It is concluded that preweaning gains are not affected by including the BO [Boer] as buck bred to AL [Alpine], SA [Saanen] or SP [Spanish] does. The growth rate of the crosses up to 100 (days) was primarily determined by the breed of doe, i.e. the milk the kids receive from the doe. Carcass quality based on rib eye depth and fat depth at 160 (days) was not affected by the breed of buck." [Goonewardene, L.A., P.A. Day, N. Patrick and D. Patrick, "Cross Breeding with Alpine and Boer Goats - Growth and Carcass Traits," (Sheep and Goats - Research Update 1996/97, Government of Alberta, Canada, www.agric.gov.ab.ca/researchupdate/97sheep11.html {website})]

17. Gipson, "Genetic Resources for Meat Goat Production," p. 1.

18. Ibid.

19. Sponenberg, D.P., "Meat Breeds: The Tennessee Goat - a forgot-

ten resource," *The Goat Farmer*, April/May 1998, p 32-33.

20. Ibid.

21. Ibid.

22. Ibid.

23. Ibid.

24. Goatex Group LLC (Breeders and Developers of Kiko Goats), "History, Development and Characteristics of Kiko Goats: An Overview," P.O. Box 34-021, Fendalton, Christchurch, New Zealand 8030, Telephone/ Facsimile 64 3 3296 255; e-mail tasman@xtra.co.nz, promotional literature, p. 5.

25. Graham Culliford, "The Genemaster Story," AKGA Update, July 1998, p. 4.

26. Ibid.

27. Alan Mowlem, *Goat Farming* (Ipswich: Farming Press Books, 1988), p 156.

28. Ibid., p. 155.

29. Lois Hetherington, *All About Goats* (Ipswich: Farming Press Books, 1988), p. 86.

30. Breeds of Livestock - Kinder Goats, p. 1., hometown.aol.com/ KGBAssn/index.htm (website)

31. Much earlier, it is said, Pygmy goats were imported to the Caribbean and North America in the 18th century on slave ships. See J.-M. Luginbuhl's article "Breeds of Goats for Meat Goat Production and Production Traits," www.cals.ncsu.edu/an_sci/extension/animal/meatgoat/ MGBreed.htm (web site), p. 2.

32. David Mackenzie, *Goat Husbandry* (London: Faber & Faber,

1980), p. 295.

33. Ibid., p. 35.

34. *Goats* (N.A.), Publication # 1704 of the Canadian Department of Agriculture (Ottawa: Government of Canada, 1981), p. 10.

35. C. Devendra, "The nutritional value of goat meat," *Goat meat production in Asia: proceedings of a workshop held in Tando Jam, Pakistan, 13-18 March 1988* (Ottawa: International Development Research Centre, 1988), p. 77.

36. Fred Homeyer, "Crossing the Boer and Angora - the 'diamond' meat," *The Goat Farmer*, Volume 12, Issue 4, p. 38.

37. Ibid.

Boer-Nubian cross.

4. MANAGEMENT

A) FORAGES: AN ECONOMIC NECESSITY

"... meat goats must depend almost solely on forages to meet their nutritional needs if they are to be economically viable."
- Bruce Pinkerton and Frank Pinkerton, "Managing Forages for Meat Goats," *Meat Goat Production and Marketing Handbook* (1996).

The truth of Bruce and Frank Pinkerton's succinct and to-the-point observation, cited here, has been substantiated and tabulated a good many times in recent years in numerous American locations, as well as in New Zealand, Australia and South Africa. It is, moreover, a premise which has been taken for granted for thousands of years in most Asian and African countries, where, by and large, goats have survived solely by foraging: rarely, have they been hand fed in confinement situations, which have invariably been considered to be impossibly expensive.

Unless special breeds are being raised as breeding stock - as most Boer goats in this country have been since their 1993 importation - pen feeding has generally been found to be too costly for animals destined primarily for the slaughterhouse. And, even if it were economically feasible, it is not necessarily a good idea for several reasons. Ideally, goats prefer to forage on their own, choosing their particular - and often to us peculiar - requirements by browsing and grazing on a mixture of vegetation, often on plants which other species abhor. Besides, as Maurice Shelton, of Texas A & M University Agricultural Research and Extension Service, has observed, the lean meat of goats is partially due to the fact that "they are seldom fed the quantity or quality of feed required to permit them to deposit large amounts of fat. Closely related to this is the fact that they are not glutinous feeders even when given an opportunity and thus fatten less readily."[1]

If meat goats were routinely hand fed large quantities of what first-time goat farmers might consider quality feed (such as grain), one of the main reasons for raising chevon would have been nullified since producers could no longer boast of their meat being the leanest on the market. Indeed, in South African experiments where Boer goats were raised in confinement, this has been proven to be so: several breeds of sheep were less fatty.[2]

By listening to the voices of experience, then, it would seem that the prospective successful producer of commercially viable chevon should have access to inexpensive land suitable for browsing and grazing. This generally means utilizing land which cannot realistically be considered for other intensive farming enterprises - though goats have been run successfully with cattle, each filling a separate ecological niche. Goats, many maintain, even improve grazing for cattle since they choose to eat weeds and brush, thus allowing grass to fill in some of these formerly unproductive (for species other than goats) spots.

Obviously some states have conditions which are more suitable for raising goats than others. Southern states have the possibility of year round foraging, whereas northern midwestern and eastern states are disadvantaged by not having year round browsing/grazing due to the severity of winter weather.

Texas is, of course, the best known state for goats. Generations of ranchers there have raised large numbers of Angora and Spanish goats under range conditions, and more recently Tennessee meat goats and crosses of these and other breeds. The dry climate in many parts of this state and generally adequate browse and grass year round (especially in regions such as the Edwards plateau) suit goats perfectly.

Other parts of the Southwest and certain portions of the Southeast too have also recently been much touted as excellent goat country - depending on the breed of goat, and, as in Texas, the reliability of the owners' guard dogs.

An Peischel has successfully raised Kiko goats* in the Sierra Nevada foothills of northern California - with Great Pyrenees guard dogs faithfully warding off such predators as mountain lions, bears and, of course, the ubiquitous coyotes, scourge of goat owners almost everywhere on this continent.[3]

Sylvia Tomlinson also attests to raising Kikos satisfactorily (together with several other goat breeds, such as Spanish and various crosses) in rugged forested hill country in Oklahoma. The guard dogs she and her husband counted on to ward off hungry predators were Anatolian Shep-

*Though it should be noted here that a substantial portion of the income she derives from these goats is from using them for brush control - which often in her region translates into fire control.

herds.

Tomlinson relates how, in the drought of 1998, their goats thrived up in the timber where "the browse was heat stressed but plentiful and some shaded forbs and grasses remained with a trace of green."[4] She also notes that their cattle could not contend with the extreme conditions and had to be sold.

Much of the Southeast, according to knowledgeable authorities such as Lynn Harwell, also has an environment suitable for raising meat goats. Although there the often high humidity levels do not always make for ideal conditions, nevertheless ample forage exists year round. Harwell states: "In the Southeast, financial arguments encourage meat goat production. An abundance of low-cost browse, coupled with nearness to eastern markets invite a close look at investment opportunity."[5]

James T. Green Jr. substantiates this view, specifically citing North Carolina as being ideally situated to become a leading supplier of chevon "because of its vast forage resources, many small landowners, and its proximity to the major markets on the East Coast." He says too that, because of the goat's varied feeding behavior, it is well suited to participate "in mixed grazing situations with cattle and sheep to better utilize the forage-browse resources found on most farms in North Carolina."[6]

On the same tack, in the same state, Shelly Andrew, an extension agent in Jackson County, has remarked: "Goats are the most underrated farm resource around today.... If properly marketed, this animal is about twice as profitable as cattle. Goats thrive on pasture land too poor to support cattle. They're perfect for mountain areas, and they are very hardy."[7]

Dr. P. Sponenberg not only pontificates enthusiastically and knowledgeably about raising meat goats in the Southeast but he does it. For his Virginia farm he has chosen Myotonic (Tennessee Meat) goats.[8] Although they are slow-maturing, this quality is not a major deterrent when forage is abundant and available year round, as is the case in Virginia. And this breed seems to be more parasite resistant than many others under these conditions.

Clair E. Terrill some years ago (in 1993) predicted that "the possible future of goat meat production in the U.S. is tremendous on forage alone, providing production and efficiency of production can be rapidly expanded."[9] It would seem that his prognostications are coming to pass.

Boer-Angora cross kids. (Crane Creek Enterprises)

B) IS BIGGER BETTER? IN MANY ENVIRONMENTS, NOT NECESSARILY!

"Considering the breeds available, the potential exists to develop a meat goat that is too big and too productive for the environment in which it has a competitive advantage. Therefore, it is imperative that breeders identify a production system appropriate for their environment, then develop a goat that effectively performs therein."
- Richard V. Machen, Extension Livestock Specialist, Texas Agricultural Extension Service, Uvalde, Texas in his article, "Great Potential in a New Industry," www.boergoats.com/library/machen.html, n.d.

When Machen cautions against opting for ever larger animals, he notes that at present the U.S. goat meat industry is at much the same stage as the beef cattle industry was in 1960. During the years between 1960 and 1975, Machen points out, beef farmers were focused on importing new breeds with heavier muscle and larger mature size while ignoring consumer concerns and environmental constraints. More recently, Machen says, "moderation, predictability and consistency are now focal points" (in the beef cattle industry), and he implies that goat producers could take their cue from this historical perspective.

As Dr. Sponenberg - having arrived at a conclusion similar to Machen's - stresses "some environments demand smaller animals."[10] Sponenberg explains that "the problem with large animals is that they have higher maintenance requirements. In a compromised environment, it can be that larger animals have trouble maintaining body weight and production, in which case bigger animals eventually outrun the support system and fail in production."[11]

C) STRESS

"It is a proven fact that stressed animals do not perform as well as unstressed ones."
- Bud Williams, "Bud Williams Stockmanship."

"Happy goats are Healthy Goats."
- P. Sponenberg, "Happy Goats are Healthy Goats," *The Goat Farmer,* www.caprine.co.nz

"There is a consensus that animals do have needs beyond the basics. If those needs are not met, chronic stress results with a corresponding loss of performance."
- Burt Smith, *Moving 'Em - A Guide to Low Stress Animal Handling,* The Graziers Hui, Kamuela, Hawaii 1998.

Smith, Williams and Sponenberg substantiate David Mackenzie's contention of several decades ago [in *Goat Husbandry* (1980)] that the owner who overlooks the social and psychological needs of his animals - even those destined for the slaughterhouse - is making a big mistake. Not only will his/her animals be stressed - thus resulting in their being less healthy than they should be - but they will tend to be troublesome rather than tractable. As Sponenberg, who is both a veterinarian and goat farmer, emphasizes, "goats are social creatures and really do need the companionship of other goats to do well."[12]

After observing closely goat hierarchies and interrelationships, Sponenberg cautions that "frequently mixing and remixing goats into different subgroups is a nightmare from a goat's viewpoint. Every change in social group means that the goats have to redo the entire social order....

Constantly mixing and remixing goats gives them no opportunity to take a rest from the work of establishing the pecking order and keeping it in shape."[13]

Smith suggests that, without attending to one's animals' social and psychological needs, the farmer/rancher will not only stress his animals, but will also lose money. He advocates a slow and calm approach to the animals in one's care.

D) MARKETING

"A current marketing study has found buyers, processors, wholesalers and consumers of goat meat to be concerned with both lack of quality and consistency of animals and carcasses [Pinkerton, et al, 1993]. Brokers, traders, auction owners and packers identify erratic quality and seasonality of supply/demand ratios as constraints to more rapid expansion."

- William Drinkwater, Frank Pinkerton, Terry Gipson, "Development of Grade Standards for Slaughter Kids, Yearlings, and Adult Goats," *Meat Goat Production and Marketing Handbook*, 1996.

The concerns raised by Drinkwater, Pinkerton and Gipson have not, according to pundits worldwide, yet been solved. To offset such difficulties some owners simply sell their animals from their own farms - one at a time, as regional consumers appear in their yard. Such an arrangement works well, it is said, in communities where there is a high ethnic population and chevon is favorite fare - particularly on special occasions. Many such customers like to choose their animals and see them butchered according to their specifications.

Farmers/ranchers serving such customers need to be aware of the various ethnic holidays so as to have the sought-after animals available at the right time. Many of these special celebrations are religious or of religious origin. The dates of these occasions differ considerably from one group to another and, frequently, from year to year as well.*

For instance, Christians use one of two calendars: the Julian (Eastern)** calendar and the Gregorian (Western) calendar. Often the two are almost two weeks out of sync which, together with the use of various sys-

* Western religions generally use a solar calendar and Eastern religions a lunar one.
** Greek.

tems of calculation, can result in Easter (a special feasting day in both Eastern and Western churches) being from 1 to 5 weeks later in Eastern than Western churches.

To check specific Christian dates, producers may call Keith Clark Calendar Cooperation at 607-563-9411.

The Islamic calendar is lunar. Months begin with the appearance of the new moon and vary from 29 to 30 days. Rarely does any day of any month fall on the same date as in the solar year. Three Islamic celebrations significant for goat consumption are: 1) Ramadan, the period of fasting from sunrise to sunset during the 9th month of their calendar year; 2) Id-al-Fitr, the festival of breaking the fast; and 3) Id-al'Adha, the festival of sacrifice, which occurs during the last month of the Islamic year. At this time in Eastern countries, the meat of goats, sheep and camels is distributed to the needy, to religious leaders and is also consumed by the donors.

There are other significant Muslim dates as well. To check on important dates for Muslim communities, producers may contact Dar-adh-Drikr Mosque, 4323 Rosedale Avenue, Bethesda, MD 20814.

The Jewish calendar, though primarily lunar, has some solar aspects. Jewish holidays celebrate events of historical importance to Jewish people and begin at sunset of the first day.

Meat consumption usually increases during these holidays. There are specific and strict periods of fasting and eating. Three particularly significant Jewish holidays are Passover (in April), Hanukkah (in December) and Rosh Hashanah (in September or October).

Many other groups with different religious and cultural celebrations also favor chevon. One source to contact for more information on this subject is: Multifaith Resources, 45 Windy Hill Court, P.O. Box 128, Wofford Heights, CA 93285-0128.

Not every goat farmer, however, has large numbers of ethnic buyers hammering on his/her door - a factor the farmer or would-be goat farmer has to take into account. Various markets are there, however, experts agree, for reliable suppliers of quality chevon. Apparently, though, the challenge of producing large quantities of high quality chevon consistently has not been met. Thus restaurants - unsure about quality and availability - tend to be leery of putting chevon on their menus.

Maurice Shelton has clearly laid out the categories in which chevon is generally marketed: 1) suckling kid (a 4 to 6 week animal) for cabrito in the Mexican community; 2) weanling kid (a 4 to 6 month animal); 3) 6 month to 1 year old, primarily for barbecuing; 4) older animals (mostly culled females). The suckling kid, Shelton notes, is inefficient in the production system unless it fetches a very high price. The weanling, he says, is "the typical market age in North America and much of Europe."[14] Age is, of course, a major concern with the older culls, the meat from which tends to need marinating and slow cooking. Goats from feral herds in Australia, New Zealand and the United States tend to make up a large proportion of this last group.

Notes: Chapter 4

1. Maurice Shelton, "Goat Production," *Encyclopedia of Agricultural Science* (San Diego, New York, Boston, London, Sydney, Tokyo, Toronto: Academic Press, 1994), p. 459.

Another reason, of course, is that goats tend to deposit much of the fat they do accumulate internally - not on the carcass.

2. N.H. Casey and W.A. Van Niekerk, "The Boer Goat II," 21 May 1998. "In these studies (Owen and Norman, 1977), total body fat (TBF) in Boer goats was considerably higher (18.31%) than in SAMM (11.8%), Merino (15.0%) or Dorper sheep (16.7%), but less than the very early developing Pedi sheep (24.5%)."

3. See *The Stockman Grass Farmer,* October 1998, a staff article entitled "California Goat Grazier Fights Fires in Fields and Forests."

4. Sylvia Tomlinson, *The Meat Goats of Caston Creek*, Redbud Publishing Co., Edmond, Oklahoma, 1999, p. 77.

5. Lynn Harwell, "Enterprise Analysis," *Meat Goat Production and Marketing Handbook,* p. 103. In this article Harwell catalogues specific available resources in N.C. for meat goat farming.

6. James T. Green Jr., "Potential for producing Meat Goats in North Carolina," *Meat Goat Production and Management Handbook,* p. 116.

7. Merle Ellis, "Demand for Goat Meat Grows," p. 1, www.boergoats.com/library/Butcher.html (website), P.O. Box 907, Tiburon, California 94920, 415-383-6585 (Telephone)

8. See references to Dr. Sponenberg's articles in Chapter 3 and elsewhere in Chapter 4.

9. Clair E. Terrill, "Goat Meat in Our Future? The Status of Meat Goats in the United States," *Live Animal Trade and Transport Magazine*, December 1993, Volume V, No. 4.

10. Philip Sponenberg, "Meat breed must suit environment," *The Goat Farmer*, www.caprine.co.nz, p. 2 of 15.

11. Ibid.

12. Philip Sponenberg, "Happy Goats are Healthy Goats," *The Goat Farmer*, Whangarei, New Zealand, July/August, 1999.

13. Ibid., p. 12 & 13.

14. Maurice Shelton, "Goat Production," pgs. 459 & 460.

Killian Boers, Des Moines, Iowa.

5. GETTING STARTED IN THE GOAT BUSINESS

"Besides the amount of work that you can do or want to do, you must examine what you have available for a food supply. How many meadows and fields do you own or can you perhaps lease? Where can you buy feed and at what price. Must you build fences? What must you spend for them?"
- Ulrich Jaudras, *The New Goat Handbook*, 1987, p. 9.

One's chances of succeeding in any goat-raising venture are much improved by careful research. Before purchasing a group of goats, it is worthwhile to read everything one can find about goats, visit with as many goat raisers as possible and look at as many goats as possible. Advice from experienced and reputable goat raisers is extremely valuable. *Ranch & Rural Living* as well as *Meat Goat News*, a publication of *Ranch and Rural Living*, published by Scott Campbell, P.O. Box 2678, San Angelo, Texas 76902, contain breeder directories for meat goats, Boer goats, Kiko goats, and Tennessee Wooden Leg - Myotonic goats, for example. Various state and province association addresses, as well as addresses of individual ranchers, are listed in these breeder directories. Some useful addresses include:

American Boer Goat Association, 232 W Beauregard, Suite 104, San Angelo, TX 76903, 915-486-AGBA(2242) (Tel), 915-486-BOER(2637) (Fax), www.abga.org (web site), abga@wcc.net (e-mail)

American Dairy Goat Association, 209 West Main Street, Spindale, NC 28160, 828-286-3801 (Tel), 828-287-0476 (Fax), info@adga.org (e-mail), www.adga.org/ (web site)

American Kiko Goat Association, Inc., P.O. Box 186, Lakeland, GA 31635, 912-244-6058 (Tel)

American Meat Goat Association, P.O. Box 333, Junction, TX 76849 (915-835-2605), contact Marvin Shurley, 915-387-6100 (Tel), 915-387-5814 (Fax)

American Tennessee Fainting Goat Association, Public Relations Director: Cindy Pollock, 955 Brentwood Drive, Eagle Point, Oregon 97525, scflock@medford.net (e-mail); goat registrations, ATFGA Registry Office, RR4, Box 4100, Houlton, ME 14730, www.webworksltd.com/webpub/goats/faintinggoat.html

Canadian Boer Goat Association, Box 1033, Glenwood, Alberta, Canada T0K 2R0, 403-783-4044 (Tel), 403-783-2489 (Fax), www.canadianboergoat.com (web site)

International Boer Goat Association, Rt.3, Box 111, Bonham, TX 75418, 877-402-4242 (Toll Free), 903-640-4060 (Fax), igba@igba.com (e-mail)

National Pygmy Goat Association, 1933 149th Ave. SE, Snohomish, WA 98290, 425-334-6506 (Tel), 425-334-5447(Fax), www.npgapygmy.com (web site)

New York State Meat Goat Association, John R. Addrizzo, MD, P.O. Box 100, Mt. Marion, NY 12456, 914-246-9052 (Tel), 718-981-8891 (Fax)

The Kinder Goat Breeders Association, P.O. Box 1575, Snohomish, WA 89291-1575, KGBAssn@aol.com (e-mail), hometown.aol.com/KGBAssn/index.htm (web site)

One of the most important ingredients of success in any livestock enterprise is to enjoy working with animals. A person who genuinely likes his or her charges and does not resent the time, energy and worry which raising livestock entails is well on the way to being a good goat raiser.

A well-cared-for, top quality meat goat is an animal anyone should be proud to own. Goats have unique personalities, are small, long-lived, hardy, readily handled and need minimal facilities.

However, like any living creature, goats can frustrate one no end. They manage to crawl under and through fences, get their heads stuck in unbelievably small holes and destroy equipment one felt was built sturdily enough for cattle. Your sense of humor can definitely be strained when, after a long day at work, you arrive home to find all your goats contentedly grazing on the wrong side of the fence - in the neighbor's about-to-be-harvested corn. When, on seeing you, the goats walk back through the multistrand electric fence as if it is nonexistent, you may indeed wonder if goat raising is for you.

While a couple of goats make interesting pets, most people who have any number expect to generate some income from them. Meat, breeding stock, milk and hides are all sources of revenue. Some meat-type goats, such as cashmere goats, grow a valuable fiber as well as superior meat. Managed carefully, goats can provide a living or a second income.

Costs of getting started vary, depending on facilities one has available, whether fence needs to be erected and cost of goats in one's area. Cost of goats generally is proportional to one's proximity to Texas and the relatively inexpensive Spanish goats found there. Prospective goat raisers considering purchasing northern goats may find them pricier than if they did their shopping in Texas. However, it is probably not worthwhile making the trek south for just a few goats unless one is planning to buy top quality registered stock. Good quality northern goats are available and they generally have the advantage of developing to their mature size at an earlier age, having been better fed than their Texas counterparts. The northern stock tends to produce more kids, particularly as yearlings and two-year-olds.

Top quality goats generally cost more than mediocre animals, and, of course, registered stock is more expensive than commercial. Prices may range from next-to-nothing for the toothless, lame old nanny to several thousand dollars for an outstanding stud buck.

If one does not plan on selling registered stock, one can start with a group of good quality commercial nannies and the best buck one can afford. Start with a manageable number. The magic number will vary depending on your energy, enthusiasm and experience with livestock: 25 nannies and a buck may be overwhelming for some, whereas 500 nannies may be easily coped with by others. Remember that, if your management is good, your numbers will multiply quickly. So, it is better to start with too few goats than too many.

If your animals will need to be housed for part of the year, plan on 15 square feet of barn space per goat and at least three to four times this space outside the barn. If goats are to be confined year round, plenty of space for hay storage will be necessary. Several hundred goats can be raised on a few acres if kept in confinement, but this is a very labor-intensive method of raising goats. Unless feed resources and/or labor are very inexpensive, raising meat goats in confinement year round is unlikely to be profitable. Pastured goats require varying amounts of land, depending on pasture quality. More than 10 goats may be grazed per acre of good quality land. Twelve to 15 goats or sometimes more can be grazed on good quality alfalfa. Where vegetation is sparse and not overly nourishing, it may take several acres to sustain a single goat. A general rule is that 6 mature goats are equivalent to one cow on native or improved pastures. Ten goats can be grazed in place of one cow if plenty of good quality browse or brush is available.

If one is ingenious and good at bargaining and scrounging, old fence, fence posts, scrap metal and lumber may be purchased relatively inexpensively or even obtained free of charge, and feeders, fences, kidding pens and so forth constructed for a minimal amount. Money is best spent on good quality breeding stock, fencing, nutrition and preventative medicine (coccidiostats, deworming and delousing agents).

6. GOAT SELECTION AND RECORD KEEPING

"Producers need to emphasize adaptability and reproduction as the key traits for a meat goat enterprise. Growth rate and carcass quality are also traits of economic interest."
- Terry A. Gipson, "Meat Goat Breeds and Breeding Plans," *Meat Goat Production and Marketing Handbook,* Clemson Extension, EC 683, October 1996, p. 11.

"Objective selection depends on having records of performance on the candidates for selection, or their relatives, or both."
- Geoff Simm, "Strategies for Genetic Improvement", *Genetic Improvement of Cattle and Sheep*, Farming Press, Miller Freeman UK Ltd, Ipswitch, UK, 1988, p. 77.

I keep records on all goats in my herd, regardless of whether they are registered or commercial animals. This helps me to select the superior goats and eliminate unworthy individuals. Culling goats is not always straightforward as goats with some good features may have less desirable features as well. For example, some goats that gain well and raise top quality growthy offspring on good quality feed may not thrive on marginal nutrition (some range land or poorer-quality pasture) without supplemental feed. So, it is important that selection be made within the environment that the animals are expected to produce in.

Some unwanted traits are more obvious than others and goats with these traits can be readily eliminated. These include low reproductive efficiency (does that abort, kid late, produce and/or raise low numbers of kids or kids that gain poorly when compared to their herd mates), physical or conformational defects (poor feet and legs, cryptorchidism, lower jaw that is too short or too long), poor growth, and small body size and low body weight relative to herd mates. Information that can easily be recorded include dates that bucks are turned out with the does, which buck each group of does is exposed to, kidding dates, age at first kidding, kidding ease, number of kids born and raised each year, birth weights of kids, rate of gain of kids from birth to weaning and postweaning, yearling weights and adults weights. Recording level of supplementary feeding (if any) is also useful. If ultrasounding is available, goats may be appraised postweaning for fat cover and loin eye area.

The simplest system is to keep a card for each goat and record general information including weights and any comments. It is quite difficult to estimate weights accurately. So, decent scales are recommended if one wants to keep proper records and do a good job selecting for the animals that do best in your environment and under your management.

INDIVIDUAL GOAT INFORMATION sheet can include:
Goat Identification - plastic tag number, metal tag number, tattoo, registration number if registered.
Dam Identification
Sire Identification
Pedigree Information (may be kept separately)
Weight records - birth weight, weaning weight, 6 month weight, yearling weight and mature weight. Record date weighed and actual weight. Appropriate weighing times will vary with the operation and marketing system. If kids are usually sold at a young age, for example at weaning, weaning weights and any weights taken before weaning are of most importance.
Carcass information - ultrasound information - back fat and rib eye area measurements. Also carcass information from any relatives that are slaughtered is helpful.
Reproductive information
-Date when buck is introduced and buck identification.
-Number of days from introduction of the buck to kidding date.
-Kidding date.
-Number of kids born.
-Kid identification.
-Abortions, stillbirths or other problems.
-Estimate of kid vigor.
-Estimate of doe milk production.
-Estimate of maternal abilities - note rejected kids or kids grafted to another doe.
-Kid deaths and record reason - weak kid, scours, predation.
-Birth weights.
-Weaning weights and/or 50 and 100 day weights (or 60 and 120 day weights) or whatever weights best suit your operation. Once kids are

weaned, they can be transferred to their own sheet and postweaning information recorded there.

Health problems should be recorded - for example, mastitis, injury, susceptibility to parasitism.

I carry a little notebook (with a waterproof cover) with me at kidding time. I use another book for the rest of the year as, with large numbers of goats, one may forget a tag number or detail by the time one returns to the office. When I make my rounds of the paddocks or pastures, I record information in these books. If kids are born in a building, a clipboard in the barn can be used to record the same information. Then the information can be transferred to record sheets or to a computerized system or both. Be very careful not to leave your records in a spot where the goats can nibble on them. It is also a good idea to make copies of records or transfer them daily in case an accident does occur.

Details recorded are as follows:

BIRTHING/KIDDING NOTEBOOK

Primary Kid Identification - number followed by international year code. For example, 1K was the first kid born in the year 2000. Tattoo is the same as the primary identification.

Secondary Kid Identification - unique metal ear tag (backup identification), combination of letters and numbers that are different from the primary identification.

Dam Identification
Sex
Sire Identification
Birth Date
Birth Weight
Birth Type
Kidding problems (if any)
Kid presentation (normal, breech)
Kid vigor estimate
Maternal qualities (or lack of)
Comments

I assign any dead or stillborn kids a primary identification so that they are part of the total tally. This helps to identify highly prolific does.

Weaning weight and day weighed can be added to this booklet or recorded on separate sheets.

Characteristics which influence profitability of meat goat operations include the number of kids reared to slaughter per doe per year and the weight and carcass attributes of the kids produced. Feed consumption, health and longevity are also considerations. Since reproduction and pounds of meat weaned are the most important items in a meat goat operation, they need to be the primary focus of any commercial operation. As well, production should be within a defined kidding season utilizing the inputs you are prepared to provide - for example, feed, labor and buildings.

Kid production is strongly influenced both by the number of kids born and kid survival. Typically, survival is lower as the number of kids born increases as birth weights are lower. As well, the ability of some does to kid approximately every 8 months (3 times in 2 years) can increase kid output per doe if adequate feed resources are available and the climate/environment and management is appropriate for this level of production.

Carcass value is usually related to carcass weight, fatness and conformation. Breed, age, sex and time of year can also influence value.

Feed costs and feed efficiency are important whether the goats are being raised intensively with concentrate feeding of kids or extensively, grazing grass or forage crops.

Some breeds or crosses are hardier and longer lived than others. Crosses of 2 breeds are always hardier than either of the breeds used to make the cross due to heterosis. The longer each doe is productive in a herd, the lower replacement doe costs are.

A commercial operation typically strives for medium-sized, hardy, long-lived maternal does that are fertile, prolific, have vigorous kids and plenty of milk for them. Terminal sires exhibiting strong growth and carcass traits are bred to these does to produce top quality kids for market. Replacement female numbers required are estimated before the breeding season and the best maternal does are bred to a maternal buck to provide top quality replacement animals. All offspring from the terminal sires should be marketed and should not be used for replacements (at least in the ideal world). This is because replacements from a terminal sire may not be as strong in maternal traits and thus less productive and will have a larger mature body size and weight making them more costly to feed.

Growth and carcass traits are moderately variable and moderately to highly heritable. Most reproductive traits are more variable and have low heritabilities. Correlations among live weights recorded at different ages are usually high, particularly later in life when the maternal influence on birthweights and other early weights has declined. Correlations between weight and carcass dimensions are usually positive. There is a tendency for genetic relationships between weight and fertility to be negative (very large framed later maturing individuals are typically less fertile). An exception is the relationship between yearling live weight and the number of kids born and raised which is usually positive (well grown yearlings tend to bear and raise more kids).[1]

Of interest to many raising goats in extensive conditions is selection for gastrointestinal parasite resistance. In sheep, fecal egg counts (FECs) are being used as an indicator of resistance to gastrointestinal parasitism. FECs are good indicators of gastrointestinal parasite infestations and are moderately heritable in sheep (0.25 - 0.3).[1]

My individual record cards do not contain routine processing information such as foot trimming, vaccinations, deworming, and so on. This information is recorded on herd sheets. For example, if I trim feet and deworm the goats, I make a note of the date, the procedures performed and which goats or groups of goats are and are not processed. Generally I attempt to process the goats in large batches.

It is particularly important to note when either groups of animals or individual animals are treated with a product such as an antibiotic or dewormer. This is so that withdrawal times can be observed when animals are marketed for meat. Some products can take weeks to be eliminated from the system. Do check with your veterinarian to find out withdrawal times for each product you treat your goats with.

Sophisticated computerized record keeping systems are becoming more readily available and the serious producer who wants to make improvements should consider and hopefully use one of these. These programs estimate the genetic value of various traits using contemporary groups (animals of the same breed, sex and genetic makeup born at the same time and raised under the same conditions) to account for environmental variation. To properly compare animals, it is imperative that goats within a contemporary group are of a similar age. As well, weights taken from individuals within a contemporary group must be adjusted for age of the individual, sex of the individual, birth type of the individual, age of the dam and so on. The phenotype (physical appearance of an animal) is the result of both genetics and environment. For example, a goat with the genetics to have the best rate of gain in the herd may not gain very well if raised on poor pasture in a drought year. However, if raised under the same environmental conditions, none of the animals in the group will grow as well as expected. When this genetically superior individual is compared with its contemporary group members, which were all raised on poor pasture and the environmental effects accounted for, this goat will be above average. Because animals within a contemporary group are raised under identical conditions, they can be compared with each other and unknown nongenetic effects adjusted for. The contemporary group concept is the foundation for genetic improvement in livestock.

When the performance of each animal in a contemporary group is compared to the average of its contemporaries, a more precise estimate of genetic value can be obtained than by evaluating individual animal performance.

Predictions of genetic values - Estimated Breeding Values or EBVs - are the result of applying genetic theory and statistics to performance records. The deviation of an individual's or relative's records from its contemporary group averages is multiplied by a weighting factor. As more information, including correlated traits, is recorded for the animal and its relatives, the reliability of the EBV increases. Information on relatives (especially close relatives) is particularly important for EBVs for traits that are not very heritable.

EPDs or expected progeny differences are half of the EBV - the half of a goat's breeding value that is passed on to its offspring.

An idea of the reliability of an EBV or EPD can be assessed by noting the accuracy value associated with these figures. Low accuracy figures are the result of little information being available on the animal being evaluated or when heritability is low for the trait.

LAMBPLAN, Department of Animal Science, University of New England, Armidale, NSW 2351, Australia, a national sheep and goat computerized record keeping system in Australia, will accept records from anywhere in the world. A comparable program exists in the US for sheep but not for goats. LAMBPLAN has a program for Boer goats for producing estimated breeding values (EBVs) for growth traits, fat and muscle traits and reproductive traits, all of which affect profitability. The weight EBVs describe an animal's genetic merit for growth rate. A positive EBV means that the animal is genetically faster growing than the average. EBVs for birth and weaning weight also provide maternal EBVs so that the genetic merit of each goat is divided into the direct effect of its own genes and the effect (milking ability) of the mother. EBVs can be determined for weaning weight, yearling weight and mature doe weight.

Goats can be ultrasonically scanned at 50 to 65 kg (bucks) and 45 to 55 kg (does) so that fat EBVs and eye muscle depth EBVs can be determined. Reproductive EBVs indicate the animal's value based on kidding and/or marking rate and the number of kids weaned.

Higher merit sires produce kids that grow more quickly. These offspring can be slaughtered faster and kids meet carcass specifications for fat and muscling. Higher merit dams have more kids as well as kids with higher growth rates and improved carcass characteristics. More information on LAMBPLAN can be found on the LAMBPLAN web pages on the internet. (www.ansc.une.edu.au/lambplan/index.htm)

Programs such as LAMPBLAN are an excellent way of comparing one animal to the next within a herd. Rapid improvement in traits can be made by selecting high merit males and females. Measurements needed for determining EBVs can easily be collected (weights, kidding records and ultrasound information) and submitted. As more animals that are related to each other are entered into the system, across flock comparisons can be performed. These are based on genetic linkages between animals. One of the best way to obtain useful across flock comparisons is to use a common sire or semen in the flocks that are being compared.

Notes: Chapter 6

1. Geoff Simm, "Strategies for Genetic Improvement", *Genetic Improvement of Cattle and Sheep*, Farming Press, Miller Freeman UK Ltd, Ipswich, UK, 1988, p. 77.

7. FACILITIES, FEEDERS AND FENCING

"It must be admitted that the goat is inherently less easy to control than other members of the farmyard community; yet the nature of the goat is disciplined, co-operative and intelligent; most of the difficulty in controlling her arises out of the fact that the goat's psychology, her requirements in the way of food and shelter, and the specifications for the fence that will control her, are so very different from those of other farm stock."
- David Mackenzie, *Goat Husbandry*, 4th ed., London: Faber & Faber, 1980.p. 67.

Fancy facilities or equipment are not necessary for raising meat goats. In fact, one can usually "make do" with old buildings and scrap lumber and metal. In many environments, housing is not essential. However, if heavy rainfall and/or severe winters plague the region you plan to raise goats in, shelter such as an open-fronted, south-facing building or even a grove of trees will help the goats thrive. Use your imagination. All sorts of goat facilities and feeders are just waiting to be designed.

Many existing farm buildings can be readily converted into goat housing. Housing can be as simple as a three-sided pole shed that is open to the south, has an insulated roof and natural ventilation. Far more elaborate (and impractical - unless it is an existing unused facility) is an insulated confinement building that can be heated, and, in the winter at least, requires exhaust or pressure ventilation to provide adequate air quality.

We have found that goats do very well with minimal facilities and, indeed, if one's operation is a serious commercial enterprise, housing is a major and often unnecessary additional expense. Well fed, mature goats tolerate cold readily. Sheds or barns really are only necessary to keep the animals dry if there is prolonged cold, wet weather and to provide a dry area for kidding, especially if one plans to have kids arrive during cold or wet weather. In a truly commercial operation, it is not usually practical to have does birthing inside. Kidding time should be planned so that good quality feed (pasture and/or browse) is available and weather is sufficiently warm that newborn kids will not freeze. Rainy seasons should be avoided as newborn kids chill quickly in cold rains.

The doors and windows of our pole shed are kept open all the time except during blizzards or severe rain storms when large quantities of snow or rain, respectively, can blow into the barn. In the spring, summer and fall, one group of our pastured goats has only trees for shelter; another has a three-sided shed; and another, a shade-shelter covered with snow fencing. All groups remain healthy. Goats kept outside as much as possible have more available space per animal and thus tend to do better than those closely confined. As well, many disease problems are perpetuated when goats are closely confined. A book containing some useful information on housing, as well as all sorts of advice about sheep equipment (some of which can be used for goats) is *Sheep Housing and Equipment Handbook*, MWPS-3, Midwest Plan Service, Iowa State University, Ames, Iowa 50011.

Confinement setup. (Crane Creek Enterprises)

In confinement, goats can be kept in groups of approximately 20 to 30 head and feeders used to divide pens. Goats need more square feet per head in a barn than sheep of comparable size and weight because of their aggressive treatment of each other. Probably 15 square feet of floor space in the barn or shed is sufficient. Depending on the size and aggressiveness of the goats, more or less space can be allotted.

Confinement setup (winter quarters) open to the south. (Crane Creek Enterprises)

If you plan to have your does kid during cold or rainy weather, your building(s) will need space to house goats at kidding time. If harvested feed is fed during periods of the year, there needs to be an area for hay and/ or grain (unless you have bulk bin(s)) and bedding. A storage spot for mineral is necessary, especially if it is purchased in bulk. The building can also have space for tools and machinery (if you have any of the latter). Space can be saved by using one area for several different things. For example, hay, straw and cornstalk bales can be stored in the kidding area for most of the year. By the time kidding season arrives, much of the feed and bedding has been utilized and there is plenty of room to set up kidding pens. A cement pad for sorting, processing or quarantining goats in one shed can serve as a parking place for the pickup and tractor, or whatever else, for much of the year. If you are planning to build a shed for goats, make it bigger than you think will be necessary. Your operation is likely to grow, not shrink, and extra space always comes in handy. As well, build things strongly. Goats, for their size, are quite hard on equipment and you do not want to spend all your time repairing things.

It is best to have a somewhat flexible floor plan, as, over time, one may find that one's initial setup is not as handy as expected and some rearranging may be in order. Thus feed bunks, panels and gates should be movable and, while they should be sturdy, they should not be so heavy that one is unable to move them. Metal or wooden 3.5 to 4 feet high and 8 to 12 feet long panels are useful for dividing or creating pens. These are a convenient size, since, when the barn is being cleaned, at least some of the equipment will probably need to be moved around.

A floor composed of lime screenings or other absorbent material that packs firmly works well and is preferable to concrete. When the barn is cleaned prior to kidding, fresh lime screenings can be spread on the floor. New screenings should also be spread in the kidding pens once in a while.

Each group of goats in a building should have access to the outside. Goats in adjacent pens will constantly butt and poke at their neighbors and, in the process, destroy almost any kind of fence. Even the most timid goat will incessantly bang on a fence, despite the fact that the goat in the next pen may be much larger and more aggressive. Goats are intelligent and seem to know that the fence provides personal protection. Of course, they are completely unconcerned about their fate once they have destroyed the fence. Anyway, we solved the problem (after the goats ruined several hundred dollars worth of fencing, including some cattle and hog panels) by running a single strand of hot wire around the inside of each pen at goat nose level (8-12 inches off the ground depending on the size of the goat). We use a powerful New Zealand type fence energizer and, after each goat tries to attack the fence once or twice, he or she leaves it alone. We have never had goats tamper with good nonelectrified perimeter fences unless inviting feed is growing right next to the fence. Then the goats will try and eat through the fence, often damaging it in the process.

Each pen or pasture should be provided with fresh water. Depending on which facility or pasture I have the goats in, I use electrically-heated two-sided horse waterers, hog nipple waterers (the goats seem to be slower to catch on to these than sheep and dribble a lot of water on the ground), energy-free waterers with lids or fifty gallon oval plastic or metal one foot high sheep or goat water tanks. Stock tanks with tall sides - 1.5 to 2 feet tall or more - should be avoided as goats or kids may climb into them and drown.

One foot tall sheep or goat water tanks can be heated with a floating stock tank heater in the winter. Some heaters will melt plastic tanks if they come into contact with the walls or base of these tanks so one needs to either avoid this type of heater or never allow tanks to run out of water. In the summer we use an automatic float in these stock tanks so that the goats have water available all day on a hot day. If the pasture is bordered by solid fence (no electric fence), about a third to half of the stock tank is pushed through a previously cut hole in the fence so that the goats cannot reach the float setup. In our rotational grazing setup, the float setup is positioned along the 2 or 3 strands of hot wire used to contain the goats. This way, the automatic float cannot be reached by the goats and flipped out on the ground. Waterers should be cleaned frequently as goats are very particular about their water supply and do not like dirty water. Wind can transfer considerable dirt into water tanks or waterers, so cleaning may need to be a daily or every-other-day event.

If you use hog nipple waterers, it is a good idea to fix the nipples initially so they drip a small amount of water. If one does this for a few days, the goats catch on to drinking from the nipple waterers more easily. When they see the water dripping from the nipples, they will start playing with them and learn to drink out of them.

Goats can also be taught to lift lids on "energy-free" waterers, but this takes some time and patience too. We wire up the lids and gradually drop them down until the goats figure out how to lift the lids.

The main challenge in making feeders for goats is to design something that the goats cannot get their feet into, or, in the case of kids, the entire body. Feeders set low on the ground are a problem because, even if they are designed so that the adults cannot get into them, the kids inevitably can. Kids love to sleep on the hay in any low bunk, and, unfortunately, they contaminate the feed with fecal material. We have had good luck with feeders that have the feed trough elevated to one to two feet off the ground, depending on the size of the goat. We also find that placing a "stand bar" a few inches off the ground encourages the goats to stand on this bar to eat instead of trying to put their feet in the feed trough. We have always lined our V-shaped hay feeders with two or four by four inch wire - either welded or woven sturdy wire will do - so the goats have to work a little to get their rations. We find we have very little hay wastage and our goats definitely do not appear to be underfed.

Make sure feed bunks are anchored to something on the side of the barn, such as metal or wooden posts. It is surprising how easily goats manage to turn feed bunks over. Since goats are hard on bunks and pens, we never use 1 by 4 inch lumber. At least 2 by 4 inch boards work well for us. Mature nannies can easily smash three-eighths inch plywood or 1 by 4

Eight-month-old Texas billies receiving extra feed. (Adams' Ranch)

Iowa goats in confinement. (Crane Creek Enterprises)

Close-up of feed bunk for confined Iowa Angoras. (Crane Creek Enterprises)

Simple wooden feed bunk (and attentive young Border Collie, "Flo"). (Crane Creek Enterprises)

Feed bunk based on design from Premier Fence Supplies, Washington, IOWA. (Crane Creek Enterprises)

An Angora doe and a three-month-old kid drinking from an automatic waterer (Midwestern United States). (Crane Creek Enterprises)

Old Iowa dairy barn converted into kidding and lambing facility. (Crane Creek Enterprises)

Savanna triplets and dam in pen in converted Iowa dairy barn. (Crane Creek Enterprises)

inch boards used to make kidding pens, particularly if they dislike a goat in the neighboring kidding pen. So, even items like kidding pens should be sturdily made or a lot of repair work will be necessary.

If one has large numbers of goats in confinement or semiconfinement and one wants to save some space - for example, if large, round hay bales are being fed, then it really is not necessary to have grain bunks in each pen - a central grain feeding area should be considered. Goats can be let into a central area, allowed to eat their grain and then released back into their original pen. The grain troughs are refilled, the next group of goats let into the central grain feeding area and so on. This cuts down on space required for grain feeders and goats quickly adapt to moving into a central feeding area and then back to their own pen once their grain has been consumed.

Our home-built creep feeders are similar to the V-shaped hay feeders, except that the sides of the feeder are made of plywood instead of wire. Other feeders that work well for creep feeding include old metal turkey self-feeders and various metal hog self-feeders. Some of these will need to be elevated on bricks or platforms so the kids do not constantly have their feet in the feed. Goats like to push and shove against their feeders, so be certain that they cannot knock any of the self-feeders over on themselves or their pen mates. Hanging self-feeders are also good: just be sure that they are firmly suspended so that the goats cannot pull them down on themselves.

Small plastic or metal hog creep feeders, hanging tires (the sides of which are spread apart with the use of scrap lumber), and sheep mineral feeders are all useful for dispensing salt and mineral.

We have had good luck getting by with existing fencing by placing one or two strands of electric wire just inside whatever old fence happened to be on land we have rented. The bottom wire is placed about 10 inches off the ground; if you need to add a second wire it can be 10 -12 inches above the lower strand.

The reason for using 1 strand of offset electric fence inside woven wire fence! (Crane Creek Enterprises)

We use 2 hot wires placed at these heights in our rotational grazing setup. Electric netting is very popular on some small farms for subdividing paddocks. Goats readily learn to respect electric fence if introduced to it when there is a good strong charge passing through the fence (5000 volts or more). For any pasture situation we use the most powerful fence energizer (a New Zealand type low-impedance fast-energy release design) we can find, but, even so, some goats always seem to be testing the fence. The fence should be checked daily with a volt meter and any repairs made before the goats escape. If you can identify individual escape artists, they should be culled.

Two strands of maxishock, fiberglass post. (Crane Creek Enterprises)

So, if you own your own pasture, it is a good idea to put up a permanent peripheral fence. Then, a large pasture can be subdivided using electric fence if one plans to do any intensive grazing. High tensile (with or without some electrified strands), welded wire or woven wire fences will all contain goats. Woven wire fences should be of the sheep variety - this type of fence allows a goat to pass its head through the fence and pull it back out without getting its horns caught. We like to place one strand of hot wire at goat nose level inside this type of fence. Otherwise the goats seem to enjoy grazing through the fence and are quite hard on it.

An excellent fencing manual can be obtained free of charge from Premier, Box 89, Washington, Iowa 52353. It contains numerous illustrations and information on fencing supplies and methods of installing fencing.

Permanent electrified fences do not need to be very tall: 40 inches is sufficient. However, they should be very close to the ground as goats are expert at crawling under things.

Electric fence showing tread-in posts. Note water line lying along fence line. Early spring/late winter. (Crane Creek Enterprises)

Installing electric fence in comfort! (New Zealand)

Very effective goat fencing; 4 strands of electric fence. (New Zealand)

Try to anticipate goat disaster areas before a goat succeeds in strangling, drowning, getting crushed or smothered. Your barn, lots and pastures should be made as safe as possible: goats seem to be attracted to trouble spots.

8. HANDLING SYSTEMS

"One of the most important and probably least understood things is how to use the movement of animals to help you."
- Bud Williams, "Bud Williams Stockmanship."

"Just as throughput efficiency can be improved, it can also be ruined by layout mistakes."
- Temple Grandin*

A few goats can be ushered into a small pen and individually captured and processed for procedures such as vaccination and deworming. However, for any number of animals, some sort of handling system, if carefully designed, can save a tremendous amount of time and energy. If the handling system works well and animals flow through it smoothly and efficiently, management jobs are likely to be performed in a more timely manner with much less stress to animals and handler(s).

Because permanent handling facilities require considerable thought and planning if they are to be effective, a portable or movable handling system should be considered. First of all, a permanent facilty must be located in an accessible, likely central, portion of the ranch or farm so that animals can be easily moved to the facility for processing. Availability of electricity should be considered as well as proximity to roads for loading and unloading. Whether the facility is inside a building or outside depends on factors such as the size of the facility, available building space and climate. Most handling systems of any size are located outside. A shade or rain shelter can be erected over the facility if necessary. One should consider what sort of procedures are routinely performed and how many animals are typically processed in a single group to help determine priority given to the different features of the systems and to decide on dimensions of pens and chutes. Vaccination, deworming, weighing and foot trimming, depending on the climate, are likely to head the list. If holding pens are too

*Temple Grandin operates Grandin Handling Systems, Inc., Ft. Collins, Colorado.

Handling facility with skylights in roof. (New Zealand)

Outside handling facility. (New Zealand)

small, a lot of time can be wasted moving animals from pen to pen. If pens are too large, the goats can scatter and, again, time and energy are used chasing animals.

Basically one needs a holding pen or pens, depending on the size of the operation, for receiving and holding the largest group size you will work with at one time. Once the animals are in this holding or gathering pen, small groups can be separated from the main group by wide gates and moved into the much smaller crowding pen. Allow anywhere from 3 to 6 square feet per animal, depending on the goat size. Long rectangular pens with slanted ends work well. Fences and gates of gathering pens should not be solid and they can be made of wood, wire or welded panels. To support wooden panels, posts should be 4 to 6 feet apart and, for wire fence, not more than 8 feet apart. If you have agile goats that jump readily when stressed, make sure that the panels are high enough, at least 42 or, better yet, 48 inches tall. Low panels encourage jumping. Make sure that entrance gates are wide enough so that animals enter the pen(s) easily.

The crowding or forcing pen is used to confine a small group of animals (15 to 30 head for a several hundred head herd; more for larger herds) within an area that has solid sides. It is adjacent to the treatment chute that the goats will move into as soon as space is available. The forcing pen also allows a way, if need be, to physically move or crowd the small group towards and into the treatment chute. For herds of 500 or so goats, a circular or semicircular forcing pen is very effective. For large herds, a rectangular shape works better for sorting larger groups of animals into one or more wider treatment chutes.

Swinging gates for the forcing pen should not be more than 8 or 10 feet long. A standard hinged gate has the disadvantage of having to be swung back against the goats in the holding pen; however, it is still better than nothing! More innovative gates include the lift-swing gate, which lifts straight up at the end of its arc and swings back over the heads of the incoming animals; the swing-slide gate, which is a single gate without a center post that can be continuously swung in one direction and, at the end of its arc, slides through itself in its own frame, the inner end becoming the outer end for the next sweep of the gate; and the center post gate, which has a center post with two swinging gates that can each swing in a full circle and so alternate between being the inner and outer gate.

A treatment chute should be narrow enough (typically 12 inches wide but up to 18 inches wide for the largest goats) so that the animals are walking single file. One needs to make the chute the appropriate width for the goats one is working. The chute needs to be narrow enough that the goats cannot turn around. Some purchased chute panels are adjustable and can be adapted to working kids or smaller goats. Chutes can be designed so that they are wider at the top (to accommodate the horns, chest and abdomen) and narrower at the bottom (where the feet are!). The chute walls need to be solid and are usually made of wood or metal. Height may be from 36 to 48 inches. If the operator is only going to work over one side of the chute and the goats have a tendency to jump, the far side can be made taller (48 inches). Sections of the chute should not be more than 10 feet long as goats tend to pile up and lie down in the chute. A sliding gate can be used to divide a 20 foot long chute into two 10 foot sections.

At the end of the treatment chute a sort gate - at least a two way sort gate - allows animals going through the chute to be sorted into a minimum of 2 different groups. Thus one needs at least 2 sort pens. The sort gate also acts as a temporary stop gate. Three and 4 way sort gates can be complicated for one person to operate but they are available. With a two way sort gate, for example, animals going to market may be sorted off from the main group into their own pen. The sort gate must be easy to use and there needs to be sufficient chute preceding it so that the operator has enough time to see the animal and make a decision about which way to sort it. Depending on the length of the chute, there may be one or more antiback-up gates in the chute so that once the goat passes a certain point in the chute it cannot back up. Scales may be placed in the chute for weighing and a turntable may be at another location in the chute for foot trimming. Usually stop gates, a center folding type of gate, whose action is across the chute, are used at the exit and entrance to scales and turning tables as well as at the entrance to a treatment or sorting chute.

For larger operations, wider chutes, treatment chutes, up to 3 feet wide and often from 18 to 27 feet long, can be used for vaccinating and deworming. The owner works in the treatment chute with the animals, instead of from the outside of the chute, and allows treated animals to pass behind him or her as he or she progresses from one end of the chute to the other. While big setups may have both a narrow sorting chute and a wider chute for processing, many smaller systems use the narrow sorting chute for all procedures. In large setups, animals progress from the wider treatment chute into narrower chutes where they can be sorted.

A cable stretched 6 feet above the chute for the length of the chute is useful for attaching containers of vaccine or dewormer. These containers can be on rolling pulleys and so can be moved up and down the length of

Curved handling system with scales just behind sort gate. (New Zealand)

Portable handling system for sheep (or larger goats). (New Zealand)

the chute as the animals are processed.

Many of the components of a handling facility can be homemade and the more complex items purchased. Turning cradles, a device that squeezes the animal from the front and the rear until all four feet leave the ground and then the animal is flipped upside down end over end, do not work well for goats as they can squirm out of the embrace of the cradle. Tilt tables do work but typically access to anything but the feet is minimal.

If one understands the behavior of his or her goats, it is much easier to erect a good working system. Dr. Temple Grandin, whose web page is at www.grandin.com, has written and edited several books and many articles on animal handling, including *Livestock Handling and Transport*, edited by Temple Grandin, Oxford University Press, Cary, NC. She has designed many of the cattle handling facilities in the United States and has a lot of information on her web page and in her books and articles on the design of handling facilities. Although her information is slanted towards cattle, much of it is applicable to other species, including goats.

Although the points outlined below seem obvious, they are worth mentioning because most chute systems that do not work have incorporated some of these problems.

Some basics of chute design include:

Lighting should be diffuse and even. Animals do not want to enter dark or dimly lit buildings and chute systems. If lights are to be used in a building to illuminate a chute, they should not shine directly into an animal's eyes. Watch for shadows and puddles in a system; they can cause animals to balk.

The single file chute and crowd pen and crowd gate should have solid fences. This will help animals to move smoothly through the system as they cannot see distractions outside.

Chutes should never look like a dead end. When the animal is standing at the chute entrance, it should be able to see at least two to three body lengths up the chute.

Chutes should not be too short. A minimum of 20 feet (two 10 foot sections for goats) is recommended so that there is a good flow of animals through the chute.

Don't make the crowd pen too large and don't overload it.

Keep noise to a minimum and speak in a normal voice. Loud foreign noises distract and upset the animals.

Don't stand or allow strangers to stand in front of the chute when animals are supposed to be entering it.

Curved systems with round crowd pens are more efficient than straight systems if laid out correctly. This is because animals going through a round pen will run up the chute without hesitating, thinking that they are headed in the direction from which they came. The best setup allows animals to travel in a 90 to 180 degree turn.

Working systems are best on a flat piece of ground. If the chute needs to be on a slope, a slight uphill slope is acceptable.

Moving animals gently and carefully pays off as, if their initial introduction to the working system is not unpleasant, they will move through it much more readily in the future.

Dogs should not be used to move animals in very small pens where animals may pile up. A dog can be used to gently move the goats from the pasture into the gathering pen. After that, if the pens are set up correctly, it should not be that difficult to move the animals through the system. Bud Williams, from Alberta, Canada, believes that the average rancher or farmer forces animals to do what he or she wants instead of LETTING the animals do what he or she wants. This, of course, means wondering what you did to make the animal behave a certain way, not just assuming that it was the fault of the animal. Treated humanely and with an understanding of animal behavior (and with some patience), goats can be made to cooperate very well and can be moved readily with a minimum of stress. Bud Williams has some interesting articles on the internet and, as well, offers animal handling schools which are often advertised in *The Stockman Grass Farmer*, P.O. Box 2300, Ridgeland, MS 39158-2300, 1-800-748-9808 (Telephone) 601-853-8087 (Facsimile).

Training a lead goat to conduct a group of animals through the chute and then return to the crowding pen to collect more goats is also very useful. A lead goat can be rewarded with food to keep him or her focused on the job! Lead animals work well because goats move towards other goats and generally follow one another.

SIMPLE HANDLING SYSTEM FOR SMALL HERDS

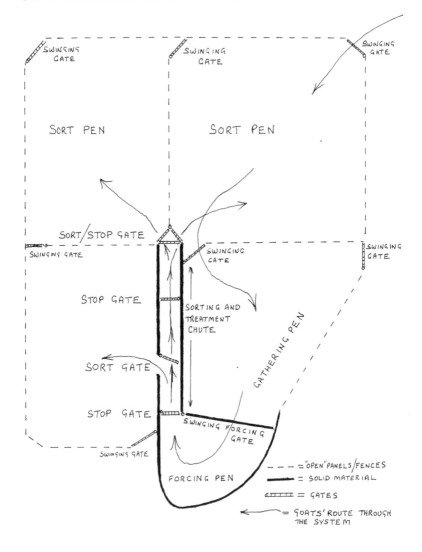

SWINGING GATE

SWINGING GATE

SWINGING GATE

SORT PEN

SORT PEN

SORT/STOP GATE

SWINGING GATE

SWINGING GATE

SWINGING GATE

STOP GATE

SORTING AND TREATMENT CHUTE

GATHERING PEN

SORT GATE

STOP GATE

SWINGING FORCING GATE

SWINGING GATE

FORCING PEN

- - - = "OPEN" PANELS/FENCES
━━━ = SOLID MATERIAL
⟨▭▭▭▭ = GATES
⟵ = GOATS' ROUTE THROUGH THE SYSTEM

9. NUTRITION

"...adequate year round grazing with only mineral supplementation is the optimum option..."

Frank Pinkerton, Bruce Pinkerton, "Feeding Programs for Meat Goats," *Meat Goat Production and Marketing Handbook*, Clemson Extension EC 683, October 1996.

The ideal situation is to have healthy, productive goats that obtain their nourishment from forage. However, because, in most locations, forage growth and weather patterns vary from year to year, supplemental feed may be needed in some grazing situations. In more northern climates, where forages grow only a little or not at all during the colder months, goats may need to be hand fed harvested feed for at least part of the winter. Since well-nourished goats mature at an earlier age, raise more and faster growing, healthier kids and have fewer health problems than their counterparts who live on poorer feed, good nutrition is essential. In some circumstances, if feed, including grain, is abundant and inexpensive, it may be worthwhile to feed goats very well, reckoning that, although some additional feed and labor costs are incurred, there are more pounds of kid to sell per doe.

One needs to very carefully assess feed and labor costs in the region one plans to raise goats in. Often it is more economical to have the goats grow and mature more slowly on forage alone or forage with minimal supplementation. Although these goats may be less productive in terms of pounds of kid raised per year, they are more profitable because there are few or no extra feed and labor costs. Feeding meat goats is a balancing act and one must be careful not to spend all one's profits and then some on feed!

To produce and raise a good kid crop it is essential that goats obtain adequate nutrition from forage and/or other feed sources. Weak small kids born to does with inadequate milk may not survive a sudden rain storm and, for one's goat enterprise to be profitable, one needs to have kids to sell. Well grown doe kids can produce at least a single kid at 12 months of age and, well nourished mature nannies can have and raise twins and even triplets. With increased numbers of kids raised, the operation has more pounds of meat to sell, and, as well, one can progress faster in selecting superior animals. A goat that has produced 5 or more kids by 3 years of age has given a strong indication of the type of offspring she will produce. Thus goats that do not suit an operation can be culled at a fairly young age. One must be careful to select goats that will thrive on the available feed and in the local environment.

One also can overfeed goats, particularly if they are kept in confinement or semiconfinement. Goats that are too fat are no more desirable than those that are too thin. It is important to assess body condition continually and feed accordingly.

Since goats store much of their fat internally, keeping tabs on body condition is useful. Animals typically receive a score between 0 and 5, based on feeling the sternal region (the chest and between the front legs) and lumbar region (along the top of the back). A 0 score is given when there is little to no fat along the spine and the tips of the vertebrae are very prominent. When the sternum is palpated and mainly bone is felt, this also is a 0 score. A 5 score is assigned when the backbone is completely covered by fat and the tips of the vertebrae can barely be felt. At this score the sternum is covered with fat that bulges backward and up over the ribs.

A healthy doe at breeding time typically has a body condition score of 2.5 to 3 and should maintain this score during early and midgestation. By kidding time, a doe should have a condition score of 3 to 3.5. A loss in body condition score of 1 to 2 points during lactation is acceptable IF the doe was in good condition at kidding time and IF the doe is producing kids once a year. If a doe is to produce kids every 8 months, she needs to be kept in good body condition during lactation since there is little time for her to regain body condition prebreeding. A breeding buck should be separated from the does (either on pasture or in drylot) if his body condition score drops below 2. Overly fat does are more susceptible to metabolic problems such as pregnancy toxemia and overly thin does are more susceptible to diseases, parasitism and may not produce enough milk for optimal growth of their kid(s).

Since feed is the major expense in any goat operation, one must strive to feed for maximal production without wasting feed by overnourishing the animals. This is a challenge for anyone and requires keeping careful records of amounts and types of feed, their costs and individual animal production. Animals under the same nutritional program do not all achieve the same production. In some regions, where nutrition is poorer, large framed goats are less profitable since, compared to a smaller animal, they have to walk farther to obtain enough feed to maintain their body weight. In hot, humid environments where internal parasites are more of a problem, breeds, crosses or particular bloodlines of goats that are more resistant to internal parasites should be selected. Since the producer's aim should be to have superior animals as well as to make money, animals that are less productive should be culled from the herd.

Goats can adapt to a wide range of feeds, but it should be remembered that changes in diet should be made gradually. In their natural environment, goats are selective browsers and prefer leaves and needles from both deciduous trees and evergreen shrubs as well as sprouts, twigs and woody plants. They also consume weeds and grasses with great pleasure. Goats typically travel considerable distances when browsing and all this activity may result in increased energy requirements compared to animals that graze. Because of the diet goats prefer, they complement cattle and sheep on woody pasture and range land. With such a complementary arrangement, more animals can be stocked per available acre because the sheep and cattle prefer to graze while the goats are busy browsing. Due to the goats' preference for weeds, they are being used to control multiflora rose in the Midwest, leafy spurge in the northern plains and mountain states and kudzu in the southern states.

Depending on the area you live in, availability of certain feeds and feed costs will vary. Thus, it is important to research your feed program with the help of a nutritionist familiar with your geographic region. Your Cooperative Extension Specialist should be able to help you or refer you to an appropriate person or persons. A publication, *Nutrient Requirements of Goats: Angora, Dairy and Meat Goats in Temperate and Tropical Countries*, National Academy Press, Washington, DC, NRC 1981 provides useful guidelines.

To maintain adequate goat performance in a grazing situation in which plants are low in protein or forage quantity is reduced, protein must be supplemented. The level at which protein needs to be supplemented depends on the age of the animals involved and/or their physiological status. The stage of gestation or lactation, whether they are young growing animals, animals about to be bred or goats simply needing to be maintained (mature does postweaning and prebreeding) all needs to be taken into consideration. Some factors to consider in supplementing protein include labor costs associated with feeding, cost of the supplemental protein, feeding equipment required and palatability. Often hay is a convenient source of additional protein but protein blocks or cottonseed or soybean meal may also be considered. Sufficient roughage, even of poor quality, is needed for goats to properly utilize the protein supplied. To compute the cost of a pound of protein, divide the price of a hundred pounds of feed by the protein content of the feed (lb protein/cwt of feed).

Supplementation with good quality hay, 0.5 to 1 pound of shelled corn or whole cottonseed is needed if pastures or rangeland are low in energy. Cost per unit of energy should be carefully considered. In some operations, protein blocks and hay are available at all times and goats can consume supplemental feed as forage quality declines.

Frank and Bruce Pinkerton, in their article, "Feeding Programs for Meat Goats[1]," mention that they have found a mixture of ground milo, cottonseed meal and 8 to 15% salt to be a useful 16 to 20% protein supplement for open, pregnant and lactating goats on dry grass or hay or limited grazing. The salt in the mixture limits supplement consumption. Initial intake is minimal but then increases to 0.75 to 1.25 pounds per head per day, depending on the amount of roughage being consumed.

Meat goat kids often do not receive creep feed; however, factors such as high prices for good quality kids as well as for heavier, better conditioned kids may encourage producers to consider creep feeding kids. For example, kids raised in the eastern United States for the hothouse Easter market are usually creep fed. Creep feeding decisions should be based on pasture quality as well as on the marketing program. Lamb grower ration works nicely (Ration B) if the ingredients can be purchased for a reasonable price. Kids consume pelleted feed or coarsely ground feed better than feed that is ground to a powder-like consistency. Simple grain mixtures of corn, oats, barley or milo may also suffice[1]. Creep feeders must be in a location that kids can easily find and entry ports to the creep area must be multiple and not so large that the nannies can enter the creep area also. Some guardian dogs may also get into the creep areas and eat the creep feed so the creep area design should also prevent this from happening.

If nannies are in thin condition prior to breeding, "flushing" or feeding supplemental protein and/or energy for 30 days before and 30 days after the introduction of the buck(s) will improve fertility and increase conception rates. If goats are in good condition, flushing may not be necessary. Increasing weight gain prebreeding may be achieved by moving the does onto a better quality pasture or by supplementing with 0.5 pound of corn and/or protein supplement per head per day.

Goat nutrient requirements and examples of some hay and grain based goat rations (for kids as well as for nannies in various stages of production) are in Appendix IX. Some corn and soybean meal based rations are in Table 1 at the end of this chapter. If you can get these rations in Table 1 pelleted at a reasonable cost, this is worthwhile. These rations can be used for show animals, developing registered breeding stock or, as a creep feed (ration A or B), in regions where grain is inexpensive. These rations are not practical for many commercial situations. In confinement, kids can be started on ration A as a creep ration and, at weaning time, changed to ration B. As kids grow they can be switched to ration C or even shelled corn if forage or hay has a good level of protein. Confined buck kids over 40 to 50 pounds may be limit-fed grain, especially if there is a concern about urinary calculi. Bucks kids can be fed anywhere from 0.5 to 1.0 pound per day of ration C or shelled corn, depending on the quality of the hay or forage they are consuming. In confinement, in most situations, these rations are not affordable for animals over 50 or so pounds. In confinement, older nannies and doe kids over 50 pounds can be fed shelled corn and/or oats and a mixture of grass and alfalfa hay. All animals should receive a good quality sheep or goat salt and mineral mix free choice. If your hay quality is poor - that is, low in protein - you can add protein in the form of soybean or cottonseed meal, for example, to the ration for the larger doe kids or mature nannies to boost the overall protein level. If you have good quality alfalfa hay which is high in protein, you do not need to add protein to the grain mix.

In most goat operations, commercial mineral mixes are offered free-choice year-round. Minerals can be provided as trace mineralized salt, individual sources of calcium and/or phosphorus, either alone or combined with salt, or as commercial mixes. As a general rule, forages contain more calcium than phosphorus and grains are high in phosphorus and low in calcium. A nutritionist familiar with your area and goat nutrition can recommend specific mineral mixes since, depending on the soil types in your area, regional needs for different minerals vary. Tim Turner, D.V.M. (Southwestern Livestock Mineral Co., P.O. Drawer 231, San Angelo, TX 76902) is an expert in goat mineral nutrition and will give advice to you and your local feed store concerning mineral mixes and rations.

In some regions, certain minerals need to be heavily supplemented.

For adequate consumption, salt and minerals are usually mixed together and the combination should be palatable. Loose salt and mineral mixes are preferable because goats may chip or break their teeth on hard salt or mineral blocks. As well, goats are unable to lick enough salt and mineral from a very hard block to fulfill their nutritional requirements. Soft trace mineral blocks for sheep are available, but they tend to be more costly than the loose mineral and salt mixtures. Salt needs to be fed free choice with some soft trace mineral blocks so read all feed-related labels carefully.

Although copper toxicity seldom is a problem in goats, I still prefer to feed sheep mineral. (Sheep are extremely susceptible to copper toxicity, so sheep minerals and feeds have little or no copper added.) I have never seen copper deficiency in goats consuming sheep mineral. In *most* situations, cattle mineral mixes should also be safe for goats. When dietary copper is less than 7 ppm and molybdenum is normal, deficiency symptoms such as poor growth, weight loss, hair decoloration, abortions and stillbirths may occur. Rations should contain 10 ppm of copper and the copper: molybdenum ratio should be greater than 2:1 and below 10:1.

Minerals that may be deficient in some areas include selenium, sulfur, magnesium, phosphorus and iodine.

Recommended levels of dietary selenium for goats are not available, but up to 0.7 mg per head per day can be added to sheep feed. Selenium and vitamin E deficiency can result in white muscle disease in young goats, and, in mature individuals, reproductive problems and a dry hair coat with scaly skin.

Goats consuming tannin-containing plants (for example, oak) or urea-based feeds have higher sulfur requirements. Sodium or ammonium sulfate can be added to the feed at levels of 0.16% to 0.32%.

Supplementation of magnesium at 8% of a free-choice mineral or 0.2% of the total diet may prevent grass tetany in goats grazing short cereal grain pastures or river-bottom pastures.

Reproductive efficiency may improve in pastured animals when the level of phosphorus is increased to 10% to 12% of the mineral mix. Feedlot animals consuming concentrates, which are already high in phosphorus, should never receive additional dietary phosphorus.

Iodine deficiency can result in unthriftiness, low reproductive efficiency and fetal and kid deaths. Feeding iodized salt will prevent deficiencies.

Vitamins A, D and E should be added to rations for confinement-raised animals, particularly kids. Vitamin A, lack of which can cause growth retardation and reproductive failure, is formed from B-carotene, the best source of which is green pasture forage. Green forage or high-quality legume hay is a good source of Vitamin E. Vitamin D, needed to prevent rickets in young kids, is obtained through ultraviolet radiation and/or sun-cured hay.

If kids are raised in confinement, a coccidiostat should be added to the kid feed. Monensin (Rumensin: Elanco Animal Health) at 20 grams per ton of feed has worked well for us and is approved for use in goats. At recommended doses, monensin is a growth promotant. Decoquinate (Deccox: Rhone-Poulenc), at 22.7 mg per 100 pounds body weight (0.5 mg per kg) per day for at least 28 days during periods of exposure, is actually more effective than monensin in the younger kids. This is because very small kids may not consume enough monensin-containing feed, and thus not enough coccidiostat, to control coccidiosis adequately. Decoquinate has a much wider safely margin than monensin in goats, produces no toxic effects and does not affect feed consumption or live weight gains. It is not toxic to horses, unlike monensin, which is highly toxic to horses and should be used with caution if horses are on the premises. Decoquinate can be added to feed and is also approved for use in goats.

Lasalocid (Bovatec: Hoffman La Roche) does not appear to be an effective goat coccidiostat at recommended lamb feed levels of 30 grams per ton. This may be because young goats are eating such small amounts of feed that they are not consuming enough lasalocid. Lasalocid is not ap-proved for use in goats.

TABLE 1 - RATIONS
(Modified Pipestone Lamb and Wool Program Rations)

RATION A - 20% Crude Protein, 72% T.D.N., 0.778% Calcium, 0.388% Phosphorus, 2/1 Calcium to Phosphorus Ratio.

1170 pounds rolled corn
670 pounds 44% soybean meal
50 pounds liquid molasses
40 pounds limestone
20 pounds white iodized salt
*10 pounds ammonium chloride
**20 grams monensin
0.3 ppm selenium
1,000,000 IU vitamin A
200,000 IU vitamin D
120,000 IU vitamin E

RATION B - 16% Crude Protein, 72% T.D.N., 0.745% Calcium, 0.355% Phosphorus, 2.1/1.0 Calcium to Phosphorus Ratio.

1400 pounds rolled corn
440 pounds 44% soybean meal
50 pounds liquid molasses
40 pounds limestone
20 pounds white iodized salt
*10 pounds ammonium chloride
**20 grams monensin
0.3 ppm selenium
1,000,000 IU vitamin A
200,000 IU vitamin D
80,000 IU vitamin E

RATION C - 13% Crude Protein, 72% T.D.N., 0.7% Calcium, 0.35% Phosphorus, 2/1 Calcium to Phosphorus Ratio.

1635 pounds rolled corn
255 pounds 44% soybean meal
50 pounds liquid molasses
40 pounds limestone
20 pounds white iodized salt
*10 pounds ammonium chloride
**20 grams monensin
0.3 ppm selenium
1,000,000 IU vitamin A
200,000 IU vitamin D
80,000 IU vitamin E

*Ammonium chloride can be omitted from rations fed only to does.
**Decoquinate can be substituted for monensin and probably should be in ration A.
Pelleting of these rations is useful if it can be done inexpensively.

Notes: Chapter 9

1. *Meat Goat Production and Marketing Handbook,* Clemson University, BC 683, Rep. October 1996.

10. GRAZING MANAGEMENT

"One of the critical decisions facing livestock producers is how to best utilize the forage resources on their farm or ranch.

"The manner in which this valuable resource is utilized often determines the profitability of a livestock operation.

"There is no class of ruminant animals that cannot be raised or maintained on a 100% forage diet."

- James R. Gerrish, "Intensive Grazing Management: Principles and Techniques", from University of Missouri - FORAGE SYSTEMS RESEARCH CENTER, Oct 7, 8 and 9, 1992.

There is a wealth of information on controlled grazing or management intensive grazing but, despite this, pastures and other grazing land are often poorly managed or neglected. A good grazing system must provide appropriate nutrition for the class or classes of goats involved and forage yield, quality and persistence must be optimized. As well, the management system needs to be practical and economically sound.

This all seems like common sense; of course, a doe raising twins needs much better quality pasture than mature stud bucks that are simply being maintained until the next breeding season. Evaluating pasture or browse quality, however, takes practice and constant observation, not only of the pasture or browse but of the body condition of the goats. Forage composition is variable and what a goat consumes depends on availability and palatability. A chart showing the composition of feed stuffs for goats (protein, TDN - Total Digestible Nutrients, calcium and phosphorus) is in the chapter "Managing Forages for Meat Goats"[1]. Legumes (alfalfa, for example) are usually higher in protein and calcium than non-legumes (such as bermudagrass, bluestems, sudangrass) but their TDN values are similar. Forages that are grazed are usually more nutritious than hay made from the same fields. Forages are typically much higher in calcium than phosphorus. Many factors, such as plant age and soil fertility, can greatly influence protein and TDN values of individual forage species. Spring growth is usually the most palatable and has the highest nutrient value. Kidding in synchrony with the best quality forage usually is the most cost effective way to utilize one's pastures. Mature goats generally consume between 3 to 5% of their body weight in dry matter intake per day.

Forages of the appropriate quality must be growing or be stockpiled throughout the grazing season to meet the needs of the particular class of goats. Although goats thrive on browse, in many regions they have no option but to graze. If pastures are to be planted, forage species should be chosen based on adaptability to the location, seasonal distribution, total yield potential, the level of management you are willing to provide and the ability of the species to meet the goats' nutritional needs. A combination of several species is usually best but one does not want to make things too complicated either.

If grazing is not controlled, goats, like any other animal, will select their favorite species and ignore the others. Over time, many desirable species will disappear in continuously grazed pastures. Dividing land into a series of paddocks or small pastures and rotating the animals from paddock to paddock will reduce selective grazing and encourage more uniform grazing, thus allowing various species in a mixture to persist and thrive. Paddocks need to be grazed according to forage availability and growth rate.

As a general rule, the leaves are the most nutritious portion of a plant. As a plant matures, the proportion of a plant that is cell wall content, the least digestible part of a plant, increases. Especially in older plants stems contain far less nutrients than the leaves. So, to maximize forage quality of grasses, legumes, forbs and brushy species, one needs to manage for maximum leaf production.

It is also important to prevent seedhead formation (reproductive growth) in forages in paddocks. As the grass tiller changes from vegetative growth (producing leaves) to reproductive growth, the stem must become more rigid in order to hold the seedhead up. So, forage quality decreases because fibers in the stem become quite indigestible. As well, nutrients from the leaves are needed for seed development so leaves also become less nutritious. Before seedhead production gets underway, it is important to graze paddocks or, if necessary, to clip and/or harvest surplus growth.

Increases in dry matter yield are mainly the result of increases in the number of tillers (leaf blade and sheath, stem and seedhead) per acre. New tillers, which originate from growing points or basal buds, are produced in response to removal of top growth (as long as the basal bud is protected.) New tillers require carbohydrates (energy) from roots and lower stem bases for growth until sufficient leaf area is developed so the tiller can produce its own carbohydrate. Once the tiller is producing its own energy, then carbohydrates are replenished in the roots, leaves and lower stem bases. New tiller development is slowed if root energy reserves are depleted. Some sunlight needs to reach the basal bud to stimulate new tiller development. Therefore, intervals between grazing must not be so long that excessive forage growth prevents sunlight from reaching the growing point. Good grazing management maximizes new tiller development and increases yield per acre. A paddock should not be grazed so often that root energy reserves do not have time to replenish. However, grazing needs to occur before tiller formation decreases and a shift toward the reproductive phase has begun.

It is impossible to have a pasture with the best quality forage and the highest yield per acre. A happy medium needs to be found; this is, in part, dependent on the class or classes of goats being grazed. Young weaned kids or does raising multiple kids need vegetative top quality forage whereas dry does and bucks will do just fine on more mature, less nutritious and higher yielding pastures.

There is no magic formula as to how many paddocks a farm needs to be divided into and how many animals can be grazed in a certain size paddock and for how long. It takes experience and trial and error to figure out guidelines for a particular ranch or farm. To complicate life, weather patterns and forage growth can vary tremendously within a growing season and from year to year. Careful daily observation of paddocks and the animals grazing them, and responding to this information appropriately both for short-term and long-term grazing planning, gives very good results. Flexibility in paddock size and layout allows one to easily remedy any mistakes made initially.

Although this discussion has emphasized controlled grazing, continuous grazing may be appropriate under certain circumstances; for example, if goats are being grazed with cattle to control brush and weeds.

Goats can be used to control and even eliminate unwanted weeds and brush in pastures by grazing the undesirable species often and heavily, grazing off growing points and depleting root energy reserves, and by stocking goats very heavily. However, it is important to note that goats used in this manner typically will not perform well in terms of growth and reproduction.

If goats are stocked less heavily and weeds and brush grazed less intensively, goats can perform quite well. Therefore, one may want to attempt to manage pastures so as to retain some weeds and brush which, if properly managed, are quite nutritious (for goats!). However, it may be difficult to maintain a combination of forage grasses (which tend to be undergrazed by goats, if they have a choice) and brush and weeds (which the goats prefer). In this situation, multiple species grazing (cattle and goats or cattle, sheep and goats) may be the solution.

Improved electric fence technology has been the single most important factor in the upsurge in interest in controlled grazing. Animals can now be contained in paddocks much more reliably and cost effectively than in the past. The references below contain information on setting up paddocks, figuring out stocking density, knowing when to move the animals and so on. As well, Chapter 7 in this book contains some more fencing details.

Simple and inexpensive above ground watering systems, also described in some of the reference texts below, for example, Bill Murphy's *Greener Pastures on Your Side of the Fence*, Arriba Publishing, Colchester, Vermont, 1998, allow ready access to abundant fresh water for all animals in each paddock.

A few useful references include:
Books
Bill Murphy, *Greener Pastures on Your Side of the Fence*, Arriba Publishing, Colchester, Vermont, 1998.

Burt Smith, et al, *Intensive Grazing Management: Forage, Animals, Men, Profits*, The Graziers Hui, Hawaii, 1986.

André Voisin, *Grass Productivity*, Island Press Edition, Washington, DC, 1988.

Magazine
The Stockman Grass Farmer, P.O. Box 2300, Ridgeland, MS 39158-2300, 1-800-748-9808 (Telephone) 601-853-8087 (Facsimile).

Pocket guide
Conservation Plants, Pocket ID Guide, Elsberry Plant Materials Center, United States Department of Agriculture, Soil Conservation Service.

Seminar
"Intensive Grazing Management: Principles and Techniques", A Three

Day Seminar at The University of Missouri - FORAGE SYSTEMS RE-SEARCH CENTER Oct 7, 8 and 9, 1992.

Notes: Chapter 10.

1. *Meat Goat Production and Marketing Handbook,* Clemson University, BC 683, Rep. October 1996

Crane Creek Enterprises.

11. ROUTINE PROCEDURES

"When working with a group of goats it is very important to be properly prepared so that the goats (and you) get as little stressed as possible."
- Stephanie Mitcham, Allison Mitcham, Chapter 8, "Routine Procedures," *The Angora Goat, its History, Management and Diseases*, Crane Creek Publications, Second Edition, 1999, pg 59.

Castration

Goats may be castrated at any age though, if one wants to allow some horn development, one may want to wait until goats are 6 months of age or more. Wethers (castrated males) with significant horn development are less likely to get stuck in fences because the horns will not readily pass through a fence and, as well, may be better equipped to cope with predators. A more developed penis and urethra (which occurs with age) may lessen problems with urinary calculi. Of course, if goats are being slaughtered at a young age or light weight and/or a higher price is being paid for intact males, one may not want to castrate them at all. Uncastrated males are typically leaner than wethers and females. However, if one intends to sell larger animals to slaughter, then castration should be a consideration because, as bucks mature, they may spend a considerable amount of time rutting, especially if they are in close proximity to does. Growth may be less than optimal in this situation.

In young goats, less than a week old, banding, or application of a rubber ring to the scrotum above the testicles and adjacent to the body wall, can be performed. A banding tool is used to stretch the rubber ring to a large enough size to pass over the scrotum. Once the ring is in position, tension on the ring is released by the person operating the banding tool and the ring settles into place, cutting off the blood supply to the scrotum. The band should not be applied too close to the body as it might trap the urethra. The nipples should always be above the rubber ring (on the opposite side to the testicles). Kids will act very uncomfortable - crying, lying down, getting up - for an hour or so. If a kid is still really miserable after an hour, the ring should be examined and, if there is any doubt about its position, the ring should be removed. Tetanus can occur as a result of banding, so, if dams have not been vaccinated with tetanus toxoid prior to kidding, kids should receive 150 IU of tetanus antitoxin at banding time. Banding is stressful to kids and should not be performed on the day of birth as it may interfere with adequate uptake of colostrum.

Castration with a knife involves cutting off the bottom third of the scrotum and then pulling out each testicle. The testicles are slippery and hard to get a good grip on; thus, in the past, anyway, some operators preferred to use their teeth to pull out the testicles. Special castrating knives are available that have clamps on the end of the handle. Kids are sore for at least a day after castration by this method. New bedding or clean pasture should be provided as the knife wound provides a source of entry for bacterial organisms. Tetanus is also a possible complication. If blood starts to drip steadily from the scrotum, a string can be tied tightly around the neck of the scrotum. An internal blood clot should form, and, after eight hours, the string can be removed.

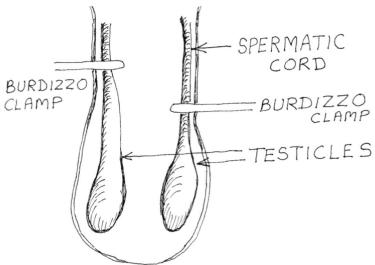

Schematic representation of castration with Burdizzo clamp.

If the bucks are to be castrated at a later age - a few months to a year - a Burdizzo clamp can be used. The clamp is applied first to one side of the scrotum, then the other, making sure that the spermatic cord does not slide out of the clamp and that the testicle is below the clamp. The clamp should never be applied across the whole scrotum: there should be a central portion of undamaged skin with clamp marks on either side. (Diagram, page 103). Some people clamp twice on each side of the scrotum; others pull on the testicle to make sure that the spermatic cord has separated. If done correctly, clamping a single time on each side should yield good results. The scrotal skin is somewhat fragile so do not pull hard on the clamp once it is closed - otherwise the scrotal skin may tear. After castration by the Burdizzo clamp method, goats walk stiffly for several days and often the scrotum swells. The clamp should not be applied too close to the body as, if the urethra is clamped in error, there could be one less goat in the herd. Tetanus is also a possible complication of this method of castration.

Dehorning

Meat goats are not usually dehorned as it requires extra time and labor. As well, the dehorning procedure may result in problems. Horns may be helpful in protecting goats against predators of the smaller, less aggressive variety and are useful for catching and restraining as well as sexing goats (the intact males have much larger horns than females of a comparable size). Dehorned goats may do better in close confinement as a nasty weapon has been removed. However, once one starts dehorning goats, one cannot stop, as dehorned animals do not thrive when penned closely with aggressive horned goats. I do not remove horns from my goats.

Dehorning is best done when the goat is very young - two to three days of age is best if the goat is a normal healthy specimen. Using an electric dehorning iron - an electrically heated metal rod with an end like a small doughnut - is the most suitable method. Most dairy goat breeders do not use an anesthetic. Problems resulting from improper dehorning techniques include horn regrowth and scur formation (dehorning iron not hot enough or not applied for a sufficient length of time) and brain damage or death because of overheating of cranial bones (when dehorning iron is too hot or applied for too long).

Allow the dehorning iron to heat up until, when the iron is applied to a pine board, it leaves a slightly depressed black ring in the wood, and, at the end of two seconds, smoke is just beginning to rise. The dehorner is applied over the horn and rocked around slowly for three and a half to four seconds. The dehorning iron and a thin cap of horn are removed. After pausing for a few seconds, the procedure is repeated for three and one half to four seconds at the same location. Then the central core of tissue overlying the bone is removed and the site sprayed with aerosol antibiotic to cool the area quickly. If the central core of tissue cannot be removed, the horn site has not been burned enough. The kid should receive 150 IU of tetanus antitoxin.

Dehorning adult goats, particularly mature bucks, is not recommended. If an older goat needs to be dehorned for some reason, call your veterinarian. This project requires anesthesia, either local or general.

Ear Tagging

The perfect goat ear tag - one that will last the lifetime of a goat - is not yet on the market. Problems with available ear tags include lettering that fades with time, particularly with exposure to sun, tags so small that the tag letters/numbers cannot be read from a distance and tags so large they are readily caught on things and torn out of the ear.

Metal tags should not be used in the ears of any goat that needs to be sheared because they are very hard on shearing combs.

We use small rectangular tags (sheep or goat tags) and, in the past, we have used small round tags (hog button tags). These come in a variety of colors so, if one so desires, a different color can be used for each new kid crop or for kids from a particular sire. Tags usually come in packs of twenty-five. They can be ordered prenumbered; for example: 001 to 0025 or 0026 to 0050, or blank. Tags may also be ordered specially that are imprinted with herd initials or other information. These tags are, of course, more costly. Special marking pens are available for labelling blank tags or re-numbering faded ones. Some brands require costly applicators, so check this out before you buy new tags.

I use ear tags on both my commercial and registered goats. If one plans on keeping any records, each kid born should be tagged with a tag that displays the number on the outer flap of the ear. The male half of the tag is numbered. The other half - the female half - of the tag lies on the inner ear and is blank (the female portion of the tag can be purchased prenumbered or can be labelled with a special marker pen if one so desires). On this blank portion of the tag one can record the sire and dam of the kid instead of the kid identification. This way, when goats are being sorted, the parentage of a particular kid can be checked on without referring to records. Also, if a kid gets into the wrong pen or pasture and is unable to find its mother, the inside portion of the ear tag can just be checked to find out who the dam is.

I prefer to use white or yellow tags as the black identification numbers and letters are more readily visible. If blank tags are purchased, a simple identification system is as follows: The first number on the male part of the tag indicates the birth order of the kid. So, the first kid born in a year is 0001. This is followed by the international year code so that one knows by glancing at the tag how old the goat is. For example, the year 2000 is represented by a K. So, the first kid born in the year 2000 is 0001K. Kids born in 1999 have tags labelled with a number followed by the letter J.

Tags for registered goats can be labelled with the flock initials if one so desires. If one has several breeds of goats, one may want to have different color tags for the different breeds. Numbers on the prelabelled tags tend to last a little longer so this is also a consideration.

Registered kids can have their ears notched and/or tattooed early in life so that all young registered stock carries two means of identification.

If there are problems keeping ear tags in commercial goats, these animals could also have their ears notched and/or tattooed or a tag could be placed in each ear. Small, less costly, plastic or metal ear tags can be used as a second tag.

Some people tag male goats in one ear and females in the other. I place my main larger tag in the right ear of the females and in the left ear of the males. A smaller metal tag is placed in the other ear. All tattoos are in the right ear.

Make sure to avoid the large blood vessels that run down the ear - the tag should be placed between the two main vessels. Bleeding is worse on warm days, so it is best to do ear tagging in colder weather.

Ear tags and applicators should be kept clean. Disinfecting tags and applicators prior to use is a good idea.

THERE'S ABSOLUTELY NO TALKING TO HER SINCE SHE GOT THOSE NEW, EMERALD - GREEN EAR-TAGS

Foot Trimming

In wetter climates goat hooves can grow at an amazingly rapid rate and, if goats are kept on soft surfaces, the hooves do not get worn down. In some situations feet may need trimming three or four times a year, or, if the climate is dry, trimming may not be necessary at all. Foot trimming can be performed in conjunction with other procedures when goats have already been collected in pens.

It is much easier to trim feet that are moist than those that are very dry, so, if there has been a dry spell for several weeks, one might consider postponing a trimming session until there has been some damper weather.

Foot trimming may also be undertaken with the goat lying on its side. In this instance, one's knee or foot needs to be placed on the neck of the goat and one's other leg is positioned between the goat's hind legs so it cannot get up. Another restraint method requires that the goat is sitting up with its rump between your feet and its neck between your legs. In this case, the goat's head is behind your legs, giving the goat the opportunity to stick its horns into the back of your legs or even bite you if it is so inclined. Trimming tables are useful if one plans to trim any number of feet. The latter are usually part of a chute system. The goat walks into a trimming table and is pressed between two adjustable panels (usually one is solid and the other is webbed). Then the table is rotated sideways so that the feet and lower legs are protruding at a convenient height for trimming. These are available in various sheep supply catalogs, for example, Townsend's Sales, 4141 S. 25 W., Trafalgar, IN 46181, Telephone: 317-736-4047.

Whichever method you choose, it is important to use good, sharp foot rot shears. Several different types of shears are available, including compressed air power-assisted shears. These are excellent for trimming hooves on large numbers of animals. However, they are dangerous and the inexperienced operator must take care not to nip off a finger or two. The main types of hand shears are Burdizzo foot rot shears, which have straight handles, and Felco shears with curved handles for easier use and more leverage. For people with small hands, Felco shears with a rotating handle are helpful. Shears can be sharpened with a file or by someone with professional sharpening equipment.

The shape of a properly trimmed hoof should resemble that of a young kid's. To achieve this shape, the hooves are trimmed so that the portion of the hoof touching the ground is parallel with the top of the hoof wall (which merges with hair). Usually the heel as well as the toe needs to be trimmed. Before starting to trim a foot, any dirt clinging to the hoof should be removed with the point of the closed shears so that the hoof is clearly visible. Any folded-over hoof wall should be trimmed off. The hoof is well-supplied with blood, so, if one trims too close, bleeding can occur. Usually this will stop of its own accord but, if bleeding is very severe, a pressure bandage may need to be applied. Until one is sure of what one is doing, it is better to trim the foot back gradually. Once the sole appears to have a pinkish hue (this is because of the underlying blood vessels), enough hoof has been removed. As one becomes more proficient at foot trimming, one or two cuts per hoof will often suffice in animals that have had their feet trimmed at frequent intervals.

Feet that have not been regularly trimmed can, over time, become misshapen. These feet cannot be returned to normal overnight. A number of trimming sessions over many months may be required to restore a normal shape to the hoof. Sometimes these feet will never appear normal. In these cases one just must do the best job one can.

The small, hard claws on the back of the leg above the hoof can also be trimmed. These sometimes get quite long in older goats.

Restraint

If each goat has to be chased for routine procedures such as vaccinating and deworming, it is hard on the goats. Groups of goats may be bunched up in a small pen or a chute system - a narrow alleyway that the goats cannot turn around in - can be made. Chute systems (Chapter 8. Handling Systems) can be very simple or quite elaborate: sorting gates and pens, scales, trimming tables, and so on, can all be part of a chute system. Portable three to four feet high and eight to twelve feet long wooden or metal panels are useful for penning animals into a corner for minor procedures.

Individual mature animals can be caught by their horns, but it is important to grasp the horns close to the skull, otherwise; a horn may be pulled off, resulting in considerable bleeding. Goats less than a year old have soft horns that will readily break off, so young goats should not be caught by the horns. Goats may also be held by their chin or caught by a hind leg. Goats should not be lifted by a front leg - a shoulder can be dislocated this way.

Goats can be positioned with their rump between one's feet and the neck between one's legs. To turn a goat over to set it on its rump, I hold on to the base of the horn nearest me, reach over the back and then under the belly of the goat and grasp the hind leg closest to me. I slide the hind leg out from under the goat and roll it over on its rump.

12. KID PRODUCTION

"In a meat production system ... reproductive performance is of paramount importance since productivity is largely a function of the number of offspring born and weaned and frequency with which they are produced."
- Stephan Wildeus, "Reproductive Management of the Meat Goat," *Meat Goat Production and Marketing Handbook,* Clemson Extension EC 683, October 1996.

Whether kidding time is a pleasant experience or a nightmare depends on one's management in the months prior to kidding. First of all, the goats - both bucks and does - should be in good body condition prior to breeding. If the does are on the thin side, "flushing" - feeding supplemental feed prior to breeding - will help ensure a good kid crop. If nannies are in excellent body condition, flushing probably will have little effect. Depending on the goats' body condition, supplemental feeding can be started 2 to 4 weeks before the introduction of the buck. A high energy feed such as corn is often used for flushing goats, but, if the goats are on a pasture that is low in protein, their diet may need to be supplemented with soybean meal or alfalfa hay as well. Feed analysis prevents feed supplementation from being a guessing game. Moving goats to a very good quality pasture will also have a flushing effect.

Bucks also need to be in good flesh before breeding, and, if at all possible, they should be kept at a separate location so that the nannies cannot see or smell them and vice versa.

The larger doe kids can be bred, but, in order for them to produce vigorous babies and sufficient milk to feed them, they should weigh at least 75% of their mature weight at breeding time. Goats weighing less than this will usually not conceive or, if they do, they may abort or resorb the fetus. Well nourished, well grown does usually get bred readily and will produce one, two, three or sometimes more healthy kids. Foot trimming, deworming, delousing and vaccinating should all be completed before the start of the breeding season. Once the bucks are put in with the nannies, and for the next couple of months, life for the goats should be as

109

tranquil as possible. This should encourage implantation and survival of all fertilized eggs.

The time of year at which the individual breeder wants to kid and thus the date the buck(s) will be turned in with the does should be given serious consideration. Cold, rainy seasons should be avoided if one plans to have the does birth outside. Newborn kids can become chilled readily in cold rain. If the kids are to be born and raised on pasture, they should be born at a time of year when there is sufficient feed for the does to sustain themselves and produce plenty of milk for their offspring.

A newly-born kid basking in the April sun (Midwestern United States: Crane Creek Enterprises).

In temperate latitudes, goats are seasonal breeders and spontaneous estrus cycle activity increases with decreasing day length. Although reproductive activity can be manipulated with hormonal therapy and alteration of lighting (by artificially reducing daylight duration) as well as the effect of the introduction of the male (the physical presence of the buck will synchronize and induce estrus in does in the transition period before the regular breeding season), the most successful natural means of obtaining a good kid crop is to breed your goats during the late summer, fall or early winter months (late August through December). Goats bred very early or late in the breeding season may not have as many kids as those bred in the middle part of the season. Some goats - either individuals or breeds - have an extended breeding season or may even breed year round. Typically the closer one is located to the equator, the stronger the tendency for year round breeding.

Goats must be bred in groups (separate pastures or pens) if one wants to know exactly which buck is the sire of which kid. Breeding the superior bucks to the best nannies and so on down the line gives the best animals an opportunity to produce superior offspring. If a particular buck and nanny combination does not work out then a different sire can be used another year. In a more commercial setting, multiple sire mating groups can be used (a group of paternal half brothers - bucks all sired by the same buck - is recommended). This way, one can still obtain useful records without having to cope with single sire mating groups in a large herd. If there is a low fertility or infertile buck in a group, the group of does will still kid on schedule and have good kidding percentages.

Marking harnesses (sheep harnesses), that house a crayon on the chest between and in front of the forelegs, can be placed on the bucks so one knows whether they are mounting the does or not. When a buck mounts a doe, he leaves colored chalk marks on her rump. Special marking paint can be painted or rubbed directly on the chest of the bucks daily or every few days instead of using a harness. Marking paint is preferred in situations where the goats can only be checked every other day and there is a chance that the harness can catch on brush or other items in a pasture or paddock. The dates when the first marks appear (or first signs of heat are observed) should be recorded so one knows when to expect the first kids. After nineteen to twenty-one days of breeding activity (one heat cycle), the crayons in the marking harnesses should be changed so one knows which does will kid late. Also, bucks can be switched at this time so that if, by chance, a buck did not breed any of the does in a single sire mating group at least they will get bred on the next heat cycle.

Although many sources indicate that kids will start arriving 7 to 10 days, plus the gestation period (145 to 150 or more days) after the buck is turned out (if the buck is kept out of sight and smell of the nannies prior to breeding), I find that some of the nannies get bred the first day that the bucks are turned out. Depending on your management (pen-breeding versus pasture breeding) and the male, one mature buck can be expected to breed 25 to 40 or more does. Probably a very vigorous stud buck could breed 100 or so does if given the opportunity. Generally younger bucks (yearlings) are expected to breed fewer does. Does are in heat for about 12 hours or more (up to 36 hours) and will typically flag their tails and show considerable interest in the buck. If you want to have your kids arrive within a 5-week period, for example, billies should be removed from the nanny pens after 5 weeks of breeding activity. Does that are consistently late in kidding should be culled.

During gestation, good nutrition is a must. Mature nannies can be maintained on feed of moderate quality until the last 6 weeks of gestation - this is when the kids do most of their growing - but very young or old nannies will benefit from better quality feed during mid-gestation.

Depending on the area goats are being raised in, certain nutritional problems may cause difficulties at or after kidding. For example, certain regions are low in selenium so vitamin E and selenium may need to be added to the feed and/or mineral mix. Many sheep mineral mixes contain vitamin E and selenium, but levels may not be high enough for animals in very selenium deficient areas. Kids can be injected with a vitamin E/selenium supplement at birth or nannies can be injected with supplement prior to kidding. Some areas are deficient in iodine and, if iodine is not present in the salt/mineral mix at sufficient levels, weak kids with enlarged thyroid glands that die soon after birth may be the result.

During the last 6 weeks of gestation the quality of feed should be increased so that the kids will have good birth weights and the nannies have plenty of milk. Since my goats often have twins and triplets I want to be certain that the nannies end up feeding the babies - not me! I find that, if the goats are well cared for before kidding time, the nannies are good mothers.

About 30 days before kidding, the does should be boostered with *Clostridium perfringens* types C and D and tetanus vaccine. Since the does are being processed anyway, they can be dewormed if need be and feet trimmed. If one is planning on having the does kid inside, the buildings should be cleaned and any preparations for kidding (kidding pens set up, if you use them) made.

It is important to prepare for kidding in advance of the expected onslaught of kids. Otherwise you will find yourself caught empty handed at some extremely inconvenient time. Supplies to keep on hand for kidding inside include: strong (7%) iodine in a wide-mouthed jar for dipping navels, paper towels and old towels and rags for drying off wet hands and the occasional kid, heat lamps and extra heat lamp bulbs, commercial milk replacer, frozen colostrum, baby bottles and nipples (lamb nipples are of-

112

ten too large for kids), milk replacer feeding system (bucket and nipples), long acting penicillin (an injection is given to does that require any assistance in kidding), ear tags, ear tag applicator, ear notcher, antiseptic scrub, lubricating agent (for assisting in difficult births), vitamin E/selenium supplement, needles and syringes, paper, pencils, thermometer, suture material and needle. I have a small plastic tool chest (Walmart, cost less than $10.00) for all my medical supplies and another for all the tagging, notching and tattooing supplies. Shelves for paper towels, heat lamp bulbs, iodine jar, towels and other supplies are helpful.

Although some people feel that the time of day the goats are fed influences the time at which most of the kids are born, there is no scientific proof of this. If my pastured nannies are not disturbed too much, most of their kids are born around the middle of the day. It does seem that the more one is out in the pastures or barn in the middle of the night, the more kids are born then. If one does need to check on the nannies through the night, it may be best to use a flashlight instead of turning on all the barn lights. Try to make as little commotion as possible. For example, filling up the feed bunks in the middle of the night is not a great idea as it gets all the nannies up. The one year I was able to feed grain at about 9 a.m. to our confined nannies, I did not have a single kid born after 8 p.m. and most nannies kidded after the 9 a.m. feeding or around noon. In other years, when I have fed early (5 a.m.), I have had more kids born in the early morning.

I check our barn (a metal uninsulated pole shed) every 4 hours or so for new arrivals when kids arrive in March, and, in very cold weather (-28 to -35 C: -20 to -30 F), the goats get checked every 2 hours. In warm weather, goat checks may be every 6 to 12 hours or so. Breeders of registered animals may use devices such as a wireless intercom, one portion of which is plugged into a barn outlet and the other into a house outlet (obtained from Radio Shack for less than $40.00). This is quite useful as one can usually hear the newborn kids as well as the anxious mothers on the intercom. Cameras for monitoring animals can also be installed in buildings. These are becoming less expensive all the time but they definitely are not essential equipment!

Goats typically do not have birthing problems. Because the pelvic bones relax before kidding, the expectant mother often has a sunken-in area just before the hip bones. The doe will be uncomfortable, sometimes will paw at the ground and often seek out a corner of the barn. Often the nannies will nibble at their own nipples prior to delivery. Perhaps this is to help remove the waxy plugs from the end of the teats so that the kids can nurse more easily. Many of my nannies do not spend a lot of time getting ready to give birth.

I have observed that my confined goats like to get their daily feed ration before they kid. Nannies in the first pen I feed often will go and gobble up their breakfast (I feed corn in the mornings) and, by the time I have fed goats in the second and third pens, the nannies in the first pen will already have delivered their kids or will be in active labor. The initial straining/contractions will produce a water bag and, after more straining, the first kid will appear. Some of the nannies will cry out during contractions. Normally, active labor is in progress for less than 30 minutes before the first kid arrives. If the nanny is in active labor for more than 30 minutes, it is time for you or your veterinarian to lend a hand.

My confined nannies are in pens which contain 20 to 30 goats, and nannies kid in these open pens. Once the kids have arrived, I move the mother and the new arrivals into a 4 by 4 foot kidding pen. The kidding pens have solid sides so that nannies do not fight with each other. We find that if the nannies cannot see each other there is less tendency for them to bang on the panels between kidding pens. The front of most of the kidding pens can have a gap in it so that nannies can eat hay outside the kidding pens and not waste so much hay. Kidding pens in one of my buildings have feeders right in the pens (see photograph in Chapter 7).

The navel cord of each kid born in confinement should be soaked in strong (7%) iodine as soon after birth as possible. I put the iodine in an open-mouthed container, put the entire cord into the bottle and then upend the bottle against the abdomen so that the whole cord from top to bottom is soaked in iodine. Kids born on clean pasture do not need to have their navels dipped.

As well, make sure that both of the mother's teats are unplugged and that she has lots of milk. If the babies do not have a full belly and if they will not nurse with some human intervention (often holding the kid up under the nanny and squirting some milk into its mouth will encourage the kid to nurse), the kid can be tube fed with a flexible rubber catheter attached to the end of a 30 or 60 ml syringe.

The kid is placed on a flat surface and the head tilted back. The tube is wetted and passed along the left side of the kid's mouth into the esophagus. If it is very cold, the tube will be less flexible so it is best to have the tube warmish prior to use. One can feel the tube slide down the esophagus and one can also feel the adjacent trachea which is fairly firm and ridged.

If one measures the distance from the mouth to the back of the rib cage, this is roughly the distance that the tube will need to be passed. Make sure that air is not passing in and out of the tube. If this is the case, you are in the trachea and the tube should be removed. The procedure should then be repeated gently until you are in the esophagus. If you are careful and take your time, it is unusual to get the tube in the trachea but you should always check to be certain that you are in the correct location. I like to be sure that the kids receive at least sixty ml of milk within the first two hours of life. This way I know that they receive colostral antibodies at the optimum time.

Usually a kid does not have to be tube fed more than once. I do not like to feed a kid large volumes of colostrum via stomach tube because, if the belly is completely filled, the typical kid will go off for a nap. Then the kid misses out on some of the early bonding that takes place when nursing occurs.

If it is cold, a heat lamp can be placed over the pen until the kids are dried off. Make sure that the nannies cannot chew through the heat lamp electrical cords and that the lamps are not too close to any hay, wood or straw. Some people put the heat lamps or heaters in a small box that is part of the kidding pen. Kids can slip into the small box and curl up under the lamp. This way, the doe cannot damage the heat lamp by butting it or chewing on it (not uncommon) or lie on the kids (which is extremely rare in my experience).

While kids are in the kidding pens they can receive an injection of vitamin E/selenium supplement and be ear tagged (I use plastic round or rectangular tags). Kids born on pasture do not receive any injections and are simply tagged when the rounds of the paddocks are made. Kids can be permanently identified - tattooed or ear-notched - when they are 30 or 60 days old - when they get their first or second overeating vaccine, respectively. Records are kept on each nanny and her kids: date of birth, comments if there are any problems or good points, ear tag numbers, dam, sire, pen that the doe and kid will go back to, etc.

Does and kids are usually left in the kidding pens for 6 to 48 hours, depending on how many babies the dam has and how the kids appear to be doing. Once kids and does go back to the main pen, kids should be bonded to their mothers. In my confinement setup, each large pen has a creep area with a creep feeder in it containing a high protein creep feed. Many lamb rations will work fine for a creep feed (see chapter on nutrition). However, most of these contain the coccidiostat Bovatec, which, at 30 mg per ton (recommended lamb creep feed levels), does not control coccidiosis in young goats very well. For kids, the best coccidiostat is Deccox (May and Baker) and you should consider adding this to your kid feed, particularly if you have large numbers of goats kidding in confinement. If pastures are poorer quality and/or grain is inexpensive in your region, it may be economical to set up a portable creep area on pasture.

In cold weather, a heat lamp can be hung over the creep area to encourage the kids to use this area. They will all pile into the creep region and sleep under the heat lamp. This way kids are less likely to get stepped on by nannies and also learn to eat solid food early on. Several entrances should be made for the creep region so the kids can get in and out easily. Be careful not to make the entrances too large or some of the nannies will worm their way into the creep region and engorge themselves on the creep feed. Feed bunks in the main pen should be about two feet off the ground or kids will crawl into the feed bunks to sleep. Unfortunately, the kids will also contaminate the feed with fecal material. The nannies will not eat this feed. As well, contaminated feed is a potential internal parasite hazard. Kids are quite fragile when first born. Most losses are in the first day or two and are the result of hypothermia (chilling) and inadequate nutrition. So, attention paid to keeping the kids warm and with full bellies really pays off. Walking through the pens or pastures at least twice daily and observing all the kids is a must. A healthy normal kid should have a warm mouth, a full stomach and should stretch when it gets up. If in doubt, take the kid's rectal temperature. The normal temperature for a goat is 39 to 40 C (103 to 105 F). After a couple of days of age, losses are uncommon and tend to be the result of accidents.

Occasionally a doe will refuse to take a kid, and, if this is the case, one can attempt to graft the kid to a nanny that is in the process of kidding or even a ewe that is lambing. I have not had great luck with this because of the high proportion of multiple births my does produce. A doe with a single kid never seems to be available at the right time. Anyway, if you smear birthing fluids from the doe in labor all over the rejected kid, the nanny in labor will usually claim the kid as one of her own.

If the orphan kid is very active (several days old), it helps to tie its feet together so it cannot run all around the pen while the foster mother is trying to decide whether she wants it or not. One problem is that the orphan kid may be much stronger than the doe's own kid, and, if one is not careful, the orphan may guzzle all of the colostrum before the other kid is up and at it. I have successfully grafted rejected kids on to nannies with single kids only to find, a few days later, that the nanny's own kid is being neglected because it is smaller and weaker. I do feed the orphans as much warm commercial milk replacer as they will drink before I try grafting but it seems that the orphans have an endless appetite for milk from the doe rather than the commercial milk replacer. Orphans can even be grafted to a willing dog. Some people keep dairy goats so that they have goat milk available for orphans. I do not feel that I have the time or energy to milk dairy goats on top of everything else or even to stanchion the goats and supervise the kid feeding, so I just stick with commercial milk replacer. Caprine Arthritis Encephalitis virus is not uncommon in dairy herds so one wants to be careful to avoid introducing this virus to a clean herd (Chapter 13. Diseases).

Occasionally newborn kids that are very chilled (rectal temperature is less than 37 C (98.6 F) are found, and, if this is the case, these babies need immediate attention. I race these ones into the house and wrap them in warm material (towels or blankets) and put them near the wood stove to thaw out. Be careful that you do not burn the sensitive skin of a young kid when using heat lamps or heating pads to warm them up. Heat lamps should not be placed too close to a kid that cannot move and heating pads should be wrapped in a blanket or a towel. A kid can be wrapped in a blanket and warmed in an open oven at a low heat. Chilled kids can also be warmed by placing hot water bottles or jars filled with hot water and wrapped in towels under or around the kid. Once the kid is warm, I tube it with colostrum (the first milk produced by the doe) either from the real mother or from the supply in the freezer.

Nannies or ewes that have large amounts of colostrum get hand milked and the excess colostrum is frozen in ice cube trays. Colostrum cubes are then popped out of the tray and placed in labelled freezer bags. Any problem kids or lambs then have access to the colostrum bank and we can thaw out a few cubes as needed. Remember to thaw this colostrum gradually. Do not boil it as boiling will destroy the antibodies it contains.

If the kid is really far gone (the rectal temperature is less than 37 C (98.6 F), the kid cannot lift its head or move and is less than 5 hours old) it can be thawed in lukewarm water that is gradually warmed up to body temperature or warmer. Only do this as a last resort as usually a doe will not reclaim a kid like this because all their scent has been washed off. Once the kid is warm it can be tube fed.

A kid more than 5 hours old that can hold its head up can be stomach tubed, dried, warmed, fed again and returned to a sheltered area.

Very chilled kids that are more than 5 hours old and cannot lift their heads up are a special problem. These babies should NOT be warmed until they have received 11 ml per kg (5 ml per lb) of 20% dextrose intraperitoneally (in the abdomen). The kid can then be warmed up. Once the kid can lift its head and sit up, then it can be tube fed or bottled. If dextrose is not given to these kids, they often will end up with severe brain damage and will die. To give an intraperitoneal injection, hold the kid up by its front legs so that its back is resting against your legs. Then swab the area one inch behind the umbilical cord and half an inch to the right or left of the midline with 70% alcohol. Using a one inch needle and aiming toward the rump, inject the dextrose into the abdomen.

Feeding orphans is a lot or extra work so it is worthwhile to train the occasional "bottle babies" to nurse from a bucket. The orphans are first fed with warm milk from a baby bottle, and, as soon as they catch on to this, they can progress to nursing from nipples attached to a bucket. For the first few feedings, the milk in the bucket is warm. After that it is kept fairly cool so that the kids do not engorge themselves.

A five gallon bucket works nicely for holding commercial kid milk replacer. Several (2 to 4) holes are drilled around the base of the bucket and nipples with a valve are screwed into these holes (obtained from Premier Sheep Supply, Washington, Iowa). The bucket is then suspended in a small pen. The kids in this little pen can nurse whenever they have the notion. In cold weather, put a heat lamp near the bucket so the milk does not freeze. In warm weather, cold packs can be placed in the milk. The buckets need to be cleaned frequently. This is quite an easy job as the nipples are easily removed from the bucket and there are no long tubes to rinse out. The kids do very well with this method. Put out creep feed, small amounts of fresh soybean meal and good hay so the kids learn to eat early on. These kids can be weaned at six to eight weeks of age, depending on their size.

Normal kids that have nursed will pass black feces within a few hours of being born. For about the first week of life, fecal material is yellow and very sticky. Sometimes if this fecal material builds up in this region, a hard mass will form over and around the rectum. This should be removed. After about a week the feces resemble that of the adult - brown pellets.

13. DISEASES

"All goat raisers have to contend with parasites, chiefly stomach worms and coccidia. Goats will thrive if parasite control and nutrition are good and if the environment is relatively stress-free. Many diseases are the result of overcrowding, inadequate feed or feed bunk space and poor sanitation."
- Stephanie and Allison Mitcham, "Diseases," *The Angora Goat, its History, Management and Diseases*, Crane Creek Publications, 1999, p. 83.

Anyone reading this chapter before acquiring any goats will quickly decide that he or she will *never* be qualified to raise goats. Do not be discouraged! Goats are basically healthy and hardy and, if well cared for, can live ten or more years. Very few of the diseases in this chapter will be a problem for the careful manager. The detailed descriptions of some of the following diseases should, however, allow the owner to better understand these conditions, and thus prevent them.

Not every goat disease is discussed in this chapter; however, most of the commonly seen problems have at least been mentioned.

I. PARASITES

INTERNAL PARASITES

Goats grazing in humid environments are very susceptible to internal parasites. This is likely because, over the years, they adapted to arid environments where the available vegetation allowed them to browse. If goats are allowed to roam over dry, rocky terrain and obtain a significant portion of their sustenance by browsing (consuming most of their feed from small shrubs, bushes, weeds and trees), internal parasite problems will typically be much less significant. Unfortunately many goats cannot be raised in this manner and must graze close to the ground, such as in a rotational grazing system.

Currently, there is an interest in selecting for goats (Kikos in New

Zealand and Boers in Australia, for example) that are more resistant to internal parasitism than the average and, as well, shed fewer worm eggs into the environment.

Coccidia

Coccidiosis, caused by host-specific protozoal parasites of the genus *Eimeria*, is of major economic significance to the goat industry. Animals of all ages can be affected with coccidiosis but the disease is most common in 3 week to 5 month old goats in confinement. *Eimeria* oocysts (eggs) are present in the feces of normal and clinically ill goats. At least 2 of the species of coccidia that infect goats do not cause clinical disease.

Goats develop age-related resistance to clinical coccidiosis by about 5 months of age. Although immunity does not eliminate infection, it slows the rate of coccidial replication in the intestinal tract. Oocyst numbers in fecal samples decline from 6 months through 6 years of age. Then, as the immune system weakens in goats 7 years of age and older, there is an increase in oocysts in the feces. The immunity that develops is specific for each *Eimeria* species so that goats of any age may become clinically affected if exposed to a species that they are not resistant to. As well, resistance may be lessened by stresses such as kidding and lactation, transport, feed changes, weather changes and even increased levels of exposure to an *Eimeria* species that the goat is already resistant to.

If conditions are right - adequate moisture, oxygen and suitable temperature (24 to 32 C or 75 to 90 F) - oocysts in the feces become infective in 2 to 5 days. Temperatures below -30 C (-22 F) and above 40 C (104 F) will kill oocysts. However, between these temperatures and in appropriate conditions, oocysts will survive for a year or more. Many disinfectants, including 5% formalin, will not kill oocysts. When conditions are optimal, synchronous sporulation can occur among oocysts accumulating in the environment, exposing susceptible goats to massive numbers of oocysts. *Eimeria* species life cycles vary and, with some species, if kids ingest sporocysts at birth, they may shed oocysts as early as 2 weeks of age.

Clinical coccidiosis is more commonly diagnosed in confinement-raised kids because of the concentration of fecal material and thus oocysts. When oocysts are ingested, digestive enzymes in the gastrointestinal tract damage the oocyst wall and sporozoites are released. The sporozoites penetrate the intestinal lining cells, causing considerable damage and initiating an asexual cycle of reproduction. After 1 to 3 asexual cycles, a sexual cycle occurs and oocysts are produced. The entire life cycle in the goat spans 2 to 3 weeks and may extend for several months.

Damage caused to the lining of the intestinal tract by asexual coccidia replication results in loss of blood and plasma into the gut lumen. Peracute cases, the result of massive blood loss into the intestinal lumen, may present as sudden death with no clinical signs. The early signs of acute cases include poor appetite, depression, weakness and abdominal pain, resulting in crying and frequent rising and lying down again. Diarrhea may develop and fresh blood in the feces or black feces may be noted - the black color being the result of digested blood. Very young susceptible animals may die of coccidiosis in a day or two while older more resistant animals may show weakness, diarrhea, weight loss and dehydration for as long as 2 weeks before dying or spontaneously recovering.

Bacteria can invade the goat's body via the damaged intestinal wall. Affected kids are very susceptible to other infections; for example, bacterial pneumonia.

Kids as well as older animals that survive are often unthrifty. They may be stunted with a poor hair coat and a potbellied look. This is because these animals are unable to absorb nutrients properly through a permanently damaged intestinal tract lining.

Diagnosis of coccidiosis is based on history, clinical signs, fecal flotation and necropsy results. Interpretation of fecal flotation results may be frustrating and misleading, since, if there is an overwhelming infection in which the coccidia are still at the stage of asexual replication, oocysts will not be seen. As well, oocysts are routinely found in all normal goats older than 2 to 3 weeks of age. Direct fecal smears can be used to identify merozoites, the formation of which precedes oocyst formation. Unless the *Eimeria* oocysts are specifically identified, oocyst counts are of limited value because some of the *Eimeria* species that do not cause disease produce an abundance of eggs. Necropsy is much more useful in diagnosing clinical coccidiosis. Gross examination of the intestine may show catarrhal, hemorrhagic or necrotic enteritis. The bowel may be filled with blood in peracute cases. Multiple raised white 1 to 6 mm diameter nodules on the intestinal mucosa (lining) are the most consistent lesions. Smears or histopathologic examination of these nodules reveal many macrogametes and oocysts.

Treatment of advanced cases of coccidiosis is generally unrewarding. Affected individuals should be removed from the group and dehydration corrected with oral, subcutaneous or intravenous balanced electrolyte solutions. Usually only very valuable individuals are treated with subcutaneous and intravenous fluids. Milk should be given in small amounts to kids that are not weaned because coccidial damage to the intestinal tract may cause maldigestion and osmotic diarrhea from the lactose that is not digested. Blood transfusions may be necessary for anemic (and valuable) kids. Anti-coccidial drugs are of limited value in advanced individual cases because most of these drugs inhibit but do not eliminate coccidial reproduction and act only on early stages of the reproductive cycle. Coccidiostats are most useful for preventing development of new cases of coccidiosis rather than for treating established cases. Drugs used for treatment include sulfonamides (sulfadimethoxine at 75 mg per kilogram (2.2 pounds) of body weight orally for 4 to 5 days) and amprolium at 10 to 50 mg per kilogram of body weight orally for 3 to 5 days. Sulfonamides must be used with care in dehydrated goats as renal damage can ensue. Amprolium given at high doses for 3 to 4 weeks can cause polioencephalomalacia, which is thought to be the result of thiamine deficiency.

Good management - low stress, good nutrition and adequate sanitation - will help control coccidiosis. Dry environment, clean bedding, prevention of fecal contamination of feed and water, properly balanced rations and moderate stocking densities are important. Most managers do use anticoccidial drugs, particularly in young kids and when conditions are wet or humid and the animals confined. Outbreaks of coccidiosis while coccidiostats are being used for prevention are usually the result of inappropriate levels of coccidiostat in the feed or salt or inadequate consumption of the coccidiostat-containing feed or salt by the goats.

The coccidiostats approved for use in goats include decoquinate at 0.5 mg per kilogram (2.2 pounds) of body weight and monensin at 20 grams per ton of feed. Monensin also is a growth promotant. One caution is that monensin is very toxic to members of the horse family and can also be toxic to goats if overdosed.

Decoquinate can be mixed in feed to approximate an intake of 0.5 to 1 mg per kilogram of body weight or added to trace mineral salt at 2 pounds (908 g) of 6% decoquinate per 50 pounds (22.7 kilograms) of trace mineral salt. If a commercial salt/mineral mix is being used, then the decoquinate needs to be added according to the percentage of salt in the mixture. For example, if the mixture is 50% salt and 50% mineral mix, then 1 pound of 6% decoquinate needs to be mixed with each 50 pounds of the product. As kids grow, the intake of feed increases, so the amount of decoquinate added to creep rations needs to be calculated on a weekly basis. Lasalocid, an ionophore, as is monensin, has the added benefit, as does monensin, of improved weight gains in addition to its coccidiostat effect. However, it should be noted that outbreaks of coccidiosis have been reported in young goats being fed lasalocid. Speculation as to why this occurred include uneven consumption of the lasalocid-containing feed by individual animals, possible drug resistance and failure to maintain good hygiene while feeding the coccidiostat.

By 5 months of age well-cared-for kids normally have immunity to reinfection by the *Eimeria* species they have been exposed to. At this time, coccidiostats need no longer be fed but kids should, if possible, be moved into uncontaminated housing or pasture.

Controlling coccidiosis in goats is a balancing act in which the manager tries to prevent massive challenge of kids by Eimeria species but allows sufficient exposure to the protozoa so that immunity and resistance can develop. Cleanliness and good management cannot be overemphasized.

Cryptosporidia

Cryptosporidiosis, caused by a protozoal parasite of the subclass Coccidia, is the most common cause of diarrhea in kids, especially those raised in confinement, that are less than a month of age. *Cryptosporidium parvum* occurs worldwide and can infect all mammalian domestic livestock species, poultry and man.

Its life cycle is similar to that of *Eimeria* species (coccidia) but the entire life cycle can be completed in a week.

Oocysts shed in the feces of goats, calves and even humans and consumed by a kid in sufficient numbers can result in disease. Disease is more severe in kids that have not received colostrum. Cryptosporidia damage intestinal lining cells resulting in both malabsorption and maldigestion, white to yellow, watery diarrhea and, in severe cases, death. Diarrhea may be apparent in kids as young as 3 to 4 days of age and may be persistent (for up to 2 weeks) or recurrent.

Since cryptosporidia are not usually found in the feces of healthy goats, their presence in an acid fast stained fecal smear or on fecal flotation and sedimentation (preferred method for detection), indicates a diagnosis of cryptosporidiosis. Gross necropsy lesions are nonspecific. Cryptosporidia are often found in conjunction with other agents that can cause diarrhea so a laboratory examination to rule in or out other causes of diarrhea is helpful. Dietary causes of diarrhea may be ruled out by taking a careful history.

Numerous drugs have been evaluated and none have been documented as useful in controlling or eliminating cryptosporidial infections. Treatment involves supportive care, mainly fluid therapy. The volume of milk per feeding should be reduced and the frequency of feedings reduced. Oral electrolytes may be substituted for milk for a few feedings but, if the diarrhea goes on for 2 weeks, milk must be reintroduced after a couple of days or kids will starve to death.

Cleanliness is of paramount importance in controlling or preventing this disease. All kids should receive colostrum at birth and any kid with diarrhea should immediately be isolated to prevent oocyst spread. Kids with diarrhea should be handled after the main flock is tended to or, better yet, cared for by a person who is not going to handle the other livestock at all. Clothes and footwear should be washed after diarrheic kids are handled and hands should be washed carefully because humans may contract this disease. Steam cleaning of pens that have been occupied by kids with diarrhea will help to kill oocysts. Common disinfectants do not destroy oocysts.

Oocysts are very resistant to environmental changes as well as to a variety of disinfectants. Only ammonia (5%) and formol saline (10%) render oocysts incapable of infecting kids.

Liver Flukes

Because the water snail is an intermediate host for *Fasciola* and *Fascioloides* species, disease resulting from infection with these flukes is typically a problem when animals are grazed on wet, marshy or irrigated pastures. *Dicrocoelium dendriticum* needs both a land snail and an ant to complete its life cycle.

1)*Fasciola* species

Adult *Fasciola* flukes, which have worldwide distribution, live in the biliary tract of the goat and eggs pass through the bile duct into the feces. Within 10 to 12 days, eggs hatch and, if the temperature is at least 10 C (50 F), the miracidia that are released invade snails. From 21 days to 10 months later (usually from 5 to 8 weeks later), cercariae are shed by snails, swim to nearby plants and encyst. When these infective metacercariae are ingested by a goat, they excyst and migrate through the intestinal wall to the liver. They arrive in the bile ducts 6 to 7 weeks after infection and need another 2 to 4 weeks to develop into egg-laying adults.

Snail infection with miracidia usually peaks in the late spring and

FASCIOLIASIS, THE MOST COMMON LIVER FLUKE
DISEASE IN MEAT GOATS

HEALTHY GOATS GRAZE ON PLANTS
WITH ENCYSTED MIRACIDIA AND THE
INFECTION
BEGINS

LIVER FLUKE

LIVER FLUKE EGGS IN THE BILE DUCT
OF AN INFECTED ADULT GOAT
ARE PASSED IN
THE FECES

THE FLUKE EGGS IN THE FECES
HATCH INTO MIRACIDIA WHICH
INVADE SNAILS CARRIED IN BY
AN OVERFLOWING STREAM

LOW-LYING PASTURE

THE WATER SNAILS SHED THE MIRACIDIA WHICH SWIM
OFF TO PLANTS WHERE THEY ENCYST

early summer in temperate regions. Thus, goats consume infective metacercariae in the late summer and early fall with most clinical signs apparent in the late fall and winter. If winters are not too cold and dry, some snails will survive so there can also be a wave of infection, though less severe, with metacercariae in the late spring and early summer. Metacercariae can be present year round in tropical regions so clinical disease may occur throughout the year. Goats do develop some immunity to *Fasciola* infection but may easily become reinfected.

Clinical disease occurs when metacercariae penetrate the liver capsule and wander through the liver tissue on their journey to the bile ducts. Acute fascioliasis, in which there is severe disruption of the liver tissue and/or capsule with resulting severe hemorrhage or, if the goat survives, hepatic insufficiency from extensive liver damage, is rare in goats. This is likely because goats prefer to browse rather than graze and, as well, they do not like really wet areas. So, they may not ingest enough metacercariae to cause acute disease. Manifestations of acute fascioliasis are sudden death or progressive weakness, listlessness, inappetence and anemia for up to 3 days at which time death occurs.

Less severe liver damage and hemorrhage as well as extensive fibrosis (formation of scar tissue), in an attempt to heal the damaged liver, occurs in subacute fascioliasis. Affected animals may have similar clinical signs to those with acute disease. Signs of illness may span several weeks.

Chronic fascioliasis, the most common form of this disease in goats, is the result of the adult flukes in the bile ducts feeding on blood. Affected animals may be depressed, have a poor appetite and lose weight for a month or more. Diarrhea may occur and animals are anemic. Intermandibular edema (bottle jaw) is often noted in more chronic cases.

Acute cases are usually diagnosed at necropsy. Migrating flukes are best seen by shaking the cut surface of a piece of liver in a container of water and looking for larvae which settle at the bottom. Fluke eggs can be found in the feces in goats with chronic fascioliasis. Necropsy of goats affected with chronic fascioliasis typically reveals hepatic fibrosis and irregular hepatic nodules as well as thickened and fibrosed bile ducts containing adult flukes.

In Australia, black disease, resulting from proliferation of *Clostridium novyi*, soil-borne bacteria present in the liver, has been documented in Angora goats that are forced to graze in wet regions during drought. In sheep, black disease often occurs in conjunction with fascioliasis because *C. novyi* organisms already present in the liver multiply in the dead liver tissue, now an anaerobic environment, resulting from the liver fluke migration.

The only drugs available for treatment in the United State are albendazole, only effective against mature flukes 10 weeks of age or more, and clorsulon, effective against all flukes 2 weeks of age and older. Neither is specifically approved for goat use. Albendazole orally at 15 mg per kilogram (2.2 pounds) was 95.9% effective against adult *F. hepatica*. Clorsulon is being used at the sheep dosage of 7 mg per kilogram (2.2 pounds) of body weight. Because these drugs are not effective against immature forms, animals need to be retreated at an interval recommended for the drug being used to eliminate the larvae as they mature. Fecal examination can be used to determine if fluke ova are being shed. If liver damage is not too severe, animals with chronic fascioliasis can be saved.

The prognosis for animals with acute and subacute fascioliasis is poor. These animals and any others at risk should be treated with diamphenethide or triclabendazole (which are not available in the United States).

Fasciola infestations can be controlled by not grazing goats in high risk regions, keeping adult fluke burdens in goats to a minimum and maintaining good nutrition and health (regular deworming and vaccination). In temperate or arid regions where flukes are known to be a problem, goats should be treated with an adult flukicide in the late winter or early spring before they are turned out onto the pasture and with a flukicide that kills immature and mature flukes in the fall to eliminate flukes ingested during the grazing season. In regions where grazing is year round, goats may need to be treated every 8 to 10 weeks with triclabendazole or diamphenethide. Intensive control methods will decrease numbers of flukes on pastures and may not need to be repeated after the first year. Molluscicides can be applied to snail habitat but these compounds are toxic to fish.

2)*Fascioloides magna*

This "large American liver fluke" may be a more serious problem in some regions of North America - including the Great Lakes region, the Gulf coast, the Rocky Mountains and the Pacific Northwest - and Europe, than *Fasciola* species. Goats are not a normal host for this fluke whose definitive hosts include members of the Cervidae family such as deer, elk and moose. The adult flukes live in the bile ducts of the definitive host and lay eggs that pass into the environment in the feces. The life cycle is similar to that of *Fasciola* species and 30 to 32 weeks after eggs are passed in feces, adult flukes in the new definitive host are ready to start laying eggs. In goats, and sheep too, migrating larvae reach the liver but never form cysts that communicate with the bile ducts. Instead, the larvae wander throughout the liver causing significant damage. Hemorrhage into the abdominal cavity and peritonitis may also occur. An infected goat usually shows signs of disease 3 to 6 months after consuming metacercariae.

Goats usually become infected in the early fall and disease is seen in January and February. The risk is increased in marshy areas but wherever deer or elk and intermediate host snails thrive is potentially hazardous for goats.

Infected goats usually die suddenly. Necropsy shows necrotic liver tissue and black tracts throughout the liver.

Because severe disease and even death can be caused by even one immature fluke, treatment is difficult. Albendazole orally at 15 mg per kilogram (2.2 pounds) of body weight is 99% effective against flukes 8 or more weeks old. In sheep, closantel is 95 to 98% effective orally at 15 mg per kilogram or intramuscularly at 7.5 mg per kilogram. Clorsulon at 21 mg per kilogram is 92% effective against 8 week old larvae in sheep.

Fencing off or not grazing wet areas as well as fencing out deer may be helpful. In northern climates, treatment with albendazole after the first killing frost and again a month later will decrease death loss.

3)*Dicrocoelium dendriticum*

Adult *Dicrocoelium dendriticum* flukes, which typically produce chronic liver fluke disease in goats that is less severe than that caused by *Fasciola* species, live in the bile ducts. Infection with these flukes is common in North America, Europe, Asia, North Africa, and the Middle East and, in endemic areas, prevalence in goat populations may be as high as 45%. Numerous regions may be contaminated with *D. dendriticum* but pastures adjacent to forests are high-risk. The fluke eggs resist drying and freezing and cercarial infections are maintained in hibernating ants so goats can be infected at the start of spring grazing. Fluke eggs are shed in the feces and ingested by land snails. Cercariae develop in snails, are expelled in slime balls and consumed by ants. Infectious metacercariae develop in ants. Metacercariae affect the nervous system of ants, causing ants to be immobilized on grasses during peak times of livestock grazing. When the ants are ingested by grazing goats, the young flukes excyst from metacercariae in the intestine and enter the biliary system via the common bile duct. *D. dendriticum* flukes are ready to lay eggs 8 to 12 weeks after ants are eaten by the goat.

D. dendriticum can cause severe inflammation of the biliary system resulting in hepatic fibrosis and insufficiency. Goats lose weight, are depressed, and may be anemic and hypoproteinemic with intermandibular edema (bottle jaw).

The most useful method of diagnosis is to identify fluke eggs in goat feces. At necropsy, adult flukes are present in bile ducts. In severe, chronic cases, fibrosis of the biliary system and the liver may be apparent.

In France, treatment includes oral albendazole at 15 mg per kilogram (2.2 pounds) of body weight with a precaution against use during the first 3 months of pregnancy. Also in France, oral thiophanate is recommended at 50 mg per kilogram. Oral diamphenethide at 220 to 330 mg per kilogram body weight is very safe and effective. Thiabendazole at 200 mg per kilogram and fenbendazole at 100 mg per kilogram are among some of the drugs reported to have efficacies of 90% or more in sheep.

Control is difficult because of the two intermediate hosts. In temperate regions where *D. dendriticum* is endemic, goats should be treated in the fall before winter feeding starts while, in tropical regions, treatment every 7 weeks will reduce pasture contamination and numbers of flukes in the bile ducts.

Lungworms

1)*Dictyocaulus filaria*

D. filaria lungworms, which may be as much as 80 mm long, live in the bronchi (airways) of the lungs. First-stage larvae are coughed up, swallowed and passed in the feces. In 1 to 2 weeks the first-stage larvae develop to infective third-stage larvae, which survive for lengthy periods in damp, cool surroundings. After the infective larvae are ingested, a month will pass before adult lungworms mature and produce eggs. Clinical signs of infection, initially rapid breathing, then coughing, difficulty breathing and weight loss, usually occur in the fall. Fourth-stage larvae can overwinter in the lungs but freezing and hot, dry weather kills larvae on pasture.

Diagnosis is by examination of feces collected directly from the rectum by the Baermann technique.

Treatment, which prevents establishment of immunity, includes oral or subcutaneous tetramisole at 15 mg per kilogram (2.2 pounds) of body weight, oral or subcutaneous levamisole at 7.5 mg per kilogram, mebendazole at 15 to 20 mg per kilogram, fenbendazole at 5 to 10 mg per kilogram, febantel at 5 mg per kilogram and ivermectin at 0.2 mg per kilogram.

Rotating pastures every 4 days is useful in controlling *D. filaria* as is starting grazing early in the season so that goats have a chance to gradually become exposed and develop immunity. Kids should be grazed on pastures that have not been stocked with yearling goats for at least a year. Pasture contamination can be limited by treating goats before winter feeding begins. Wet, overstocked pastures should be avoided.

2)Protostrongylid lungworms: *Muellerius capillaris* and *Protostrongylus rufescens* (other species are recognized in Europe and India)

All of these lungworms have an indirect life cycle with snails and slugs, which remain infective for a year or more, as intermediate hosts. Consumption of the mollusc or third-stage larvae after death of the mollusc results in infection of the goat. *P. rufescens* adults live in bronchi and *M. capillaris* in alveoli. Infections with the latter usually are not clinically apparent.

Treatment for *Protostrongylus* is as for *Dictyocaulus*. Levamisole is not effective against *Muellerius*. Fenbendazole or ivermectin treatment has been suggested at 35 day intervals because it appears that immature *Muellerius* in the lungs resume development after the adults are killed. Fenbendazole at 2 mg per kilogram (2.2 pounds) of body weight per day for 14 days when the goats are confined may decrease shedding of larvae for 5 to 7 months.

Wet pastures should be avoided. It might be useful to prevent grazing in the early morning and evening when the vegetation is moist and snails are more mobile. To prevent contamination of molluscs, goats should be treated before they start grazing in the spring.

Meningeal Worm (Parelaphostrongylosis)

Goats may become infected with *Parelaphostrongylus tenuis*, whose definitive host is the whitetail deer, by eating larvae-containing terrestrial slugs or snails. No clinical signs of disease are seen in deer infected with the meningeal worm; however, in aberrant hosts such as goats, sheep, llamas and other wild cervids, infection with the meningeal worm can cause myelitis (inflammation of the spinal cord) or encephalomyelitis (inflammation of both the brain and spinal cord). The disease is present wherever whitetail deer are to be found, essentially throughout North America and extending into northern Mexico.

Adult *P. tenuis* worms live in the subdural spaces of the whitetail deer brain as well as in cranial venous sinuses (blood vessels). When eggs laid on the deer's meninges (membrane enveloping the brain and spinal cord) hatch, they travel in blood vessels to the lungs. Eggs laid in the venous sinuses are carried by the blood stream to the lungs where they hatch. Larvae climb up the airways, are swallowed and passed in the feces. Land snails and slugs consume the larvae and, over a 3 to 4 week period, infective larvae develop. When the snails and slugs are consumed by grazing animals, the infective larvae are released and begin their travels. In deer and other animals, larvae reach the spinal cord 10 days after ingestion. In deer, larvae mature in the spinal cord for another 20 or 30 days, at which time the adults migrate to the brain. In the goat, larvae in the spinal cord mature abnormally and larval migration throughout the spinal cord is random. Larvae do not reach the brain to complete their life cycle but, in their attempt to do so, can cause tremendous spinal cord damage. Clinical signs in the affected goat depend on the location and severity of the damage in the brain and spinal cord.

The goat can control infection to some extent and recovery has been noted in both experimentally and naturally infected individuals.

Goats grazing pastures where whitetail deer browse are at risk of contracting this disease. There appears to be an increased risk of exposure to slugs and snails in low lying, wet pastures, croplands and woodlands. Cool, moist weather appears to enhance infectivity of first stage larvae and promote snail activity. In the northern portion of North America, pastures are most dangerous during the late summer and early fall and most infected goats show clinical signs in the fall and early winter. Disease has been noted in April in Texas.

From 10 to 27 percent of animals in a herd may become clinically affected and, of these, up to 65% may die.

Any age goat can be affected and clinical signs vary, depending on the severity of spinal cord and brain damage. Goats may have a gradually progressive lameness (wobbly, swaying gait, weakness, toe dragging), paresis or paralysis affecting any combination of front and hind limbs, or may be found down and unable to rise. Usually goats remain bright and alert and continue eating and drinking. If the brain is involved, the affected animal may circle, have a head tilt, be blind and separate from the flock. Infected goats may develop more severe signs, may remain stable or may occasionally improve without treatment. If the goat is up and about, it should be given at least a month to see if it will become stable, improve or recover. The prognosis is poorer for animals that are down.

MENINGEAL WORM LIFE CYCLE

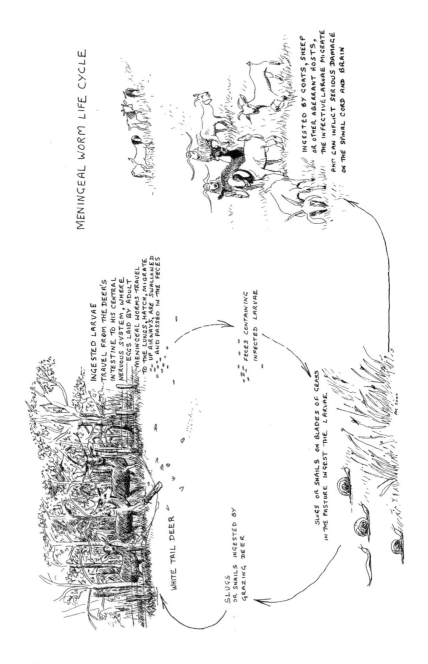

INGESTED LARVAE
TRAVEL FROM THE DEER'S
INTESTINE TO HIS CENTRAL
NERVOUS SYSTEM, WHERE
EGGS LAID BY ADULT
MENINGEAL WORMS TRAVEL
TO THE LUNGS, HATCH, MIGRATE
UP AIRWAYS, ARE SWALLOWED
AND PASSED IN THE FECES

FECES CONTAINING
INFECTED LARVAE

WHITE TAIL DEER

SLUGS
OR SNAILS INGESTED BY
GRAZING DEER

SLUGS OR SNAILS ON BLADES OF GRASS
IN THE PASTURE INGEST THE LARVAE.

INGESTED BY GOATS, SHEEP
OR OTHER ABERRANT HOSTS,
THE INFECTIVE LARVAE MIGRATE
AND CAN INFLICT SERIOUS DAMAGE
ON THE SPINAL CORD AND BRAIN

MS 2000

This disease can only be definitely diagnosed at necropsy by microscopic identification of the parasite in nervous tissue.

Although various drugs have been used to treat *P. tenuis* infections, including diethylcarbamazine at 40 to 100 mg per kilogram (2.2 pounds) of body weight for 1 to 3 days, ivermectin at high doses and fenbendazole, there is no known effective treatment. Steroids may be useful to reduce swelling caused by larval migration.

The disease can be controlled by preventing goats from grazing wet pastures near woodlands, restricting deer access to pastures (easier said than done) and removing goats from pastures before the weather turns wet and cool. Since ivermectin will kill migrating larvae before they reach the spinal cord, goats could be treated every 10 days while pastured. While this might be feasible for a few very valuable goats, this is not very practical for a large herd.

Oestrus ovis (Nasal Bots)
This parasite, which causes an impressive nasal discharge but no pneumonia, is less common in goats than in sheep. The adult fly deposits larvae around the nostrils of pastured animals. The first instars invade the nasal cavity and develop into second instars, which then enter the sinuses. After two to ten months mature larvae return to the nostrils, if they are small enough to leave the sinuses, and are sneezed out into the environment. Pupation occurs on the ground, and, after 4 weeks or more, adult flies emerge.

Apart from nasal discharge, frequent loud sneezing in the late summer may be noted. If feed consumption is not affected, treatment is not necessary. Ivermectin, at 0.2 mg per kilogram, is very effective against all stages of nasal bots.

Stomach Worms (Nematode Gastroenteritis)
Of major economic significance to goat enterprises worldwide, particularly where goats are being grazed, is gastrointestinal tract infestation with a variety of nematode parasites.

Numerous nematode families can infect the gastrointestinal tract, including the Trichostrongylidae (*Haemonchus, Ostertagia, Trichostrongylus, Cooperia* and *Nematodirus* are some of the genera in this family), Trichuridae (*Trichurus* species [whipworms]), Oxyuridae [pinworms], Trichonematidae (*Oesophagostomum* species [nodular worms]), Ancyclostomidae (*Bunostomum* [hookworms]) and Strongyloididae

(*Strongyloides papillosis*). With the exception of the latter, all of these have a direct life cycle so that an intermediate host, such as a snail, is not necessary for completion of the life cycle.

Adult Trichostrongylidae lay eggs that are passed in the feces. If conditions are optimum, development to infective third stage larvae typically takes 7 to 10 days. When moisture is adequate, infective larvae migrate 10 to 20 cm (4 to 8 inches) from the fecal material. Early or late in the day, when dew is on the grasses, larvae can migrate to the tops of the grasses and the goat may consume this grass along with the larvae. Once ingested, larvae develop to adults in 15 to 20 days at which time they start producing eggs.

Nematodes that live in the abomasum, one of the goat's four stomachs, and that cause sickness and death include *Haemonchus contortus*, *Ostertagia circumcincta*, and *Trichostrongylus axei*. Small intestinal nematodes of major significance include *Trichostrongylus colubriformis*, *T. vitrinus*, *Cooperia curticei*, *Nematodirus filicollis*, *N. spathiger*, *Bunostomum trigoncephalum* and *Strongyloides papillosis*. *Trichuris ovis* inhabits the cecum and, though it contributes to ill thrift, it is not considered to be a major pathogen. *Oesophagostomum columbianum* adults live in the colon but the infective larvae produce nodules throughout the intestines.

Domesticated goats may have little opportunity for browsing and instead must graze pastures. Under these conditions, especially where forage is lush, dense and moist, and pastures are heavily stocked, risk for gastrointestinal parasite infestation is high. Diarrheic fecal material, either the result of lush pasture or parasitism, which covers a large area when it hits the ground instead of being distributed in pellets, will also increase the spread of gastrointestinal nematodes.

Nematode eggs are killed by temperatures over 40 C (104 F) and at 0 C (32 F) remain alive but do not hatch. Eggs hatch within 8 to 9 days at 30 to 35 C (86 to 95 F) whereas hatching takes 14 days at 20 to 25 C (68 to 77 F).

Eggs of *Haemonchus* species and *Oesophagostomum columbianum* will not hatch at 10 C (50 F) or less and are very susceptible to drying. Thus these nematodes thrive in tropical and subtropical regions. Larvae are hardier and can survive dry periods. Hypobiosis, voluntary dormancy or a state of arrested development of infective larvae consumed by the goat when environmental conditions are less than optimal, increases survival of these nematodes.

Hookworms do best in humid subtropical and temperate regions, especially where bedding or pastures are wet. Damp conditions increase opportunities for larvae to penetrate the skin of the feet and legs.

Trichostrongylus species and *Ostertagia* species are well adapted to cooler, temperate regions and are capable of overwintering as well as of hypobiosis. Hot, dry summers do not agree with *Trichostrongylus*. *Ostertagia* species can tolerate colder winters and hot, dry summers and some larvae can survive on pasture for up to a year. *Nematodirus* species are very resistant to cold and dryness.

Though parasite resistance to anthelmintics is becoming more common in small ruminants and is positively correlated with deworming frequency, it is difficult to document the presence of true parasite resistance in goats because the pharmacokinetics of many anthelmintic agents used in goats are not known. Cases in which resistance to an anthelmintic is suspected may actually be the result of underdosing of the drug because of incorrect estimation of body weight or faulty automatic drenching equipment. As well, closing of the esophageal groove at the time of oral anthelmintic administration will lead to deposition of the drug in the abomasum instead of the rumen, resulting in shorter contact time of the anthelmintic with gastrointestinal nematodes. Also, drug doses recommended for sheep or cattle may be ineffective in goats. Goats may also react differently to gastrointestinal parasite infection than sheep.

Depression of the immune system, removal of adult worms by deworming, birthing and lactation can all encourage dormant nematodes to mature and start producing eggs. Fecal egg counts are highest in goats a week after kidding and remain elevated for 4 weeks. Thus kidding time is a good time to deworm goats.

Immunity to gastrointestinal parasites develops with age and with continuous exposure, although goats show the weakest immunity of the domestic ruminants. Strong resistance to parasite infection likely did not develop in goats because of their browsing behavior.

H. contortus, which feeds on blood, causes a gradually progressive anemia. If infection is very severe, then death from acute blood loss may occur. Most of the other gastrointestinal parasites damage the lining of the intestinal tract with resulting plasma protein loss, hypoproteinemia, mild to moderate anemia and diarrhea. Most parasitic infections are the result of multiple species so it is often difficult to sort out which clinical signs are the result of which nematode.

Infections with *Trichostrongylus, Ostertagia, Cooperia* and *Nematodirus* species typically affect young grazing animals and result in condition loss, poor growth, listlessness, decreased feed intake and, in severe infestations, a dark green to black diarrhea. Intermandibular edema (bottle jaw) and subcutaneous ventral abdominal edema, the result of hypoproteinemia, may develop in chronic cases and there may be occasional deaths. Goats with *H. contortus* infections will have pale mucous membranes (gums, vulvar lips), conjunctivae and horn bases as well as intermandibular edema and weakness. Subcutaneous edema (fluid under the skin) may also be present along the ventral abdominal wall and down the legs.

Examination of fresh or refrigerated feces for parasite eggs may be useful although serious damage may have been done by immature nematodes before eggs are even present in the feces. Eggs may also be counted, but, again, there may be no correlation between the severity of the infection and the number of eggs present. There is considerable variation in the numbers of eggs laid by different species and some of the prolific egg producers may not cause much in the way of disease. Egg counts of 2000 or more per gram are considered to indicate serious infection in lambs and counts of 500 or more in multiple specimens indicate the necessity of further evaluation of the situation in a goat herd, especially if individuals are hypoproteinemic (serum albumin less than 2.5 g/dl) and/or anemic (packed cell volumes less than 25% and as low or lower than 10% in severe haemonchosis).

Fecal egg counts can be used to monitor anthelmintic efficacy. If fecal egg counts are performed before deworming and again a week later, an idea of the efficacy of the anthelmintic agent can be determined. A 90 to 95% reduction in the eggs per gram of feces should be obtained if the anthelmintic is to be worthwhile using in one's parasite control program.

Emaciation at necropsy is suggestive of gastrointestinal parasitism. Subcutaneous edema and/or anemia may also be noted. The red and white striped females (barber pole worms) of haemonchosis can be seen on careful examination of the abomasal mucosa (interior lining of the abomasum, one of the four stomachs). *Ostertagia* causes edema of the abomasal wall and a grainy appearance of the abomasal mucosal surface, the result of larvae filling the gastric glands. Gross (that can be seen with the naked eye) necropsy findings for most of the intestinal worms are nonspecific and the worms are difficult to see except on microscopic examination of stained mucosal impression smears.

Apart from anthelmintic treatment, goats with clinical signs of gastrointestinal parasitism need supportive care, including separation from healthy individuals who are likely to pick on them, good quality, readily digestible high-protein feed and injectable iron dextran. If the individual is very anemic and valuable, blood transfusions may be considered. Many anthelmintic drugs are available but most are not approved for use in goats. The benzimidazoles, such as thiabendazole (at 44 mg per kilogram (2.2 pounds) of body weight), fenbendazole (at 5 mg per kilogram), oxfendazole (at 5 mg per kilogram), parbendazole (at 30 mg per kilogram), albendazole (at 7.5 mg per kilogram), mebendazole (at 12.5 mg per kilogram) and cambendazole (at 25 mg per kilogram), are safe, broad spectrum oral anthelmintics. Grain should be withheld for 24 hours before dosing with cambendazole as this drug may be toxic to goats on high grain diets, The benzimidazoles are not very effective against *Trichuris* but are highly effective against adult and immature stages of most of the other gastrointestinal nematodes. Newer compounds, such as oxfendazole, febantel (a probenzimidazole given at 5 mg per kilogram), fenbendazole and albendazole are also highly effective against hypobiotic (dormant) larvae of *Ostertagia*. As well, the benzimidazoles kill ova, so, once treated, goats can safely be moved onto clean pastures, pastures that have been grazed by another species or hayed during the previous grazing season so that they are free of gastrointestinal nematodes.

Overdosing with oxfendazole and its precursors albendazole, fenbendazole or febantel during the first 45 days of pregnancy can produce fetal defects in rats. Such abnormalities have not been documented in goats.

Ivermectin, an avermectin, has a wide spectrum of efficacy against pulmonary and gastrointestinal adult and immature nematodes as well as arrested (hypobiotic) larvae. Ivermectin is not effective against tapeworms or flukes. The recommended dose is 0.2 mg or 200 ug (micrograms) per kilogram (2.2 pounds) of body weight, although doses as low as 50 ug per kilogram have been found to be highly effective in goats. It has a wide safety margin and can be administered orally or subcutaneously though some goats find it highly irritating when given subcutaneously. No lasting effects have been noted in these individuals that react to subcutaneous administration.

Levamisole and the pyrmidines, pyrantel (orally at 25 mg per kilogram) and morantel (orally at 10 mg per kilogram), have similar spectrums of activity against gastrointestinal nematodes when compared to the benzimidazoles but have little effect against hypobiotic larvae and ova. As well, levamisole and the pyrmidines have no activity against tapeworms (cestodes) and flukes (trematodes).

Levamisole, which has a narrow safety margin, can be given orally or subcutaneously. Even at the recommended dose of 8 mg per kilogram (2.2 pounds) of body weight, some goats may appear depressed, salivate, froth at the mouth and have muscle tremors. These signs subside without treatment.

To decrease development of gastrointestinal nematode resistance, all animals being introduced to the herd should be dewormed with double doses of broad spectrum anthelmintics from at least 2 different anthelmintic classes. Animals should be overdosed with anthelmintics rather than underdosed and treatments during a year or grazing season should be kept to a minimum. Because it is now felt that resistance occurs just as quickly with the use of multiple anthelmintics as with a single one, only a single anthelmintic should be used during an entire grazing season. Where grazing is continuous, a single anthelmintic should be used until resistance develops. When anthelmintics are changed, an anthelmintic from a different class should be selected.

Totally confined goats that are carefully managed (dry, clean facilities with feed bunks that the animals cannot defecate in) can be kept relatively free of gastrointestinal nematodes. So, if the pastures available are small and overgrazed, it may be better to raise the goats in confinement. In semiconfinement situations, goats should be dewormed with an anthelmintic effective against both adults and hypobiotic larvae before being turned out onto pasture - preferably pasture that was not grazed the previous year - in the spring. Fecal egg counts on composite fecal samples should be performed periodically throughout the grazing season and goats dewormed as deemed necessary. At the end of the grazing season, goats should be dewormed again.

When the grazing season is lengthy or continuous, the body condition of the goats should be carefully observed in conjunction with assessment of the consistency of the feces and periodic determination of fecal egg counts. In regions where it is known, for example, that rapid *Haemonchus* larval development may occur after heavy rains, treatment before the advent of clinical signs is recommended. As well, animals should be moved onto clean pasture following treatment. Ideally, animals should be drylotted for a day or so after anthelmintic treatment so that any parasites are passed *before* the animals are turned back out to pasture. With rotational grazing, paddocks must be large enough to support the number of goats. Supplemental feeding should be done in feed bunks or feed should be well spread out and in new, clean sites daily. Water should not be allowed to overflow and accumulate in areas where goats gather to drink. In tropical regions, with little seasonal variation in temperature and humidity, deworming every 3 weeks may be necessary.

Grazing several species together will also help control parasitism and will allow better pasture use as different species prefer various pasture components. If given the opportunity to eat a variety of items, goats will consume about 60% browse and 40% grass. Cattle, on the other hand, will eat 80% grass and sheep are intermediate. These amounts vary with the season and breed.

Tapeworms (Cestodes)

Although tapeworms are generally of little clinical or economic significance, they can cause great concern and excitement when owners spot proglottids, which resemble grains of rice, in the feces. The most common intestinal tapeworm worldwide is *Moniezia expansa*. At least 50 tapeworms need to be present in the intestinal lumen before there is significant competition with the host for nutrients. If tapeworm infestation is the cause of ill thrift and a pot-bellied appearance, it usually is in kids less than 6 months of age. Occasionally the lumen of the intestine may be blocked by tapeworms. These individuals will display abdominal pain and decreased fecal output. If the intestine ruptures, kids will initially be depressed or may simply be found dead.

Resistance to tapeworm infection develops with age and in animals constantly exposed to tapeworms.

Tapeworm eggs may be detected on fecal flotation and/or proglottids may be found in the feces. On necropsy, tapeworms are readily apparent in the small intestinal lumen.

Tapeworms are more of a problem in pastured goats. However, the intermediate host infective mites may be present in barnyards, so heavy tapeworm infestations are often indicative of heavy nematode infections.

Proglottids shed in the feces contain eggs which, when consumed by mites common on herbages and in soils, develop into infective cysticercoids over a 4 month period. When the mites are consumed by goats, cysticercoids are released in the intestine and mature tapeworms develop.

Anthelmintics that will eliminate adult tapeworms in goats include niclosamide at 50 mg per kilogram (2.2 pounds) of body weight (very safe and effective), praziquantel at 5 mg per kilogram of body weight (effective but can cause severe irritation at the injection site), oral febantel at 5 mg per kilogram, mebendazole at 15 mg per kilogram, fenbendazole at 15 mg per kilogram, cambendazole at 20 mg per kilogram, and oxfendazole and albendazole at 10 mg per kilogram. Albendazole is effective against tapeworms, nematodes and *Fasciola hepatica*. It should be noted that ivermectin is not effective against tapeworms.

Cambendazole may be toxic to goats on high grain rations. Thus, if this drug is to be used, goats should not be fed grain for 24 hours before treatment.

EXTERNAL PARASITES

Lice

Goats may become infested with bloodsucking lice (order Anoplura) and/or biting lice (order Mallophaga).

All species of goat lice are quite host-specific. Eggs are attached to hairs and hatch into nymphs, that resemble tiny adults, in 5 to 18 days. The young lice become mature 14 to 21 days after hatching.

Biting lice are pale and difficult to see. These lice, when present in large numbers, cause goats to bite and pull at their hair and scratch themselves with their horns and hooves.

Bloodsucking lice are bluish gray and their presence can result in blood loss anemia and secondary bacterial skin infections as well as severe pruritus (itching). Severe infestations may kill kids.

Lice are often more abundant on certain animals: these goats, which are considered to be louse carriers, are typically malnourished, heavily parasitized or have some debilitating disease. If the underlying problem cannot be resolved in these "carrier" goats, they should be culled from the herd.

Lice can be observed by parting hair and carefully inspecting the base of the hairs near the skin.

Delousing goats with considerable fiber will be mentioned because some meat goats are raised for both meat and fiber (cashmere goats, for example) or are Angora crosses that have longer fiber than, for example, a Spanish goat with its naturally short coat. If goats are being sheared regularly, it should be noted that lice leave the goats for up to a month or more after shearing. Thus, it is best to delouse goats 30 to 50 days after shearing. As well, waiting for some hair regrowth is beneficial because the insecticide tends to adhere to the hair, giving better louse control. Delousing goats with considerable hair is generally not very successful as, even with a high-pressure sprayer, insecticide does not readily reach the skin. Of course, naturally short-coated goats can be deloused at any time.

Insecticide can be applied with a high-pressure sprayer or utilized as a pour-on. Many larger operations use dip tanks with good success, although older goats can become quite inventive when it comes to escaping dipping. Most dip tanks are concrete vats that the goats enter at one end. As the goats swim across the tank, the head is submerged for a few seconds. However, in very cold weather or if the goats are in poor condition, using a pour-on insecticide is recommended. Many different agents are available for louse control. Several of these should be selected and then rotated, as lice develop resistance to insecticides quite rapidly. Goats should routinely be deloused after shearing as it is difficult to completely eradicate lice from large groups of goats. Many Texas Angora goat ranchers will tell one "that the only way to eliminate lice is to get rid of the goats." Lice are much easier to eradicate from a herd of short haired goats.

Many of the newer permethrins, for example, Expar Pour-on Insecticide (Coopers Animal Health Inc., Kansas City, Kansas), are quite safe and effective. Two treatments, two weeks apart, 30 to 50 days post shearing, with 15 ml of Expar per 45 kilograms or 100 pounds of body weight (or 7.5 ml per 22.7 kilograms or 50 pounds of body weight) gives good control of lice until the next shearing, unless the lice are resistant to this insecticide. The solution is oily and does not run off the goats like the water-based insecticides. It can be applied with a 30 ml syringe if small numbers of goats are to be deloused or with a dosing gun and backpack for large groups.

Fenvalerate is also commonly used as a dip (0.05% solution) or as a pour-on. An example is Ectrin WDL (Fermenta Animal Health, Kansas City, Missouri). An ounce of Ectrin can be mixed with 12 ounces of water and one teaspoon of liquid detergent. Then an ounce of this mixture is applied to the back of each 22.7 to 45 kilogram (50 to 100 pound) animal. Ectrin has a residual effect, so a single treatment after shearing should suffice. Fenvalerate can also be applied with a pressure sprayer (see malathion below).

Malathion can be applied as a 0.5% solution with a high-pressure sprayer (300 to 350 psi). Each goat must be well soaked with the insecticide, making sure that the belly and legs are not forgotten. Each animal must be thoroughly sprayed with one and one half to two quarts of malathion and, because this drug does not have enough residual activity to kill lice hatching from eggs present at the time of the first treatment, malathion needs to be applied a second time 2 to 3 weeks after the first treatment.

Ivermectin at 0.2 mg per kilogram (or 2.2 pounds) as a subcutaneous injection, will kill sucking but not biting lice. Ivermectin can also be used as a pour-on.

For pets and young kids, rotenone, cat flea powders and flea collars can be used.

New insecticides enter the market at fairly frequent intervals, so check with your veterinarian from time to time for an update on new agents.

Maggots/Fly Strike

Any regions of the skin that have been traumatized (for example, a castration site, shearing injury or other open wound) or intact skin that has been subject to bacterial multiplication (urine scald, fecal contamination, vaginal discharge from a recent birthing) may attract flies that lay their eggs in these areas. When fly larvae hatch out, they initially feed on the debris on the skin surface or in the open wound. Eventually they will burrow under the skin and into the underlying tissues, and, if not arrested, will cause considerable damage. The affected goat will be depressed and go off feed, and, if on pasture, not graze with the other goats.

Treatment consists of clipping off all of the hair in the affected region(s), removing as many maggots as possible with warm soapy water and then spraying the affected area with insecticide spray. Necrotic (dead) tissue may need to be trimmed away. Animals that are very ill with secondary bacterial infections should also be treated with a broad spectrum antibiotic. Good nursing care should be provided and the area carefully checked for more larvae several days after the initial treatment. If more fly larvae are apparent, the area should again be sprayed with insecticide.

This problem can be prevented by trimming away wet urine-stained hair or otherwise contaminated hair as necessary. As well, areas that are traumatized during fly season should be carefully watched and, if necessary, sprayed with an insecticide spray.

Mange
Chorioptic Mange

This mite lives on the surface of the skin and some goats may be carriers with no signs of disease. The mite may live in the environment for up to 10 weeks. The most severe signs of clinical disease occur in cold weather.

Papules, crusts, hair loss, skin reddening and ulcers are first present on the lower limbs, scrotum, udder and perineal region. Pruritus is typical.

All in contact goats must be treated at the same time to eliminate the carrier state. As well, the environment should be disinfected. Lactating dairy goats can be treated with lime sulfur 4 times at weekly intervals. Other agents such as coumaphos (0.25%), trichlorfon (0.2%), amitraz (0.05%) and lindane (0.03%) must be applied twice at 10 to 14 day intervals. The mite is too superficial for ivermectin to be completely effective.

Sarcoptic Mange (Scabies)

In some regions this disease, caused by a mite that tunnels through the skin, must be reported to government authorities.

Several weeks after contact with an infected goat, small pruritic (itchy) nodules, typically on the head, may be noted. In some goats the disease may progress no further; in others extensive skin thickening and hair loss, the result of scratching and mite damage, may affect the head, neck, thorax, inner thighs and udder. A secondary bacterial infection may develop and, in rare cases, death may occur.

Diagnosis is by microscopic examination of skin scrapings or, in some chronic cases, response to therapy.

Five to 10 applications of 2% lime sulfur solution every 5 to 7 days is recommended for lactating animals. Subcutaneous ivermectin may be very effective. A cleansing shampoo should be used to remove crusts.

Psoroptic Mange (Goat Ear Mite)

Mites are commonly found in the goat external ear canal, with most kids infected by 3 weeks of age. The mite that infests the ear canal may also cause body mange.

Typical signs include head shaking and scratching. Body mange resembles sarcoptic mange with less scab formation. This disease may also need to be reported to government authorities, depending on where one lives.

Diagnosis is by otoscopic examination or microscopic examination of ear wax.

Goats with ear mites are often not treated. Canine ear mite preparations are effective if mites have not spread to the body but, unless the ear is properly cleaned and several weekly treatments undertaken, recurrence is likely. As well, the mite can survive for extended periods in the environment. One injection of ivermectin at 20 mg per 100 kg should be effective in non-lactating goats. Amitraz, as a dip or spray, or 2 treatments of ivermectin one week apart can be used to treat body mange.

Ticks

Many tick species can infest goats. Papules or pustules may initially be present at the attachment site. Then crusts and ulcers develop. Tick damage to skin may result in secondary bacterial infections or fly strike/maggots. Blood loss may also occur as well as transmission of a variety of diseases. Damage to hides, most of which are produced in developing countries, can be significant.

If there are only occasional ticks to deal with, simply removing individual ticks from the affected goat is recommended. The same sprays, pour-ons and dips that are effective against lice will decrease the tick population and give temporary protection. Ticks often lodge in the ear canal or perineal region so local insecticide treatment may be all that is necessary.

It is very difficult to eliminate a tick species totally, but numbers can be reduced by insecticide treatments at 2 to 3 week intervals for the entire tick season for two- and three-host ticks. One-host ticks are more likely to be on the host and killed by one or two treatments. Ticks sometimes may be controlled by cultivating or burning the pasture.

II. NUTRITIONALLY RELATED DISEASES

Nutritionally related problems in goats can be the result of over- or underfeeding or dietary imbalances.

Bloat

Bloat can occur in goats of any age whose rumen, the largest of the goat's four stomachs, is mature. Goats are less commonly affected with bloat than cattle or sheep but, when it does occur, if it is severe, it is considered to be a medical emergency.

Frothy bloat, the most common type of bloat in goats, is the result of sudden dietary changes. Consumption of growing alfalfa or clover or even grass - especially when wet - can induce frothy bloat. Even very lush, leafy alfalfa hay may cause this problem. Bloat-producing concentrates include corn, soybean meal and barley. In cases of frothy bloat, signs usually develop within a few hours of the animal eating the offending feed. Gas that normally would accumulate in the dorsal sac of the rumen and be released or "burped up" from time to time becomes trapped in a foam or froth that is formed in the liquid phase of the rumen contents. Because gas formed cannot be expelled, pressure builds up in the rumen, the rumen expands and the abdomen of the goat becomes swollen, particularly on the upper left side. As the swelling continues, the goat becomes more and more un-

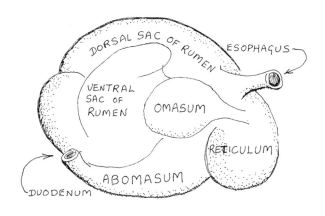

GOAT STOMACH : FOUR COMPARTMENTS
— ABOMASUM, OMASUM, RETICULUM AND
RUMEN

SURFACE ANATOMY GOAT, RIGHT SIDE
(SOME RIBS CUT OUT)

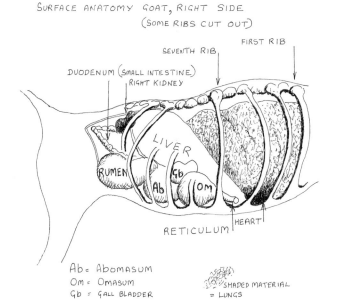

Ab = ABOMASUM
Om = OMASUM
Gb = GALL BLADDER

SHADED MATERIAL
= LUNGS

145

comfortable as evidenced by foot stamping, vocalizing, salivating, rapid, labored respiration, urinating frequently and moving stiffly. Eventually the goat will lie down and, if severe cases are not treated, the animal usually will die.

Free-gas bloat results from inability of a goat to eructate or release the gas that is normally produced in the rumen. Esophageal choke, the result of an apple or carrot piece, for example, getting stuck in the esophagus, is the main cause in goats. Diseases causing this problem include tumors, foreign bodies, abscesses, scars or enlarged lymph nodes that push on the esophagus, preventing the normal release of gas. As well, damage to the vagus nerve, which supplies the rumen, can impair normal eructation. Animals that have chronic bloat problems usually have free-gas bloat. Usually the obstruction in chronic cases is partial so that gas will be intermittently released.

Treatment includes passing a stomach tube down the esophagus into the rumen in an attempt to let off some of the gas. In cases of frothy bloat, this will not be effective until the foam is broken down. Mineral oil or cooking oil (vegetable oil) (100 to 200 ml or cc per animal) or an antibloat agent such as 15 to 30 ml or cc of dioctyl sodium sulfosuccinate can be given by stomach tube. Make sure that the stomach tube is in the stomach and not in the respiratory tract before giving oil or other agents. The tube can be felt in the smooth esophagus by palpating the midsection of the neck while gently sliding the tube up and down. If the tube is encased in a ridged structure (the trachea), it needs to be removed and the tube passed again. Exercise will help break down foam once oils or antibloat agents (surfactants) have been administered. Gently rolling a goat that is unable to rise and massaging the rumen may help to distribute the oil or surfactant. Passing a stomach tube periodically as the foam breaks down will help the goat to expel excess gas more rapidly.

In really severe cases, an opening with a trochar or sharp knife may need to be made into the upper left abdomen, over and into the rumen, to allow escape of the pent-up gas. There is a chance of peritonitis (infection in the abdomen) occurring after this method so the animal should be placed on broad spectrum antibiotics for 5 days.

Bloat can be prevented, or the incidence reduced, by careful management. Goats should be introduced gradually to lush pastures or feeds, or 50% or more grass can be seeded with alfalfa or clover in pastures or hay fields. Avoiding wet legume pastures early in the grazing season is prudent. Once animals are acclimated to pastures with a heavy component of alfalfa and/or clover, it is best to leave the animals out on these pastures for the entire grazing season. Bringing animals off these pastures and then reintroducing them increases the chance of bloat. Bird's-foot trefoil is a legume that does not cause bloat so this could be substituted for clover or alfalfa in pastures. Hay and other feeds should not be chopped or ground too fine. An antibloat agent, poloxalene, can be fed, either in the feed or in a molasses salt block, prior to introducing goats to rich alfalfa or clover pastures. Poloxalene does not prevent grain concentrate bloat. Concentrates can be top dressed with some oil, such as corn oil or peanut oil, to decrease the incidence of bloat.

Goiter/Iodine Deficiency
Goiter, caused by inadequate uptake of iodine or excessive consumption of plants containing goitrogenic compounds, can affect goats of any age. Iodine is essential for normal thyroid function and, without adequate iodine uptake, the thyroid gland enlarges in an attempt to produce thyroid hormones. The thyroid gland is in the upper neck on either side of the trachea (windpipe).

In adult goats, the most common sign of iodine deficiency is an enlarged thyroid gland. Reproductive performance may also be decreased. Kids are most severely affected and may be stillborn or be born weak and die within a few hours. Affected kids are born with thyroid glands that may be up to 10 times normal size. Iodine deficient kids may be hairless, born with a very fine hair or have a normal hair coat.

Adequate iodine in the salt and/or mineral mix will prevent this problem. For lactating does, the dietary iodine requirement is 0.8 mg per kilogram of dry matter. For the rest of the herd, 0.2 mg per kilogram of dry matter will suffice. If cruciferous plants containing goitrogenic compounds, such as the Brassica species, are in the diet, iodine requirements may be as much as 2 mg per kilogram of dry matter.

Does can be given potassium iodide or iodate orally at 60 and again at 30 days before kidding to protect the kids if a deficiency state is discovered in late gestation. Iodine can also be injected intramuscularly 60 days prior to kidding.

Grain Overload/Lactic Acidosis
Although goats can adapt to a variety of feed stuffs, any changes in the diet should be made gradually. Goats typically are not placed on high concentrate rations but, if they are, preferably it should take 2 to 4 weeks or

a minimum of 10 days to 2 weeks to make the transition.

Goats, like all ruminants, are susceptible to grain overload (lactic acidosis). This occurs when there is a sudden increase in the amount of grain or concentrate fed. The microorganisms in the rumen of goats eating mainly roughage are bacteria that ferment cellulose. When the goat over-indulges in starchy food, new microflora replace the old. The new population of bacteria quickly ferment the carbohydrates to form lactic acid. Prolonged exposure to this acid damages the delicate rumen lining. As well, water from the bloodstream flows into the rumen, dehydrating the tissues and concentrating the blood. Lactate is absorbed into the blood and, when the liver and muscles can no longer absorb the excess lactate, systemic acidosis occurs.

It takes from 1 to 3 days after consumption of excess grain for clinical signs to appear. At this time, affected animals are depressed and will not eat. Without treatment, rumen motility ceases and constipation followed by diarrhea, muscle tremors, teeth grinding, elevated heart and respiratory rates, may be noted. Rumen contents may be more liquid than normal because of water flowing into the rumen from the bloodstream and the goat becomes dehydrated as evidenced by sunken eyes and less elastic skin.

Any goat that has access, either chronic or acute, to large quantities of readily fermentable carbohydrates and goes off feed should be suspected of having overindulged. If the pH of rumen contents obtained by stomach tube is less than 5 and rumen contents are milky gray, a diagnosis of lactic acidosis is confirmed. As well, gram-stained smears of rumen contents will reveal mainly Gram-positive organisms. At necropsy, the rumen is filled with large amounts of grain.

Treatment with oral antacids or mineral oil should halt acidosis development unless massive amounts of grain have been consumed. Suggested dosages of oral antacids in adult goats are 10 to 20 grams of magnesium oxide, 50 grams of magnesium hydroxide or 20 grams of sodium bicarbonate. Antacids or mineral oil can be given by stomach tube. This should be done carefully making sure that the tube is in the esophagus. Mineral oil is best given by stomach tube as it has little taste and, if the goat becomes agitated when it is given as a drench, it may be inhaled into the lungs quite easily. Mineral oil in the lungs will kill a goat. One treatment with oral tetracycline at 0.5 to 1 gram or oral penicillin at 1,000,000 international units (IU) will help prevent bacterial multiplication in the rumen. Affected animals should be placed on poor quality hay or straw and no concentrate. If the rumen is not starting to move (placing an ear or, better yet, a stethoscope, to the left side of the abdomen will allow a person to hear normal rumen sounds and movement) after a day, retreatment with antacid or mineral oil may be necessary. Thiamine (300 to 500 mg several times a day), other B vitamins and subcutaneous calcium gluconate are often administered. After the goat is back to normal, concentrate can gradually be reintroduced to the diet.

Animals which are down or very ill may require intravenous treatment with a bicarbonate solution. The bicarbonate will buffer the acid in the bloodstream and hopefully return the acid-base balance of the animal to normal. A rumenotomy with removal of the rumen contents can be performed on an acutely ill, very valuable animal. If rumen contents are very liquid and the rumen pH is near neutral, draining as much fluid off as possible with a stomach tube and administering warm water, antacids and brewer's yeast by stomach tube, may be beneficial.

If large amounts of concentrate are to be fed, feeding 3 or more times a day is helpful as is feeding hay or other roughage before feeding grain in the morning. Whole grain is digested more slowly than finely ground grain. Supplementing regularly with buffers such as bicarbonate of soda or calcium carbonate at 1.5 to 2% of the ration also reduces problems with acidosis.

Feeding alkali-treated grain with an ionophore (monensin) will allow feeding moderate amounts of grain to unadapted goats. This might be necessary in range animals.

Hypomagnesemia (Grass Tetany, Grass Staggers)

This is a rare condition. However, goats, especially those in early lactation, may be susceptible to hypomagnesemia if they are grazing short cereal grain pastures, river bottom pastures or lush immature grasses that are growing rapidly. Forages containing less than 0.2% magnesium on a dry matter basis have been associated with hypomagnesemia.

Clinical signs of hypomagnesemia include excitement, rapid breathing and tremors followed by a loss of coordination. Progression to recumbency and convulsions may occur, with eventual death. Plasma magnesium levels of less than 0.5 mg per dl are consistent with a diagnosis of hypomagnesemia. Mortality usually is high (80%) and treatment with 25 ml of 50% magnesium sulfate solution usually is ineffective.

When goats are grazing forages low in magnesium, supplementation with a mineral containing 8% magnesium or ensuring that 0.2% of

149

the total diet is magnesium may be useful. Under normal confinement or grazing conditions, the total daily consumption of magnesium for a 60 kg animal should be about 1.0 gram for maintenance and an additional 1.5 grams for late gestation.

Laminitis (Founder)

Overconsumption of concentrate (grain overload), sudden ration changes, digestive disturbances and diseases such as pneumonia that can cause a high fever, all can result in laminitis, which may be a chronic or an acute condition. One or more of the feet - most commonly the forelimbs, though all 4 feet can be affected - become tender and hot. This condition is very painful and affected animals can actually end up walking on their knees and losing considerable amounts of weight.

Treatment involves correcting the underlying problem such as grain overload, pneumonia or whatever. Pain killers, such as aspirin at 100 mg per kilogram of body weight (45 mg per pound) orally every 24 hours or phenylbutazone at 4 mg per kilogram (1.8 mg per pound) once every 24 hours or flunixin meglumine at 1 mg per kilogram (0.45 mg per pound) subcutaneously once daily will help alleviate the pain and keep the goat mobile. The latter two analgesics are more useful than aspirin in acute cases but, if long-term therapy is needed, aspirin is less expensive. Exercise may help restore proper circulation of blood to the foot in acute cases. Only grass hay should be fed to recovering goats and grain should be reintroduced cautiously.

If the animal is to be kept in the herd, frequent foot trimming likely will be required to maintain normal hoof shape.

Animals with chronic laminitis tend to develop "slipper feet" with the unworn toes turned upwards.

To prevent laminitis, avoid abrupt feed changes and excessive grain feeding. Adding a buffer such as sodium bicarbonate to the ration should be considered if high energy rations are to be fed.

Listeriosis (Circling Disease)

Listeria monocytogenes, a bacterial organism which affects many species of birds and mammals (including man), usually causes encephalitis (inflammation of the nervous system) in goats, but infection may also result in septicemia and abortion. Because the organism can be shed in the milk of clinically normal "carrier" goats as well as in sick goats, it is a potential zoonotic disease.

The organism is readily killed by ordinary disinfectants but can survive in silage, feces and tissue for 5 years or more. The occurrence of clinical listeriosis in a herd is often associated with abrupt changes in weather and/or management, stress from poor nutrition, parasitism or other disease, late pregnancy, and feeding of silage. Usually older goats are affected. Sources of infection are considered to be stressed carrier goats that shed the bacteria in feces or poor quality silage with a pH above 5.0 that allows proliferation of *L. monocytogenes*. When silage from around the edges of the silo is fed, where proper fermentation and acid production has been prevented by increased oxygen levels, bacterial organisms may multiply, resulting in outbreaks of listeriosis. *L. monocytogenes* may be present in large numbers in feces, milk, birth fluids, placenta, fetuses and newborn kids from goats with the septicemic or abortion form of listeriosis. Tissues from these animals should be handled with care so that other animals, including the in-contact humans, do not contract the disease.

Damage to the lining of the mouth by rough or coarse feed or loss of deciduous teeth, for example, allows *L. monocytogenes* to migrate up nerves to the brain stem, where it induces a local inflammation. The incubation period may be as long as 2 or 3 weeks. Initial signs include depression, decreased appetite, and transient fever. As the disease progresses, the goat appears disoriented and will lean or move in one direction. This progresses to circling in one direction and facial paralysis. (The ear and eyelid on the affected side will droop and food may accumulate in the cheek on the paralysed side of the face. Drooling may also occur on the affected side.) Coma and death usually result if the animal is not treated.

Goats with the septicemic form, which may have an incubation period as short as a day, have the same initial clinical signs as goats with the encephalitic form. The organism is thought to enter the body via the intestinal tract lining. Most goats infected show few or no clinical signs and recover rapidly. Some infected animals become carriers while only a few go on to develop persistent fever. These individuals become weaker over a several day period. Diarrhea, which may be bloody, is fairly common. Death may occur within several days or the animal may be ill for several weeks.

Does will abort several days after the onset of septicemia but may not necessarily show severe clinical signs. These animals usually recover.

Culture of *L. monocytogenes* from the appropriate body tissues and silage may be helpful in establishing a diagnosis. Brain stem changes can usually only be detected microscopically. Small white dots (necrotic tissue) may be evident in the liver, spleen, kidney and heart of goats dying from the septicemic form. Many small yellowish spots on aborted fetus livers are very suggestive of listeriosis.

Goats that are down and cannot rise have a poor prognosis. For treatment to be effective, it should be started as soon as possible. The organism is sensitive to a variety of antibiotics including ampicillin, erythromycin, gentamicin, penicillin, neomycin and tetracycline. Treatment of the encephalitic form with intravenous sodium penicillin at 40,000 IU per kilogram every 6 hours until there is improvement, followed by procaine penicillin intramuscularly at 20,000 IU twice daily for 7 days, should be effective. Oxytetracycline can be used instead at 10 mg per kilogram twice daily for a minimum of 3 days. A minimum of 3 consecutive days of intramuscular treatment with penicillin or tetracycline is recommended for the septicemic form of the disease.

In an outbreak, aborting does should be isolated from the herd and fetuses, placentas and discharge handled and disposed of carefully. Carcasses should be burned or buried in unslaked lime. Gloves and face masks are recommended. Silage should be packed carefully and not fed if it is mouldy or the pH more than 5.0. Preventing fecal contamination of feed and water troughs is essential. Buildings should be cleaned and disinfected. To eliminate the infection from a herd after an outbreak, fecal cultures can be performed on all herd members and carrier animals culled.

Overeating Disease or Enterotoxemia

A common, often fatal disease seen worldwide, enterotoxemia, also known as overeating disease, occurs in goats of any age. The bacterial organism responsible for this condition, *Clostridium perfringens* type D, lives in the soil and in the digestive tract. Normally, low numbers of *C. perfringens* live in the intestinal tract, multiply slowly and cause no ill effects. However, when animals suddenly consume large amounts of readily fermentable carbohydrate-rich feed, more undigested starch passes into the intestines allowing *C. perfringens* to multiply rapidly and form a deadly toxin known as epsilon toxin. The extra feed, typically grain, consumed may slow down movement of intestinal contents and this, combined with increased permeability of the intestinal wall resulting from epsilon toxin production, allows the toxin to pass into the blood, causing brain injury, toxemia, shock and death.

Though sudden changes in feed stuffs or feeding practices have been associated with enterotoxemia outbreaks, this is not necessarily the case.

Peracutely affected animals, usually kids and often the largest and

152

most vigorous in the group, die suddenly and unexpectedly. Clinical signs, if observed, include appetite loss, depression, severe abdominal discomfort, screaming and watery diarrhea containing blood and mucus. A fever may be noted. Individuals become weak, recumbent and comatose and death occurs within hours. In some cases, paddling and convulsions occur. Even with treatment, few animals recover.

The acute form, which usually affects mature goats, has a course of 3 to 4 days instead of the 24 hours for the peracute form. Clinical signs are as above but less severe. Pasty or soft feces may be noted initially but then profuse watery diarrhea and associated dehydration and acidosis ensues. Most animals die if not treated.

Goats with chronic enterotoxemia are typically mature and have intermittent bouts of illness manifested by listlessness, poor appetite, progressive weight loss and pasty or loose feces.

Diagnosis is based on history, clinical signs (if any are seen), post mortem findings (enteritis or enterocolitis), culture of the organism from intestinal lesions and detection of epsilon toxin in the feces or intestinal content.

A related bacterium, *Clostridium perfringens* type C, causes hemorrhagic enterotoxemia in fast-growing kids less than 3 weeks of age. This organism accumulates where animals are concentrated around buildings, in kidding pens and so on. The organism, once in the intestinal tract, produces a potent toxin. The toxin causes the death of cells lining the small intestine and the result is an acute and usually fatal hemorrhagic enteritis. After an incubation period of 12 to 24 hours, kids stop nursing, are depressed and have a painful abdomen. Feces are fluid and tinged with small amounts of blood. After a short period - 2 to 12 hours - most affected kids die.

Even with treatment, the prognosis is guarded. *C. perfringens* type C and D antitoxin should be administered promptly; if given intravenously before the disease has progressed too far, the antitoxin will be able to neutralize the toxin being formed. Double or even triple (or more) the recommended (label) dose of commercially available antitoxin may be needed to elicit an improvement. Response to treatment may be temporary and affected individuals may need to be retreated every 3 to 4 hours, with the same or decreased dose of antitoxin, until the animal's condition has stabilized. Sulfonamides given orally may also be helpful. In an outbreak, all at risk animals should be boostered with vaccine and feeding of carbohydrate reduced if possible.

Although routine vaccination with *C. perfringens* types C and D toxoid will control enterotoxemia by decreasing the incidence and severity of the disease, it does not prevent it. Immunity produced by this vaccine is short-lived, likely less than 6 months. If problems with *C. perfringens* type D enterotoxemia continue despite vaccination, decreasing the amount of carbohydrate in the diet should help. A vaccine containing *C. perfringens* types C and D is available; this vaccine may also contain *C. tetani* toxoid, which protects animals against tetanus. Kids should be vaccinated at 30 and 60 days of age and then every 6 months. On farms where enterotoxemia is a problem, kids may need to be vaccinated 3 times by 60 days of age and adults may require vaccination every 4 months. Vaccinating nannies 3 to 4 weeks before kidding should afford kids protection via colostral antibodies for the first month of life.

Polyvalent clostridial vaccines containing as many as 8 different clostridial toxoids may not be as effective in controlling enterotoxemia in goats as a simpler vaccine containing *C. perfringens* types C and D and/or tetanus. Goats are not very susceptible to the other clostridial diseases represented in these complex polyvalent vaccines and these complex vaccines are more costly.

Plant Toxicities

There is a horrifying array of plants that may be toxic to goats, depending on the amount consumed and the stage of growth or development of the plant when eaten. Soil type, amount of rain, availability of alternate forage, and time of year can all influence plant toxicity. However, it should be noted that, unless a pasture or paddock is overgrazed or there is a drought and the animals are hungry, plant toxicities are seldom seen. Many potentially toxic plants are not very palatable.

A variety of clinical signs, many of which are related to damage to the nervous or gastrointestinal system, are the result of various toxic compounds in the plant(s) consumed. Toxicities may be acute or chronic and, with most, there are no specific treatments. Animals need to be removed from the problem pasture or paddock or, if left to graze the problem area, offered supplemental feed. A balanced mineral mix should be available at all times as animals deprived of minerals may consume toxic plants. Very hungry animals should not be turned out to forage as they may consume more of one plant than normal. Typically, goats move from plant to plant and species to species when grazing, so under normal conditions, they are unlikely to consume large amounts of any one item. As well, goats should not be allowed access to ornamental plants (including shrubs and trees) and their clippings.

Polioencephalomalacia (Cerebrocortical Necrosis)

This disease, which occurs sporadically in goats, and results in swelling and death (necrosis) of brain tissue, can result from overgrowth of thiaminase-producing rumen microorganisms, ingestion of thiaminase-containing plants or treatment with antithiamine drugs such as amprolium (a treatment for coccidiosis). Normally, adequate thiamine (vitamin B1) is produced by the rumen bacteria. Anything that upsets the normal rumen bacterial population, such as grain overload or lactic acidosis, can lead to proliferation of gram-positive bacteria that produce thiaminases. Thiaminases destroy thiamine in the rumen or produce analogues of thiamine that act as antimetabolites. As well, competitive thiamine antagonists may be produced by moldy feeds, thiabendazole, levamisole and some fern species.

Although animals of any age can be affected, usually young animals, weaned kids and young adults, become ill. Cases are more common when concentrates are being fed (in the winter in North America) or the goats are on very lush pasture. Sudden feed changes, increased grain feeding, stress or recent digestive disease predispose animals to polioencephalomalacia. Only rarely do outbreaks occur.

Occasionally, animals may have a 1 to 7 day course of depression, poor appetite and/or diarrhea with gradual development of nervous signs. Usually, however, affected individuals show acute involvement of the central nervous system. Early signs include elevation of the head with the head tilted back (opisthotonos), stargazing, wandering aimlessly, blindness, staggering, circling and muscle tremors. Extensor rigidity, head pressing, abnormal eye movements (nystagmus), recumbency and convulsions occur as the disease progresses. Unless the convulsions are severe, there is no fever. Animals usually die 24 to 72 hours after clinical signs become apparent unless treated.

If treatment is undertaken early in the course of the disease, there should be a good response. The diagnosis of polioencephalomalacia is most often confirmed by response to thiamine hydrochloride at 10 mg per kilogram (4.5 mg per pound) of body weight every 6 hours for 24 hours. The first dose should be given intravenously if possible; the remaining injections can be given intramuscularly. If only multiple B vitamins are available, be certain to dose according to the concentration of thiamine in the mixture. Affected animals should respond within 12 hours. In advanced cases, there may only be an incomplete response to treatment (for example, there may be permanent blindness) or the animal may remain stable or continue to deteriorate. Severely affected goats may be given prednisone at 2 to 4 mg per kilogram of body weight (1 to 2 mg per pound) or dexamethasone at 1 mg per 5 to 10 kilogram (10 to 20 pounds) in an attempt to reduce brain swelling.

Feeding more roughage and less concentrate should control the problem. In problem herds, thiamine mononitrate or brewer's yeast can be added to the grain.

Secondary Nutritional Problems

Various problems can result in the inability of a goat to obtain or utilize feed. These include oral problems, lameness or blindness.

Older does, particularly those grazing in areas where there is little forage or the soil is sandy, are prone to excessive wear of teeth or loss of teeth. A calcium-phosphorus imbalance may also result in softer teeth. Teeth should be checked regularly, and, if older nannies are doing poorly on pasture because of teeth problems, they should either be culled or moved to an area where feed is more plentiful. These very old goats may need to be raised in confinement or semiconfinement and fed some grain year round. Sharp molars that are wearing unevenly can be filed smooth with a flat file.

Periodontal disease may result from coarse feeds or plant awns packing between the teeth and gums causing infection, tooth loosening and deterioration of the alveolus (the bony socket holding the tooth). These animals can be treated in the same manner as nannies with worn or missing teeth.

Infections of the mouth and lips; for example, soremouth (contagious ecthyma) or abscesses, can result in loss of condition because of pain associated with eating. Soremouth lesions usually resolve in 3 to 6 weeks. During the time lesions are present, animals that are not eating well should be separated from the herd and fed palatable high-quality feeds. Abscesses that are detected promptly can be drained surgically and the animals treated with antibiotics or, depending on the type of abscess, with sodium iodide intravenously.

Causes of lameness include foot rot, foot abscesses, arthritis, fractures and lacerations.

Pinkeye, polioencephalomalacia and vitamin A deficiency can result in blindness. These animals need to be penned and fed individually while recovering.

Tumors and internal abscesses can cause wasting and eventual death. Individual animals that are losing body condition should be carefully examined, and, if the cause of the weight loss cannot be determined and/or treated, these animals should be removed from the herd.

Undernutrition/Pecking Order

Poorly nourished goats grow slowly and do not attain their potential full size. Small, thin goats are more susceptible to the effects of internal and external parasites as well as to infectious diseases. They may only have a single kid, abort, or, if they are very small (less than 75% of their optimal weight), they may not have heat cycles at all. Kids from these goats are typically small because the dams have little milk and do not compete well with larger goats, particularly in confinement or semiconfinement, and these kids, in turn, are susceptible to the same problems their mothers had. One of the most common "diseases" seen in confinement and semiconfinement situations - the poor-doing goat - is the result of intergoat aggression. Even among apparently well-fed goats in confinement, small, stunted goats can still be found.

Goats have an extremely well-defined pecking order and the smaller, less aggressive goats do not thrive, particularly where large groups of goats are kept together in small pens. Confined goats should be penned together in small groups - 20 to 30 or so - depending on management. Goats should be grouped together based on size and aggressiveness and adequate bunk space should be provided. Unless free choice feed is available, there needs to be enough space at the feeders so that all the goats in a group can eat at once. Groups of goats should be observed at least daily, and, if there are individuals in a pen that are not holding their own, they should be sorted into a pen with smaller goats. This may sound obvious but it is one of the most common problems in confinement-raised goats. A small goat may literally starve to death while the aggressive pen mates grow stouter and nastier.

Urinary Calculi (Obstructive Urolithiasis)

Not uncommon in young, male, castrated goats fed large amounts of grain is a condition known as obstructive urolithiasis. Although this condition typically occurs in castrated males, it may be seen from time to time in intact males on high grain diets. Goats that are castrated early - before 5 months of age - do not complete the normal development of the penis and urethra. Because of this, the urethral diameter is narrower than normal and calculi (stones or sludge formed in the urinary tract) readily lodge in the urethra. The urethra of the doe is much wider as well as being short and straight so any calculi in the urinary tract of does pass readily in the urine.

When high grain diets containing large amounts of phosphorus and little calcium are fed, serum and urine contain high levels of phosphorus and magnesium, which promotes phosphate calculi. If grass and cereal hays are the main diet, silicate stones may form, particularly in arid regions. Oxalate calculi can occur if rations are high in oxalates. Low molecular weight peptides are also present in the urine at high levels. As well, bacterial infections of the urinary tract may contribute to the problem by increasing the pH of the urine, creating an environment in which magnesium and phosphate ions are less soluble and ammonium ions more available. Calculi form out of these ions. For the actual formation of calculi, a nidus may be necessary. Bacterial infections or vitamin A deficiency cause increased loss of the epithelial cells lining the bladder into the urine. These cells may initiate formation of calculi.

If conditions are right; for example, the animal is deprived of water or the water is dirty (if the animal is drinking regularly the urinary tract will be flushed out more often and calculi will have less chance to build up), castration has occurred at an early age and the ration is poorly balanced, calculi will form, and, if they are large enough (1 to 2 mm diameter or more), they lodge in the urethra. Usual places for the calculi to "stick" are the sigmoid flexure or the urethral process (the squiggle of tissue at the end of the penis). If the stone is not passed, urine builds up behind the stone and eventually the bladder or urethra ruptures.

Early clinical signs include ever more frequent bouts of straining, with the animal stretched out to full length with a dip in the back, followed by arching of the back. An affected goat may cry in pain while trying to urinate. Sometimes crystals can be seen or felt on the hair around the prepuce. Blood-tinged urine may be noted in the same location. Over time the animal loses interest in food and water and, if the bladder ruptures, the abdomen distends with urine. This may not be particularly evident in an already fat goat. If the urethra ruptures, urine accumulates below the skin along the lower body wall or in the perineal region. Unless an affected animal is treated (and treatment is most effective early in the course of this disease), death usually occurs after 5 to 10 days.

Treatment in many cases is disappointing. If the calculus is lodged in the urethral process and it is sludge, instead of a firm stone, it may be possible to gently milk out the offending material. Otherwise, the urethral process can simply be snipped off with a pair of scissors. The animal should be able to urinate right away. If the animal is not completely blocked and is able to urinate, though with difficulty, feed can be removed for 24 hours and the animal dosed with ammonium chloride. Smooth muscle relaxants may help to relieve the pressure around the calculus, allowing it to be passed.

If a calculus is lodged at a location other than the urethral append-age and the obstruction is complete, sometimes passing a catheter up the urethra and injecting sterile saline up the catheter may help dislodge a calculus. If this is not effective, surgically removing the calculus by an incision in the urethra or, in some cases, a urethrostomy (amputation of the penis) may be necessary. Results of surgery are variable because the urethra has a tendency to fill in with scar tissue postoperatively. These procedures are a job for your veterinarian and, in most cases, the expense of these procedures cannot be justified.

As with most problems, prevention is a much better solution than treatment. To prevent urinary calculi, males should not be fed large amounts of grain. If grain is to be fed, the total ration should have a 2:1 or 2.5:1 calcium:phosphorus ratio. Sodium chloride (common salt) can be added to the diet at 1 to 4% of the ration. Up to 9% can be added if necessary. This causes the animals to drink more and thus urinate more, keeping the urinary tract flushed out. Ammonium chloride, which acidifies the urine, can be added at 2% of the concentrate ration. Fresh water should be provided at all times and, in the winter, should not be too cold. Delaying castration so that the urethra has time to develop properly may also be helpful.

White Muscle Disease (Selenium - Vitamin E Deficiency)

White muscle disease, one of the most common manifestations of selenium and/or vitamin E deficiency, is most common in kids up to 6 months of age although it can occur in older kids and more rarely in adults. Continuous consumption of plants that either grow on selenium-deficient soil or have a low capacity to extract selenium from normal soil (for example, alfalfa and clover) results in this problem. Selenium is essential to normal cellular function and, in selenium-deficient animals, a whole host of problems - white muscle disease, retained placenta, abortions, stillbirths, neonatal weakness, diarrhea, unthriftiness, infertility, immunosuppression and so on - can occur. Vitamin E is a separate nutrient but its biochemical role is believed to be similar to that of selenium.

Clinical signs of selenium deficiency are the result of muscle damage and include stiffness and reluctance to move. Muscles are sore and feel firm. Kids maintain a good appetite even if they cannot rise. The body temperature is normal. If the cardiac muscle is involved, sudden death may occur. If cardiac muscle involvement is less severe, signs of congestive heart failure may be apparent. Inhalation pneumonia may occur because the muscles necessary for swallowing may be weak.

Definitive diagnosis of white muscle disease depends on finding white or grey (necrotic) patches of involved muscle, be it skeletal or cardiac, at necropsy or decreased levels of selenium and/or vitamin E in blood (not often done since tests are expensive and not commonly available) or tissues. Characteristic clinical signs and response to treatment, in conjunction with laboratory findings, are more commonly used to make a presumptive diagnosis.

If the case is not too far advanced, one intramuscular treatment with a sodium selenite-alpha-tocopherol preparation and a second treatment 24 hours later, if the animal is not yet up, is recommended. If there is no improvement after the second treatment, the prognosis is poor or an alternate diagnosis should be considered. In cases of white muscle disease, treatment with both vitamin E and selenium yields the best results.

In the United States, selenium can be supplemented in a complete sheep ration (this has not yet been approved for goats) at up to 0.3 ppm (parts per million), in a feed supplement so that the intake of selenium does not exceed 0.7 mg per head per day, and in salt/mineral mixes at 90 ppm as long as daily consumption is not more than 0.7 mg per head per day.

Vitamin E deficiency alone can cause white muscle disease or nutritional muscular dystrophy. Because vitamin E deficiency reflects forage quality, deficiency usually occurs in confined animals receiving old hay or silage. Typically, hay has the least vitamin E content when does are birthing in the spring. The vitamin E content of colostrum depends on the nutrition of the dam during gestation.

Vitamin E deficient animals display similar clinical signs to those with selenium deficiency. Vitamin E deficient kids may not have sufficient Vitamin E at birth and may not be able to rise. Kids may die suddenly from necrosis of heart or diaphragmatic muscles. If the muscles around the larynx and pharynx are weak and the kid cannot swallow properly, aspiration pneumonia may develop. Stiffness may develop after exercise. As with selenium deficiency, the fastest growing animals are most prone to development of white muscle disease. Deficient does may have poor uterine involution and retained placentas. The daily requirement of vitamin E is 0.1 to 0.3 IU per kilogram of body weight and should be doubled when milk replacer is being fed. Vitamin E cannot be overdosed.

If there is a deficiency of vitamin E, one should be careful to read the label of vitamin E preparations. When vitamin E is present in combination with selenium, for example, typically vitamin E in the mixture is at a very low level. Injectable alpha tocopherol, which is pure vitamin E, can be purchased.

Zinc Deficiency

National Research Council recommended dietary levels of zinc are a minimum of 10 ppm. However, higher levels (45 to 75 ppm) are often used in rations.

Excessive dietary calcium, caused, for example, by overfeeding alfalfa to males or females that are not lactating or pregnant, may contribute to a relative zinc deficiency. Other animals may be unable to properly absorb zinc and need constant treatment.

Clinical signs include hyperemia (reddening) and pruritus of the skin, hair loss, thick crusts over the hind legs, face and ears and scales resembling dandruff over the rest of the body. Hair is greasy and matted.

Though skin biopsies are useful, in many instances diagnosis is by response to treatment; 1 gram of zinc sulfate orally per day and balancing the ration with regard to calcium. Usually there is a response after 2 weeks.

III. REPRODUCTIVE PROBLEMS

Abortions

Noninfectious causes of abortion in goats include malnutrition, stress and trauma. Ingestion of certain toxic plants - *Gutierrezia* species (broomweed), *Lupinus formosus*, *Conium maculatum*, *Nicotiana tabacum* and skunk cabbage (*Veratrum californicum*) - at the appropriate stage of gestation can result in deformed kids or abortions.

Trace mineral deficiencies may result in lowered conception rates and abortions. Copper deficiency causes enzootic ataxia (swayback) in kids and is the result of demyelinization of the cerebrum and motor tracts of the spinal cord. Kids may be born dead or with flaccid paralysis. The birth of dead, premature, or weak live term kids with an enlarged thyroid gland and a sparse hair coat may be the result of iodine deficiency. Selenium is important for maximizing reproductive performance in both the male and female and a deficiency of this nutrient can result in a lowered conception rate (but not abortions) or birth of weak kids. Selenium toxicity may cause abortion and conception failure.

It is thought that a combined deficiency of energy and protein in the diet is required for early embryonic mortality.

It should be noted that, while this is not a normal occurrence, goats and sheep can interbreed and thus should be separated during the breeding season. If a fertile male sheep breeds a doe, an embryo does develop but usually will not survive past the second month of pregnancy. At this time the embryo degenerates and it, along with a placenta, is expelled. Sometimes the fetus mummifies and is expelled later than the sixth week of pregnancy. This, of course, can disrupt a complete breeding season because by the time the fetus is lost and the uterus recovers it may be too late for the doe to be rebred during that breeding season.

A variety of agents cause abortion in late gestation but the two most common ones in the United States are *Chlamydia psittaci* and *Toxoplasma gondii.*

Chlamydial abortions, caused by the Gram-negative intracellular organism *Chlamydia psittaci*, usually occur during the last 2 weeks of pregnancy although they can occur any time during the last 2 months. The organism enters the placenta and fetus via the bloodstream after the organism multiplies in cells of the intestinal or genital tract. As the chlamydial organisms multiply in the placenta and fetus, inflammation and tissue death occurs and the fetus is aborted. Other animals ingesting placenta or uterine discharges may become infected and abort during their next pregnancy or, if sufficient time (40 days) remains for placental damage to occur, the current pregnancy may be aborted. The organism may be shed in vaginal secretions as long as 9 days before abortion occurs or as long as 12 days after the abortion. The fetus(es) usually are fresh and live weak newborns are not uncommon. Aborting does are not usually ill, but some may be slightly depressed and have a blood-tinged vaginal discharge 2 to 3 days before aborting. Retained placentas are not usually a problem. Up to 80% of does in a herd can abort. Once a goat has aborted, fertility should be normal though some feel that natural immunity decreases after 3 years, at which time the doe is susceptible to aborting again.

Examination of the placenta will reveal thickening and necrosis of cotyledons (the circular raised regions on the placenta) and the intercotyledonary areas.

Treatment with tetracyclines may have some use in controlling an outbreak and decreasing shedding of the chlamydial organism. Oral tetracycline at 400 to 450 mg per head per day can be fed until kidding has finished or long-acting tetracycline can be given at 20 mg per kilogram of body weight subcutaneously every 3 days (or even every 10 to 14 days) during an outbreak.

A sheep chlamydial vaccine is available that needs to be given 4 to 6 weeks before breeding. Animals being introduced to the breeding herd need 2 injections a month apart prior to breeding. In following years a single dose of vaccine prior to breeding will suffice. Animals may be sore for a day or two after administration of this vaccine. As an alternative to vaccination, tetracycline can be fed for 2 to 3 weeks before breeding and may be continued for the first half of gestation.

It should be noted that *Chlamydia psittaci* is contagious to humans. During kidding season, pregnant women assisting with births may become infected with the ruminant strain of *C. psittaci* and abort. Men and women assisting kiddings in an infected flock may also develop an influenza-like disease. Anyone working with a herd during kidding season, whether there are any abortions or not, should wear gloves to assist with births and when picking up placentas or fetuses for disposal or diagnostic purposes. During kidding season, pregnant women should have no contact with the herd.

Although I often vaccinate against vibriosis because the sheep abortion vaccines usually contain this organism as well as *C. psittaci*, reports of *Campylobacter fetus* infections in goats are rare. Vibrio abortions are similar to chlamydial abortions, with abortions occurring in the last 4 to 6 weeks of gestation. Usually the fetus is autolyzed. The vaccine is given at the same time as the chlamydial vaccine and control is the same as for chlamydial abortions.

The domestic cat is the primary host of *Toxoplasma gondii* and can shed millions of infective oocysts in the feces. Cats become infected by eating uncooked meat, placentas and small rodents. Cats usually shed oocysts for 3 to 19 days after infection but *T. gondii* oocysts may live in the soil in moist and shaded areas for as long as a year and a half. If goats consume feed, usually grain, contaminated with cat feces, the result of infection depends on the stage of pregnancy. *Toxoplasma* organisms ingested by a goat invade the small intestine and then spread to other tissues by the bloodstream. If the goat is pregnant when the initial infection oc-

TOXOPLASMOSIS IN MEAT GOATS

CATS BECOME INFECTED BY CONSUMING UNCOOKED MEATS, SMALL RODENTS AND PLACENTAE

AND DEPENDING ON THE STAGE OF THE PREGNANCY, ABORTION OCCURS

CATS ARE THE DEFINITIVE HOSTS

TOXOPLASMA OOCYSTS ARE SHED IN THE CAT'S FECES WHICH CONTAMINATE THE GRASS, HAY, GRAIN CONSUMED BY THE GOATS

TOXOPLASMA INVADES THE PLACENTA AND FETUS OF PREGNANT GOAT TWO WEEKS AFTER INITIAL INFECTION curs, *T. gondii* organisms infect the fetus and placenta about two weeks later. The result of *T. gondii* infection depends on the stage of pregnancy. Infection in early pregnancy may result in resorption or mummification whereas, in late pregnancy, abortion or birth of infected young may occur. Fetuses infected during the second half of gestation are less likely to die than those infected during the first half. Goats with multiple fetuses may produce clinically normal as well as infected kids. Usually goats that have been infected once are resistant to future abortions.

To control toxoplasmosis, the number of barn cats should be limited and they should not be allowed access to the feed. If cats persist in defecating in the hay, strategically placed litter boxes may be helpful. An adult cat population of mature neutered cats is preferable as kittens and stressed adult cats are more likely to shed *Toxoplasma* oocysts. Raw meat should not be fed to cats.

Since, in sheep, addition of monensin (Rumensin) or lasalocid (Bovatec) to the concentrate at the normal anticoccidial rate results in a significant reduction in toxoplasma-induced perinatal lamb mortality, it seems likely that monensin or lasalocid would have a similar protective effect in goats. Monensin- or lasalocid-containing feed must be fed prior to exposure of susceptible sheep (and presumably goats) to oocyst-contaminated feed.

Other, less common, causes of infectious abortions in goats include *Coxiella burnetti* (Q fever), *Brucella melitensis*, *Brucella abortus*, *Leptospira* species, *Listeria monocytogenes*, and *Salmonella* species.

Infections that cause a fever, such as bluetongue, anaplasmosis, sarcocystis and yersiniosis, can result in abortions in goats.

In the event of an abortion storm, multiple fresh fetuses and placentas should be collected from does that have aborted. These should be kept cool and immediately transported to your veterinarian. In turn, he or she will perform a gross examination and possibly do some smears as well as submit samples to a diagnostic laboratory for further work up. Because it may take several weeks for results to become available, treatment and control should be instituted right away. Does can be placed on oral tetracycline, depending on the type of abortion suspected and all contaminated bedding, fetuses and placentas should be destroyed. Aborting animals should be kept isolated and facilities kept as clean as possible. Animals should not be fed on the ground.

Congenital and Inherited Defects

Most kids born are normal but, from time to time, a defective kid will be produced. Congenital defects that can occur in kids include atresia ani or atresia coli, a condition in which the anus or colon is solid in one or more places, instead of being a tube, so that an affected kid cannot defecate. The kid will nurse normally to start with and then, over a several day period, as the intestines become distended with fecal material, the kid becomes uncomfortable and gradually weakens, strains to defecate and eventually stops nursing. Kids like this should be euthanized as soon as the problem is recognized. Other congenital abnormalities include ventricular septal defect (developmental defect involving the heart), microphthalmia (tiny eye), cleft palate, rectovaginal fistula (a condition in which the rectum and vagina do not properly separate during development), hydrocephalus, flexion deformities of the legs, spinal abnormalities, overshot and undershot jaw, sex anomalies, entropion (rolled in eyelid) and umbilical hernia. Kids affected with these problems should be culled from the herd or sold as meat.

Of the above-mentioned defects, only overshot and undershot jaw and cryptorchidism (failure of one or both testicles to descend into the scrotum) are known to be inherited. It is uncertain as to whether these other conditions are inherited or not.

If a stud buck is producing significant numbers of defective kids - for example, offspring with jaw defects or cryptorchidism - he should be eliminated from the breeding program. Dams of affected kids should also be culled. The odd defect - one out of several hundred kids - should be noted in your records and an eye kept on the offspring of the involved dam and sire.

Hypocalcemia (Milk Fever)

This rare condition, which is the result of an increase in calcium and phosphorus requirements at the start of lactation, may occur at parturition or 1 to 3 weeks after parturition in goats producing large quantities of milk. An affected goat is ataxic (unsteady on her feet), constipated and depressed to comatose. Treatment should be given as soon as possible and consists of 25 to 100 ml of a 25% calcium borogluconate solution given slowly intravenously. Additional calcium may be given subcutaneously and, in mild cases, calcium may be given subcutaneously and/or orally instead of intravenously. Several treatments may be needed as even mild cases can recur. If alfalfa hay, which is high in calcium, is being fed during late gestation, it has been suggested that other mineral supplements be removed from the ration for the last 3 weeks of gestation.

Ketosis (Pregnancy Toxemia and Lactational Ketosis)

Pregnancy toxemia, which occurs in the last 6 weeks of gestation, is not usually a major problem but, if feed intake is decreased for any reason or if the doe is very fat or very thin, ketosis may occur. Ketosis may also be seen during early lactation.

In starvation ketosis, the doe has not received enough nutrients, especially energy, to support herself and the rapidly growing, usually multiple, fetuses. Interference with feed consumption as a result of a disease process may also result in ketosis. The obese doe may reach a point at which, between the massive fat stores in the abdomen and the distended uterus, the abdominal cavity is so full that not enough dry matter can be consumed to meet the increased demand for energy. Pregnancy toxemia is usually more of a problem in very prolific animals.

Affected animals will initially be listless, weak and have a poor appetite. These signs progress to nervous signs - tremors, stargazing, incoordination, circling, teeth grinding, head pressing and blindness - and then coma. Treatment should be instituted as soon as the problem becomes apparent since, once nervous signs are evident and the animal is recumbent, the prognosis is guarded and treatment is typically unrewarding.

Diagnosis is based on history, clinical signs, the odor of ketones on the breath of the affected doe and/or ketone bodies in the urine. Tablets or strips are available for ketone detection in urine. These change color when dipped in urine containing ketone bodies.

If the ketotic goat is still eating grain, treatment includes improving the diet to contain better quality roughage and increased concentrates. Two ounces (60 ml) of propylene glycol can be given 2 or 3 times a day with a dosing syringe or by stomach tube. Many goats really resent the taste of propylene glycol so, if the goat becomes upset and struggles considerably when propylene glycol is given with a dosing syringe, it should be given by stomach tube instead. Dosing with propylene glycol can be continued for several days until the doe is feeling more like her usual self. B vitamins should also be given for several days.

If the animal will neither eat nor get up, the prognosis is guarded. Treatment should include intravenous glucose (25 to 50 grams as a 5 to 10% solution), mixed B vitamins and force feeding (propylene glycol, rumen stimulant and 2 quarts of calf oral electrolytes can be mixed together and given by stomach tube). Hand feeding leaves and tender twigs, if available, may encourage the goat to eat.

Near term pregnant does (within 1 week of kidding) can be induced to kid with 10 mg of prostaglandin F2 alpha. If the kidding date is unknown and the owner would like to try to save the doe and kids, 20 to 25 mg of dexamethasone may be given. Dexamethasone will stimulate the appetite and, while late term fetuses will be born approximately 2 days after treatment, more immature fetuses may be carried to term if the doe responds to medical therapy.

If the goat has not responded to treatment a day after its initiation, a caesarean section should be performed. It should be noted that recumbent does in late pregnancy have a poor prognosis, despite caesarean section and fluid therapy. The kids from these does are often dead at the time of surgery or die a few hours later.

Since it is not uncommon for goats to develop polioencephalomalacia (vitamin B1-responsive disease), and, because this could result in the secondary development of ketosis, goats with vague nervous signs should receive vitamin B1 at 500 mg intravenously initially followed by 250 mg every 12 hours for 3 to 5 days intramuscularly or subcutaneously.

If one goat in a group develops pregnancy toxemia, the rest of the group should be evaluated. Goats in late gestation should be fed good quality roughage and adequate concentrate. Any stress such as concurrent disease, parasitism, cold rainy weather and outdoor feed bunks that the goats will not use because of inclement weather, should be minimized. Goats should be able to exercise for at least 2 to 3 hours a day. Smaller, more timid individuals should be housed together. If goats have been ultrasounded for pregnancy and fetal numbers estimated, goats should be grouped and fed according to fetal counts.

Kidding Problems (Dystocias)

If a nanny has been in active labor (straining) for half an hour or more, there likely is a problem and it is time for you to lend a hand or call the veterinarian. One word of caution: do not interfere with the birthing process before the nanny has done her part. If you try to extract a kid from a doe before the feet and head of the kid are up in the birth canal, you will have your work cut out for you. So, give the nanny a fair opportunity. If, after 5 minutes of active labor, you cannot bear to watch her straining, walk away for a while. Also, leave the nanny in the place that she has chosen for kidding. Do not try and move her once active labor has started. The doe can be moved to a kidding pen or wherever once the kid(s) are safely on the ground and she has mothered up to them. Especially with triplets, give the doe time to identify and clean off her offspring. Do not rush in and grab the kids and move the nanny to a new location. In the confusion, the mother may become scared and reject one or all of her kids, creating a major headache for you (bottle babies). It is not often that goats have problems kidding and, if you have a goat that needs assistance two years in a row, you should consider culling her from the herd.

If you are lucky, the problem will be relatively straightforward: the kid will just be a bit larger than usual and unable to fit through the birth canal readily. Make sure that your hands and the area around the vulva are very clean. Apply a generous amount of lubricant to your gloved hands. Special lubricant can be obtained from your veterinarian or a sheep supply catalog for assisting in these difficult births. When you pass your hand through the vulvar lips into the birth canal, make sure that you do not drag any debris (fecal material, straw) in with you. You should be able to feel the tips of the front toes and the nose nestled between and above them - this is the typical birth presentation - and the doe should be straining at regular intervals. Smearing some lubricant on your hands and around the kid will often loosen things up. Gentle traction on the front feet will help the doe move the kid along the birth canal. Pulling should coincide with the contractions/straining of the doe. The kid should be pulled downward and outward, in a normal birth arc. Often gently pulling one front leg and elbow out will make a bit more room for the head and other front leg and the birth process will then proceed normally.

Kids may also arrive backwards, so do not immediately panic if you feel two legs and no head. The presence of hocks and a tail indicate that this is a normal posterior presentation. The hind legs can be grasped and the kid removed with gentle traction, again pulling in concert with the normal birth contractions of the dam. If the kid is backwards (posterior presentation) but upside down, it will need to be gently rotated into a normal position and then pulled as described above. Sometimes, the rump of a kid will get stuck in the birth canal and only a tail can be felt because all 4 legs are pointing forward (toward the nose of the dam). After washing your hands carefully and putting a generous supply of lubricant over the gloved hand and arm that you choose to use, gently enter the vagina of the goat. The kid will need to be pushed forward and the hind legs found. After the hind legs are gently pulled up and into the birth canal, this kid can be delivered as a posterior birth. Make sure that the kid is manipulated carefully. The uterus is fragile and can be damaged or torn with rough handling. The hooves of a kid can cause some damage if they are scraped hard against the uterine wall. The uterus can be protected by cupping your hand around the hooves when the feet are going to be pulled along or pushed against the uterine wall.

If the kid is presented with the head back - initially the front legs are all one can feel - the kid needs to be gently pushed back into the uterus, the head retrieved, and the head and front legs introduced into the birth canal. A lamb puller (snare) or even clean baling twine can be used in any of the above instances. Placing the wire loop of the lamb puller around the head, neck or leg(s), depending on the situation, and applying firm but gentle traction will help extract a slippery kid. Be very careful that the appropriate legs are paired up. One does not want to be attempting to pull out a front leg and a hind leg in the same breath. As well, one wants to make sure that twins or triplets are not present and that the legs you are trying to sort out are not from two or even three different individuals. If this is the case, the extra kid(s) will need to be pushed gently back into the uterus so that the kids can be delivered one at a time.

A subcutaneous injection of long acting penicillin or tetracycline should be given to any doe that needs assistance at kidding time. If no long-acting broad spectrum antibiotics are available, the doe should be treated with shorter-acting antibiotics for a minimum of 3 days and for 5 days if it was an extremely difficult birthing.

Retained Dead Fetus
On occasion a full term or near term kid or kids may die inside the doe as the result, for example, of trauma (the doe's abdomen being butted by another goat) or an unrecognized birthing problem (if the presentation of the kid is such that the head and legs do not enter the birth canal [sideways or rear end first], the doe may never initiate very obvious contractions). If the kid(s) are not removed from the doe quickly, they will decompose, the doe will become very sick and, in a few days, die. An indication that there is a problem is a bloody or brownish discharge from the vulvar lips, occasional straining and poor appetite. The dead kids must be removed gently using the same procedures as for assisting delivery of live kids. In this case, however, more lubricant will be needed as the dead kids may be quite dry. After the dead kid(s) have been extracted, the doe should be treated with broad spectrum antibiotics for 5 to 7 days and given good nursing care.

Retained Placenta (Retained Afterbirth)

The afterbirth is usually passed within a few hours after kidding and should be passed within 24 hours. Sometimes the doe or a guardian dog will eat the placenta (or a barn cat will drag it away) so it is possible to panic unnecessarily. If the afterbirth has been retained, penicillin should be given at 45,000 IU per kilogram (20,000 IU per pound) twice daily (every 12 hours) for 5 to 7 days. Prostaglandin F2 alpha at 8 to 10 mg per doe may help expel the placenta. This drug causes the uterus to contract.

Udder Problems
Enlarged (balloon) Teats

If a nanny has plenty of milk and just a single kid, the kid may only nurse from one teat. In the kidding pens, single kids should be encouraged to nurse from both sides of the udder. If the doe simply has too much milk, she will have to be milked out once or twice a day until the kid can keep up with the milk supply. If these does are not milked out, one side of the udder, as well as the corresponding teat, will swell up and get larger and larger each year. These enlarged teats are unsightly and can get large enough to impede the progress of a lactating doe around a pasture. As well, kids find it very difficult to nurse from these swollen teats and will need lots of coaching. This, of course, means more work for the owner at an already busy time of the year (kidding season). Does with single kids can and should be grouped separately from those feeding twins or triplets. The nannies with one kid can be fed less which cuts down on feed costs.

Udder Problems
Mastitis

Mastitis should not be a common problem in meat goats if the environment is kept clean and dry, particularly at kidding time. Goats with mastitis may have half or all of the udder affected. Milk from a goat with mastitis may contain clots of varying size and be discolored (watery or brown- or red-tinged). Milk volume is typically decreased. In acute cases of mastitis, the affected portion of the udder is warm, swollen and painful. Sometimes mastitic goats will appear lame as it hurts them to walk and move about. Kids trying to nurse mastitic does will often look thin and hungry. Goats with acute mastitis may be systemically ill with a fever and lack of appetite. Examination may reveal teat lesions such as trauma, soremouth or warts that were a precursor to the mammary inflammation.

The affected gland is atrophied (smaller than normal because of scar tissue and loss of functional mammary tissue) in chronic cases of mastitis. One or more abscesses may be palpated.

In cases of acute mastitis, aseptic collection of a milk sample by first disinfecting the teat end with 70% alcohol is essential to identify the causative organism. Culture of the organism followed by bacterial sensitivity testing will aid in antibiotic choice. Unfortunately, by the time culture and sensitivity results are available several days will have passed and the goat needs to be treated immediately. Many of the bacteria that cause mastitis are resistant to penicillin so ampicillin or amoxicillin, both of which have a broader spectrum of activity than penicillin, could be used. Many of the broad spectrum antibiotics do not penetrate mammary tissue well. Some of the newer antibiotics such as florfenicol do achieve good concentrations in mammary tissue after subcutaneous or intramuscular administration. If the animal is not systemically ill, infusion of the udder with bovine intramammary infusion tubes may be helpful. Unfortunately the applicator tips are often too large to enter the teat canal of a goat readily. While smaller bore syringe tips can be purchased, damaging the teat canal lining is still of concern. In any case, whether or not infusion tubes are to be used, the udder should first be stripped out and it is essential that as much fluid be removed as possible. The udder can be infused 2 or 3 times at 12 to 24 hour intervals.

If one has sufficient time, the best results can be achieved by stripping out milk, bacteria and toxic material from the udder as many times a day as possible. The fluid should be milked into a container, not squirted onto the barn floor, and carefully disposed of. One does not want to contaminate the environment further with the organism that caused the mastitis, especially in a confinement situation. Continued stripping of the milk from the affected udder, in conjunction with a broad spectrum antibiotic administered parenterally (subcutaneously or intramuscularly) will often, if the mastitic udder is noticed promptly, give excellent results.

Occasionally a gangrenous mastitis will occur. In these cases, there will be rapid cessation of milk production and the skin over the affected half of the udder is cold and blue. These goats are really sick and, in some cases, intravenous fluids, antibiotics and steroids are necessary to save the life of the doe. As well, the damaged udder will often slough off and/or scar in so that, if the goat survives, the affected mammary tissue will not be functional in future lactations. In severe cases, amputation of the udder or teat may be necessary to save the life of a valuable animal.

If only one out of a large group of goats has a problem with mastitis, it may be best to cull her. She may be a source of infective bacteria for other goats. It is best to select for healthy animals not predisposed to mastitis or other disease problems.

Udder Problems
Trauma
Sometimes a large udder can be damaged; for example, butted by another goat or bumped by something in a pen. If, in these cases, a blood vessel is ruptured, the milk will be pink or reddish in color but will otherwise be normal. The udder will also feel normal and the goat will have a rectal temperature within normal range. This problem should resolve over time and without treatment, but a close watch should be kept on the damaged udder just in case mastitis does occur.

Uterine Prolapse
A goat may prolapse the uterus after a difficult kidding. This is a problem that is not likely to occur in subsequent kiddings. If an animal with a uterine prolapse is cared for promptly (within twenty-four hours) and damage to the uterus is not too extensive, the outlook is good. Your veterinarian should be called immediately. In the meantime, the goat should be haltered and otherwise restrained so she cannot move about dragging the uterus on the ground behind her. The uterus should be carefully washed with warm water (body temperature) and a mild disinfectant and placed on a clean sheet or towel. To make replacement of the uterus less difficult, the hindquarters of the doe can be elevated - for example, over a straw bale - and the uterus gently replaced. Retaining sutures are placed in the vulvar lips for 7 to 10 days. Antibiotic therapy - procaine penicillin G at 20,000 to 45,000 IU per kilogram of body weight (10,000 to 20,000 IU per pound) every 12 hours subcutaneously or intramuscularly for 5 to 7 days - is a necessity. Oxytocin can be given to contract the uterus. If tetanus vaccines are not up to date, the goat should receive antitoxin and toxoid.

If the uterus has been out for 36 hours or more and damage is severe, amputation of the uterus may be required.

Vaginal Prolapse
Vaginal prolapse, which occurs in late gestation, is not commonly seen in goats. A large fetus or two combined with a bulky rumen and weak musculature around the vagina are thought to contribute to this condition. Straining may also aggravate this problem. This is thought to be at least in

part inherited in sheep. Certainly any goat that exhibits this problem, as well as her offspring, should be culled from the herd.

To keep the vagina in place until kidding, the prolapsed tissue is carefully cleaned and washed in nonabrasive disinfectant soap and gently pushed back into its normal position. Then the top two thirds of the vulvar lips are sutured together, leaving a small orifice for urine to pass through. The doe will need to be watched carefully because the sutures will need to be removed when active labor begins.

A baling twine prolapse harness can be made for sheep: this would also work well for goats and could be substituted for suturing the vulvar lips. To make the harness, several pieces of baling twine are tied together and the twine midpoint located. The midpoint of the twine is draped over the back of the goat in the shoulder region. The twine ends are crossed over the chest and brought back under the armpits. Then the twine ends are brought up over the back of the goat, crossed again and brought down under the hind legs. The twine is then pulled up over the back of the goat, on either side of the vulva and rectum, and threaded through the twine where it crosses over the back and the shoulders. Then the twine is tied, as tightly as possible, so that the animal can barely stand up. A separate piece of twine is threaded back and forth between the twine strings running up either side of the vulva. This twine or pieces of twine can then be loosened at kidding time. This harness does not encourage the doe to strain or cause secondary infection like the plastic bearing retainers commercially available.

IV. MISCELLANEOUS DISEASES

Bacterial Skin Disease
Dermatophilosis (Streptothricosis)

Dermatophilus congolensis causes skin infection in goats as well as in other species. During dry weather, the organism may survive in soil or the goat's hair. Any kind of injury to the skin, such as damage by external parasites or shearing cuts, allows the organism to penetrate the epidermis. Multiplication of *D. congolensis* occurs during rainy or humid weather.

Ears (especially in young kids), nose, muzzle, feet, scrotum and the underside of the tail are regions most commonly affected. Lesions begin as raised scabs, which may become covered with matted hairs. Healing or chronic lesions are characterized by dry crusts, scaling and alopecia (lack of hair). Infection with secondary bacteria may cause pruritus (itching) and/or pain.

Diagnosis is by impression smears of the underside of moist lesions, or, in dry lesions, skin biopsy. The organism can also be cultured by a diagnostic laboratory.

Penicillin-streptomycin or tetracycline are effective treatments for individual animals. Treatment and prevention also include shelter from the rain, bathing with iodophors or 2 to 5% lime sulfur, grooming to remove crusts, control of external parasites and improved nutrition. People can occasionally become infected with this organism. Because carrier animals appear to harbor the organism, these individuals should be culled.

Bacterial Skin Disease
Staphylococcal Dermatitis

Staphylococcal skin infections, which are common in goats, are the result of infection and inflammation of hair follicles. The main lesion is a pustule which may discharge exudate and become encrusted. Features of the chronic or healing stage are hair loss and scaling. Many small pustules may appear on the teats, udder, perineum and the underside of the tail. If the disease remains localized, it is of minor significance except that teat lesions may lead to staphylococcal mastitis. In some goats, the infection becomes generalized and can affect skin of the abdomen, inner thighs and even the back and neck.

Diagnosis is usually based on physical examination.

Localized lesions on the udder can be washed with a chlorhexidine or iodophor shampoo, dried and then treated with an antibiotic ointment.

Culture of the organism and determination of antibiotic sensitivity should be performed in suspected generalized infections. Treatment with penicillin can be started while waiting for culture and sensitivity results. Animals need to be treated for 1 to 2 weeks.

Bluetongue

This insect-borne virus infection rarely causes clinical disease in goats. Viral antibodies may be present in blood samples from apparently healthy goats. The disease is of economic significance in sheep, however, because of deaths, fetal deformities, damaged wool, chronically-ill animals and the cost of preventative programs.

Broken Horns

Although some people dehorn their goats, most do not. As goats get older, the horns, particularly those of the nannies, seem to get more fragile. Horns may be weakened in one region by an illness, a period of poor nutrition or an injury. Sometimes the horns of aged nannies will break off with very little encouragement or, more commonly, a curious goat will poke its head through or into something and, when it tries to escape, ends up cracking or even pulling off a horn. The amount of blood produced can be unsettling.

The affected goat should be penned separately so her/his pen mates are not able to butt her/him. If the bleeding is considerable, pressure should be applied until the bleeding slows down or halts. Strips from an old but clean sheet or towel tied around the head will work if bleeding is profuse. If the horn has not completely broken off and is just dangling, it can be quickly pulled or twisted off. If it is more firmly attached, it can be sawed off at the base of the horn above the point at which the horn enters the skull of the goat. A length of Gigli wire with pliers attached to either end makes a useful saw. During fly season, insecticide spray should be sprayed around the horn until healing is complete.

Caprine Arthritis-Encephalitis (CAE)

Goats with caprine arthritis-encephalitis virus (CAEV), a retroviral infection, have usually been in contact with infected dairy goats. Caprine-arthritis encephalitis (CAE) is not typically a problem in range-raised meat goats. CAEV is usually transmitted via the colostrum of infected does but horizontal or goat-to-goat transmission by infected secretions in feed bunks or water troughs, aerosol exposure, use of blood-contaminated needles or tattooing equipment on one goat after another, may also occur. CAE infections have a prolonged course with persistence of the virus in the host, involvement of multiple organs and a chronic course with acute episodes. Apart from subclinical infections, which are common, CAE has a variety of presentations. Encephalomyelitis, the neurologic form of this disease, usually occurs in 2 to 6 month old kids but may occur in any age goat. A chronic respiratory form can occur in adults and may be noted in conjunction with the arthritic form. In young does, the udder form may result in little or no milk at parturition. Weight loss may occur as the only sign of CAE or it may occur along with any of the other forms.

In adult dairy goats, CAE is a significant cause of chronic arthritis. The encephalitic form of CAE starts out as lameness or weakness in the hind quarter and is characterized by ataxia (unsteady gait) and posterior paresis. There is no treatment for CAE although the life of an affected animal can be prolonged with supportive care.

Definite diagnosis and management of this disease in a herd can be a challenge because a negative agar gel immunodiffusion (AGID) test, the test most commonly used for diagnosis, either in a clinically ill goat or in an individual that is clinically normal, does not rule out the possibility of CAE infection. The AGID test is only moderately sensitive and false-negative results may occur in cases in which there is not sufficient circulating antibody for the test to detect. Circulating antibody levels may be depressed further by concurrent disease, poor nutrition and during late pregnancy, when serum antibody is being transferred into the colostrum. The enzyme linked immunosorbent assay (ELISA) is much more sensitive and much less likely to produce false-negative results. Where available, this is the test of choice.

If low numbers of animals are affected, control is by serologic testing at least once a year and culling. Otherwise, immediate separation of newborns from the dam at birth before they have a chance to nurse, using pasteurized colostrum or bovine colostrum, feeding pasteurized milk and keeping healthy goats separated form seropositive goats all are steps to ward controlling CAE in a herd. Blood-contaminated equipment - for example, ear taggers and notchers - should be disinfected after use and separate sterile needles and syringes should be used for injecting each animal.

Caseous Lymphadenitis (Contagious Abscesses)

This chronic bacterial infection is a common cause of abscesses, both internal and external, in goats and sheep worldwide. The causative organism, *Corynebacterium pseudotuberculosis*, enters the body via a skin wound or the mucous membranes and eventually settles in one or more lymph nodes. There, slow-growing firm abscess(es) form that eventually rupture(s) and release(s) thick white, yellow or greenish odorless purulent material. This material contaminates the environment and may infect other goats. Abscesses may be the result of butting, ear tagging or notching, contaminated needles or trauma from sharp edges of feed bunks. Abscesses may be located anywhere but are most common in the lymph nodes of the head and neck. Goats with external abscesses seldom appear ill but goats with internal abscesses may have a history of chronic weight loss.

Culturing contents of an abscess, a sample for which is obtained by inserting a sterile needle through shaved, disinfected skin into the mass and aspirating contents, will confirm a tentative diagnosis. Animals should be kept isolated once a mass has been aspirated and while awaiting culture results since abscess contents are very contagious to other goats.

Because these abscesses have a very thick wall, antibiotic therapy is not a very successful method of treatment. It is preferable to isolate the goat, clip the hair and disinfect the skin over the mass, lance the abscess with a scalpel blade and express and then burn the contents. The abscess cavity is then flushed with hydrogen peroxide or other dilute disinfectant. This should be continued for several days and then the incision allowed to heal. Goats with open abscesses should be kept separate from the herd until the incision has completely healed over. If it is fly season, a fly repellent should be applied to the area daily.

Abscesses may be removed intact surgically in valuable show animals or outstanding breeding stock. This requires anesthesia.

The organism causing these abscesses can survive for months in the environment so abscesses should be opened in areas not frequented by the rest of the herd.

Caseous lymphadenitis can be controlled by keeping a relatively closed herd and not introducing animals with evidence of external abscesses, culling affected animals and removing or disinfecting sources of contamination. Currently available serologic tests are not specific enough to use in a culling program. Vaccination to protect against this disease is a possibility. However, available vaccines, which are said to be useful, may cause lumps at the injection site.

Diarrhea

In kids less than a month old, especially in kids less than ten days of age, the most commonly diagnosed cause of diarrhea is cryptosporidiosis (see Internal Parasite section). Enteropathogenic *Escherichia coli*, a common cause of diarrhea in young calves and lambs, is not diagnosed very often in kids. *E. coli* infections in kids may be more often associated with septicemia than diarrhea. Rotavirus and coronavirus are often isolated from kids with diarrhea but their significance is uncertain. Other agents that are associated with diarrhea in kids less than a month old include adenovirus, herpesvirus, *Salmonella* species, *Clostridium perfringens* and *Eimeria* species. Many cases of diarrhea in young kids may be the result of a nutritional problem; these are difficult to diagnose without a complete history.

Diarrhea in kids a month of age or older is more likely to be the result of coccidiosis or gastrointestinal parasites. Other causes in older kids include enterotoxemia caused by *Clostridium perfringens* type D, salmonellosis, yersiniosis and gastrointestinal upsets resulting from the transition to and consumption of solid feeds.

Regardless of the cause, diarrhea results in dehydration, acidosis, depletion of electrolytes and, in very young kids, hypoglycemia. Electrolyte imbalances, resulting from the loss of sodium, chloride, potassium, bicarbonate and water into the intestinal lumen, may be fatal if not corrected. Therapy is aimed at trying to resolve the above effects while the diarrhea runs its course. Oral, subcutaneous or intravenous fluid therapy can be instituted depending on the severity of the dehydration and electrolyte imbalances and the value of the animal. Oral electrolyte preparations should contain sodium chloride, potassium chloride, sodium bicarbonate, glucose and glycine. In very acidotic animals, additional sodium bicarbonate may need to be added. Diarrheic animals should be moved to warm, dry surroundings and isolated from the rest of the herd. Lactose in milk or milk replacer can aggravate diarrhea. Alternating oral electrolyte preparations with small feedings of milk will decrease the hyperosmotic diarrhea associated with feeding only milk. Kids should be gradually reintroduced to a milk only diet as the diarrhea resolves. In prolonged cases of diarrhea, especially in young kids, milk products will have to be fed or starvation may occur. Feeding milk in smaller amounts and more often will hopefully give the best results. Antidiarrheal medications such as kaolin/pectin may be helpful. Yoghurt or lyophilized *lactobacillus* cultures may help restore more normal bacteria to the gastrointestinal tract.

If a bacterial diarrhea is suspected or confirmed, broad spectrum oral or injectable antibiotics such as trimethoprim/sulfonamide may be considered. Antibiotics may also protect against opportunistic bacterial infections such as pneumonia.

Immediate and strict isolation of kids with diarrhea will help control the spread of the problem. If possible, kids exposed to those with diarrhea should be moved to a new clean pen or moved temporarily so that their pen can be cleaned. Good management practices such as ensuring that the environment, particularly in a confinement situation, is clean and dry and that kids get adequate colostrum (50 ml per kilogram of body weight or 20 ml per pound) as soon after birth as possible are essential. Vaccination of the does thirty days prior to kidding with *Clostridium perfringens* types C and D toxoid is recommended.

Floppy Kid Syndrome
This disease, for which no cause has been found, is characterized by a

sudden onset of muscle weakness, depression and severe metabolic acidosis, an increase in anion gap, decrease in bicarbonate, normal to increased chloride and occasional hypokalemia (low potassium). No specific organ system appears to be involved and kids have no gastrointestinal or respiratory abnormalities. Affected kids are normal at birth and develop the condition at 3 to 10 days of age. Kids are often reluctant to suckle but can swallow. From 10 to 50% of kids in a herd may be affected with mortality rates as high as 30 to 50%. Cases tend to occur toward the end of the kidding season. Kids of all breeds, from all ages of dams and from various management systems seem equally susceptible. Many diseases mimic floppy kid syndrome; white muscle disease, abomasal bloat, septicemia, enterotoxemia and severe diarrhea all can lead to a very weak and/or acidotic kid.

Diagnosis is based on clinical signs and blood chemistry results.

If the condition is detected early, the base deficit corrected and supportive care given, response to treatment is good. Owners can treat less severe cases with oral bicarbonate (1/2 a teaspoon of baking soda in water) when clinical signs are noticed. Kids may need to be tubed with milk or electrolytes until they are able to nurse. More severe cases may need to be treated with isotonic intravenous 1.3% sodium bicarbonate solution. Some severely affected cases have recovered without treatment. Antibiotic therapy does not seem to affect the outcome of the disease.

Foot Abscess

A foot abscess is the result of infection of the deeper structures of the foot. The causative agent(s) are bacteria other than *Bacteroides nodosus*, which are introduced into the deep structures of the foot by trauma and puncture wounds.

Foot abscesses may affect the heel or the toe and usually only affect one claw of one foot. The foot is hot, swollen, painful and the goat may refuse to bear weight on the affected foot. Swelling or purulent material may be apparent above the coronary band (hoof/skin junction). Paring the affected area of the foot will reveal a pocket of purulent material and perhaps a foreign body in the deeper structures of the foot. The abscess should be allowed to drain and broad spectrum antibiotics administered for a few days.

Foot Rot

Goats are more resistant to foot rot than are sheep. However, an infected goat or sheep can introduce the disease to a goat herd, so breeding stock should never be purchased from a farm or ranch where foot rot has been or currently is a problem. The disease is thought to be more difficult to eradicate on goat farms where sheep are also present. Foot rot is a contagious disease and is the result of a bacterial infection with *Bacteriodes nodosus* of the skin of the interdigital cleft - the area between the two claws of a foot. When conditions are wet and warm (above 50 F or 10 C), bacteria invade the skin and inflammation and infection then extend into the horny and laminar structures of the foot. The disease can persist in sheep flocks for years because pastures are contaminated by carrier animals. *B. nodosus* can survive for up to 14 days in the environment. Foot rot is rarely seen in hot arid environments.

Lameness may be severe with affected goats walking on their knees, or, if all four feet are extensively involved, the affected individual may refuse to walk at all. There may be swelling of the interdigital tissue or separation at the hoof wall and skin junction. There may be a small amount of purulent material around the hoof/skin junction (coronary band) and there may be a characteristic necrotic aroma. Chronically affected animals may lose weight and fly strike and/or tetanus may occur. Healed hooves may be deformed.

Culture of *B. nodosus* from foot lesions confirms a tentative diagnosis of foot rot.

Treatment involves radical foot trimming followed by application of topical bactericidal agents to the exposed diseased tissue. Quaternary ammonium antiseptic solutions, iodophor antiseptic solutions, iodine or 10% zinc sulfate in water are all useful. If large numbers of goats are involved, foot bathing can be substituted for individual treatment. In recent years, a 10% to 20% zinc sulfate solution with 2% sodium lauryl sulfate has proved as effective as copper sulfate or formalin. The former solution also has no irritating fumes like formalin, is less toxic than copper sulfate and does not stain the hair like copper sulfate. A fertilizer-grade zinc sulfate can be used to make a zinc sulfate solution. Zinc sulfate is more soluble in warm water and a wetting agent, for example, lauryl sulfate, or a heavy-duty laundry detergent with nonionic surfactants at a 0.2% volume:volume ratio, is useful. A 10 to 30 minute soak at 5 day intervals should cure most cases of foot rot. For severe cases, 1 hour soaks weekly for 3 treatments may be needed. Animals should be kept on a dry surface for a least an hour after topical treatment. Foot trimming equipment should be disinfected in 10% formalin after footwork on each goat is completed. This helps prevent spread of foot rot to uninfected animals.

Antibiotic therapy is also useful. One intramuscular injection of penicillin at 40,000 IU per kilogram in conjunction with foot trimming and placing the animal(s) in a dry environment, is very effective and has a high cure rate.

A vaccine is available - Footvax (Coopers Animals Health) - but it is expensive and may not provide complete protection in goats. It needs to be given twice at a 30 day interval and then given yearly. Vaccination, if used along with foot trimming, foot soaking and culling of severely affected animals, can help eliminate foot rot from a herd.

As with many diseases, prevention is the best way to deal with foot rot. Closed herds that use artificial insemination to introduce new genetics and do not show their animals should not have to worry about foot rot. Persons coming to visit or tour a farm and who have mud or manure contaminated footgear should be asked to change their boots or place plastic boots over their dirty boots. It is a good practice to have visitors who own goats or sheep don plastic footgear or at least dip their footwear in a disinfectant foot bath before entering your facilities. If goats are being raised in a humid environment and have access to good feed, they likely will need regular foot trimming.

Footscald (Interdigital Dermatitis or Benign Foot Rot)

Footscald is a contagious infection of the skin between the toes and does not extend into the deeper structures of the foot as in foot rot. This problem is caused by weakly virulent strains of *Bacteroides nodosus*. Lameness is mild and the skin between the toes is red and/or swollen.

Treatment and prevention is as for foot rot.

Johne's Disease (Paratuberculosis)

It is possible that this disease, which mainly affects the digestive tract and is the result of bacterial infection with *Mycobacterium paratuberculosis*, is a frequent cause of chronic weight loss in confinement-raised goats. The disease may be more common in temperate climates but does occur worldwide. It is difficult to diagnose because the clinical signs are nonspecific, rapid, reliable laboratory tests are not readily available and gross postmortem lesions are minimal.

M. paratuberculosis is shed in the feces of infected adults and, when ingested by susceptible young goats, the infection is carried in a latent state in the intestine and associated lymph nodes. Although kids are most susceptible to infection, especially those in crowded, heavily contaminated environments, adult animals in crowded conditions may also become infected. At some stage, probably as the result of stress, infected animals begin to shed the organism in their feces and, at the same time or at a later date, begin to lose weight. Diarrhea is characteristic of this disease in cattle but is not observed in goats (or sheep). Clinical disease rarely occurs before a year of age and most clinically ill individuals are 2 or 3 years of age. Although the appetite is normal initially, as the disease progresses the appetite diminishes and the affected animal becomes lethargic and depressed. Flaky skin and poor hair coat are common. Hypoproteinemia, as evidenced by intermandibular edema (bottle jaw), may be apparent in the later stages.

Fecal bacterial culture is the most reliable method of diagnosing Johne's disease, but, if the goat is not yet shedding the bacteria in the feces, the results will be negative. The agar gel immunodiffusion (AGID) test is also useful for identifying subclinical cases although false-negatives can occur. Gross necropsy lesions, if present, include diffuse or focal thickening or edema of the intestinal tract. Microscopic lesions are characteristic.

Joint Ill (Bacterial Polyarthritis)

Infection of one of more joints in young kids is usually the result of inflammation of the umbilical cord or bacteremia. Many bacteria, all common environmental contaminants, have been isolated from the joints of goats with arthritis. These bacteria gain entry into the bloodstream via the umbilicus and localize in joints resulting in joint inflammation. Animals that are born in dirty environments, do not have their navels dipped or are immunodeficient (for example, do not receive colostrum) are more susceptible to polyarthritis.

If it is economically feasible, it is useful to perform a bacterial culture on material from infected joints as well as antibiotic sensitivity testing. In most cases, broad-spectrum antibiotic and anti-inflammatory drugs are administered. Treatment may need to be prolonged (two or more weeks) and the prognosis is guarded.

To prevent this problem, goats should kid in clean, dry areas. Kidding pens should be well cleaned and bedded and disinfected regularly. Insuring early and adequate consumption of colostrum is essential. Umbilical cords of confinement-born kids should be thoroughly dipped (right up to and including the ventral abdomen) as soon after birth as possible in strong (7%) iodine solution. If the herd is having problems with this disease, dipping navels again on the second day after birth may be helpful.

Pinkeye (Infectious Keratoconjunctivitis)

Chlamydia and *Mycoplasma* species, both bacterial organisms, are the two most common causes of keratoconjunctivitis in goats in North America. Mycoplasmal infections can also cause mastitis, pleuropneumonia or arthritis while chlamydial infections can result in abortions, arthritis and respiratory disease.

Early clinical signs of keratoconjunctivitis are tearing and reddened and swollen conjunctivae. Later, small blood vessels form on the surface of the cornea giving the cornea a hazy or opaque appearance. Corneal erosions or ulcers may develop. The eye is painful and blinking is frequent. Animals, especially those with both eyes affected, have impaired vision or may be blind.

Affected animals need to be separated from the flock and given easy access to feed and water. Tetracycline eye ointment administered at least twice daily and more often if possible is recommended if not too many individuals are affected. Otherwise, an intramuscular injection of long acting tetracycline is helpful. In goats in which perforation of an ulcer is imminent, the eye should be sutured closed until the ulcer heals. A third eyelid flap is the easiest surgical technique to aid ulcer healing.

Pneumonia, Bacterial

The bacterial organism, *Pasteurella haemolytica*, is usually involved in cases of acute pneumonia. *Pasteurella multocida* is often a secondary invader. Pneumonic pasteurellosis usually develops in animals stressed by weaning, transportation, exposure to inclement weather after recent shearing, chilling, overheating, exposure to drafts, confinement in poorly-ventilated barns, overcrowding, abrupt ration changes, malnutrition and severe parasitism. Stress impairs normal respiratory tract function, and, as a result, *Pasteurella* bacteria, which are normal upper respiratory tract inhabitants, are inhaled, colonize the lower respiratory tract and initiate inflammatory disease. Viral infections may also predispose the lung to bacterial invasion.

Animals with pneumonia may not be obviously ill, particularly in the very early stages of the disease. Finding a dead goat may be the first sign an owner notices. However, careful observation will reveal that the appetite is poor and the goat is depressed. Respiration may appear labored and the respiratory rate is elevated. The body temperature usually is elevated (104 to 106 F or 40.0 to 41.1 C). However, animals in the terminal stages of any disease, pneumonia included, can have a normal or subnormal temperature. Coughing and/or nasal discharge may be apparent. Mortality may be 10% or more.

Bacterial cultures performed from material obtained from a tracheal wash or lung from a necropsied goat (that has not been treated with antibiotics) will determine the organism(s) involved. If many goats or valuable animals are involved in the outbreak, antibiotic sensitivity testing should be performed so that the appropriate antibiotic can be selected. At necropsy, the cranioventral lung lobes are usually dark, red to purple and firm. Fibrin (white material) may be on the pleura (lung surface covering). If the goat has been ill for weeks or more and the dorsal lung lobes feel meatier/firmer than usual, the primary problem may be CAEV infection. Histologic examination of lung tissue will help confirm this.

Goats with pneumonia must be treated early in the course of the disease and for an appropriate length of time - for at least 3 days after the body temperature returns to normal. The affected animal(s) should be isolated and provided with good quality feed and clean water. Useful antibiotics include ampicillin at 5 to 10 mg per kilogram (2.2 pounds) twice daily, tetracycline at 5 mg per kilogram once or twice daily and tylosin at 10 to 20 mg per kilogram once or twice daily. Aspirin can be used in conjunction with an antibiotic to control pain, fever and inflammation.

If ventilation and high humidity are problems in a building, the situation should be corrected. Newly acquired animals should be kept isolated from the rest of the herd for a minimum of 2 weeks. Kids should receive adequate colostrum.

Chronic pneumonia may result from infection with *Corynebacterium pseudotuberculosis*, the agent that causes caseous lymphadenitis (contagious abscesses). Treatment is not effective in curing lung abscesses and the long-term outlook for afflicted animals is grave. Often these animals are thin, poor-doing individuals. Sudden death may occur after rupture of an abscess.

Posthitis, Ulcerative (Pizzle Rot)

This chronic disease results from the combination of a high protein diet (18% or more protein) and a bacterial organism, *Corynebacterium renale*. Male goats on high protein diets may excrete urine containing as much as 4% urea. Bacteria colonizing the skin around the preputial orifice hydrolyze the urea to ammonia. Ammonia is very irritating and causes ulcers, scabs and scar tissue to form. This condition is more of a problem in wethers than intact males. This is likely because, in castrated males with a less well developed penis, urination frequently occurs without exteriorization of the penis. Excessive hair, which tends to remain wet, around the preputial orifice, and allows prolonged bacterial contact is also a predisposing factor. If enough scar tissue and inflammatory exudate is present around the preputial orifice, it may be blocked. Severely affected goats are restless, strain to urinate, kick at the abdomen, have a stiff gait or an arched back and may continually be getting up and lying down. If the preputial orifice is completely occluded, the animal may die. Because of the moist environment in this region in affected animals, secondary fly strike with maggot development can be a problem.

Posthitis can be prevented by lowering dietary protein and providing lots of clean drinking water. Altering the diet of goats on pasture or range can present problems.

Animals that are unable to urinate must first have the tissue removed from the preputial orifice. Then treatment involves shearing hair away from the region if this is the problem, removing dead tissue and applying a broad spectrum antibiotic-containing ointment into the sheath and onto the preputial region. Intramammary infusion tubes are useful for administering antibiotics into the sheath. Topical penicillins, ampicillins and cephalosporins should all be effective. Affected animals should be moved to a clean, dry environment while their lesions heal. If posthitis occurs during fly season, a maggot check should be performed daily and insecticide spray should be applied to the diseased area until it heals up. Most animals, except those with severe scarring of the preputial orifice, will recover nicely with treatment.

Rabies
Cases of rabies are rarely reported in goats. However, this viral disease should be considered whenever a goat shows nervous signs. Goats are moderately susceptible to rabies, which places them in the same category as dogs, sheep and cattle. The virus is introduced into the goat by the bite of a rabid animal such as a fox, skunk or dog. Vampire bat bites may cause rabies outbreaks in the tropical parts of Mexico. The virus replicates in the muscle at the site of the bite wound for days and then enters local nerves and moves up nerve trunks to the central nervous system. The incubation period can range from 14 to 24 days, mainly because of the varying distances the virus has to travel to the central nervous system. For example, a

goat bitten on the face will have a shorter incubation period than one bitten on a hind leg. When the virus reaches the central nervous system, it continues to replicate and move throughout the brain and spinal cord. Virus particles also move back down nerve trunks to nerve endings, which is how the virus ends up in the salivary gland.

Affected goats typically display aggressive behavior and excessive bleating. Salivation and paralysis may be seen in some individuals. The clinical course is from 1 to 5 days and all affected animals die.

Cases may be confirmed by histopathologic examination of the brain, immunofluorescence staining of brain sections (rapid and accurate) or intracerebral inoculation of mice with brain, spinal cord or salivary tissue (most definitive but more time-consuming).

This is a difficult disease to diagnose because it resembles all other diseases affecting the nervous system in goats. Any animal with nervous signs should be handled as if it has rabies. Do not get saliva from the affected goat on cuts in your skin. Do not put your hands in the mouth of these animals! Gloves and masks should be worn when handling suspect animals and hands washed carefully afterwards with disinfectant soap. If a goat is suspected of having rabies, it should be euthanized so a definite diagnosis can be made.

Currently there is no vaccine approved for use in goats in the United States although there is a killed vaccine available for use in sheep and cattle. In endemic areas, vaccination of goats may be possible. Your veterinarian should be consulted about this matter.

Ringworm

Poor nutrition, infection with other disease(s) and damp, dirty environments predispose goats to fungal infections.

A goat with ringworm usually has hairless, scaly, crusty and reddened regions on the face, ears, neck and legs.

Diagnosis is based on physical examination and microscopic examination of hairs and keratin from the edge of an active lesion. If species identification is required, culture and colony examination is essential.

Most cases of ringworm regress without treatment in 1 to 4 months. Infected animals should be isolated from the herd and, if treatment is to be undertaken, the body sprayed with lime sulfur (2 to 5%), iodophors or 0.5% sodium hypochlorite daily for 5 days and then weekly. If possible, the environment should be disinfected with sodium hypochlorite and all exposed animals treated. If only small lesions are present, topical thiabendazole paste or iodine ointments can be applied. Treatment does decrease environmental contamination and spread to other animals and humans.

Scrapie

Although goats are not commonly affected with this contagious degenerative neurologic disease, characterized by an incubation period of months or years, it is very significant because of import and export regulations preventing movement of animals from countries not free of the disease. In most, but not all, cases of caprine scrapie, there is a history of contact between infected sheep and the affected goat(s). It is thought that prions, the infectious agents, are transferred to goats by direct contact with infected placentas or nasal secretions of infected sheep. Early replication of prions is first in lymphoid tissues and later in nervous tissue.

Clinical signs of scrapie have not been seen in goats less than 2 years of age. Usually signs progress gradually over 1 to 6 months. Initially, affected animals may position the rear limbs forward so that the rump is elevated and the withers held low. The tail is held up and the ears pricked forward. Infected individuals become increasingly restless and hypersensitive to handling. Over time, incoordination becomes more evident and eventually animals stumble and fall and have trouble rising. Animals eventually stop eating, become prostrate and die. Various nervous signs may be noted during the course of the disease, such as salivation, local pruritus (itchiness) and blindness.

Diagnosis is based on the clinical picture and characteristic histologic brain lesions. There is no treatment.

Control of the disease is by maintaining a closed herd or introducing new genetics by artificial insemination. Live animals should be purchased from flocks with excellent health status. If the health status of sheep is unknown, they should not be mixed with goats. Regulatory control programs for scrapie vary from one country to the next.

Soremouth (Contagious Ecthyma)

Soremouth, or contagious ecthyma, is a contagious viral disease that occurs worldwide and is characterized by the formation of vesicles, pustules, and scabs on the lips as well as the udder, coronary band, scrotum, face, ears and vulva. Humans may also be infected with this virus so affected goats, especially those that are being treated, should be handled with gloves. The virus is transmitted directly, from animal to animal, or indirectly via contaminated equipment, bedding, manure, feed and fences.

Scabs that fall to the ground may be an infection source for months or years. Carrier animals may also be responsible for outbreaks. Goats and sheep of any age can be affected, although animals less than a year of age most commonly succumb to the disease. An entire group of kids may show lesions. The condition can be aggravated by poor management - feeding rough feeds that traumatize the soft lining of the mouth, overcrowding and poor nutrition.

The disease, the course of which ranges from 1 to 4 weeks, causes great discomfort and affected animals may be reluctant to nurse or eat. Very few animals die from soremouth, however, and those that do usually have contracted a secondary bacterial infection. Mastitis, secondary to lesions on the teats, making it too painful to allow the kid(s) to nurse, is of concern in lactating does affected with soremouth.

Severely infected lips and nostrils can be treated with an ointment containing a broad-spectrum antibiotic. Salve can be applied to teats to keep them pliable. Soft, high-quality feeds may encourage animals to eat.

In early stages of an outbreak, vaccination is useful. This live vaccine should never be used in herds free from the disease. Vaccination consists of applying the vaccine (basically ground-up scabs) with a brush to a scarified region on the inner surface of the ear. The vaccine can also be dropped onto a scarified site from a syringe. If vaccination has been effective, a scab will form at the vaccination site a few days after vaccination. Pregnant goats can be vaccinated annually several weeks prior to kidding so that colostral antibodies will provide some immunity. Kids can be vaccinated at 50 to 60 days of age.

Tetanus

This disease of animals and man is caused by spores of the bacterium *Clostridium tetani* that enter the body via a deep puncture wound, obstetrical intervention, tattooing, castration, hoof trimming, dog bites or fighting among bucks, and, under anaerobic conditions, vegetate and produce tetanospasmin. Spores of *C. tetani* are present in the intestinal tract of livestock and may be passed in the feces in large numbers, especially by horses. Spores accumulate in the soil, and goats kept in a confinement setup shared with horses, or where horses have been kept previously, may be at higher risk than the average. After an incubation period of 10 to 20 days, clinical signs, all of which are related to muscular spasticity, become apparent.

In the early stages of the disease, a stiff gait, mild bloat and an anxious expression may be noted. A wide base or "sawhorse" stance becomes apparent, ears are erect, the head extended, the jaws firmly set and the third eyelid (nictitating membrane) prolapsed. Over time, an affected goat becomes hypersensitive to stimuli and responds to touch or loud noise by stiffening and collapsing to the ground. Seizures may follow. Eventually the goat cannot rise, all limbs are rigidly extended and the respiratory rate increases. Once the animal is down and cannot rise, death usually occurs within 36 hours.

Most affected animals die despite treatment. If a potentially contaminated wound is noticed, the area should be first infiltrated with tetanus antitoxin and then opened to the air, scrubbed, flushed with hydrogen peroxide and infiltrated with penicillin. Goats suspected of being afflicted with tetanus can be given tetanus antitoxin intravenously at 10,000 to 15,000 units twice at 12 hour intervals and for longer if the site of bacterial proliferation cannot be found and treated. To decrease the intensity of clinical signs, anticonvulsants, tranquilizers and muscle relaxants can be administered.

The disease can be controlled by good management - removing sharp objects from the environment and paying attention to sanitation. Vaccination of does with tetanus toxoid annually 4 weeks before parturition will provide passive immunity via the colostrum for the newborn kids. Two doses of toxoid, one 8 weeks before kidding and the second 4 weeks before kidding, are necessary for initial immunization of the doe if a bred doe is purchased and has not been vaccinated previously. Kids are vaccinated at 30 and again at 60 days of age; this toxoid is available combined with *Clostridium perfringens* types C and D toxoid. If the vaccination history of young kids is unknown, 150 to 250 units of tetanus antitoxin as well as penicillin should be given when routine procedures such as castration are performed. When treating wounds or assisting with birthings in adults of uncertain vaccination status, 500 to 750 units of antitoxin and penicillin should be administered.

Umbilical Hernia
Umbilical hernia, resulting from incomplete closure of the umbilical ring during fetal development, is rare in goats. There does not appear to be a genetic predisposition to this condition in goats.

If a swelling in the umbilical area can easily be reduced; that is, the tissue in the umbilical swelling can be gently pushed back into the abdomen, then it is probably a hernia and not an abscess (see umbilical abscess section).

In does less than a month or so of age, binding the abdomen with adhesive tape for 2 to 4 weeks may encourage the hernia ring to close. If the hernia is large or the kid is a male, surgical repair is advised.

Umbilical Abscess

Inflammation of the umbilical cord, as the result of contamination of the cord at birth with bacteria present in the environment, may result in an umbilical abscess. An umbilical abscess may be a warm and/or painful swelling or a firm mass in the umbilical region.

Umbilical inflammation can be readily prevented by dipping the umbilical cord as soon after birth as possible in strong (7%) iodine solution. Kids born on clean dry pasture probably do not need to have their navels dipped.

External abscesses should be drained and the kid treated with a broad spectrum antibiotic for a week or more.

14. ARTIFICIAL INSEMINATION

"The techniques of artificial insemination (AI) and more recently embryo transfer (ET) in livestock production present producers with unique opportunities to maximize the number of progeny from animals with superior genetic makeup and move their germplasm around with relative ease."
- Stephan Wildeus, "Reproductive Management of the Meat Goat," *Meat Goat Production and Marketing Handbook,* Clemson University, BC 683, Rep. October 1996.

Artificial insemination is, at this time, not widely used in the meat goat population. However, if superior sires can be identified by a record keeping program, artificial insemination (AI) is an excellent method for introducing new genetics to a herd. AI allows producers to use genetics that might not otherwise be affordable or attainable and, as well, limits spread of disease from herd to herd. One outstanding male can be bred to any number of females.

For AI to be effective and economical, semen must be of top quality - properly and carefully collected and processed. Much better results can be obtained with fresh semen but, unless the buck one wants to collect semen from lives near or on the farm where one will be inseminating the does, one is limited to working with frozen semen. Each thawed straw or pellet of semen must have an adequate number of viable spermatozoa or the AI program will be a failure. Most reputable semen collection sites thaw a unit of semen from each ejaculate to make sure that post thaw motility is adequate. Semen that is too dilute or of poor quality (abnormal spermatozoa morphology) should not be frozen in the first place. Each ejaculate should be carefully examined microscopically to make sure that it is worth freezing. Bucks can produce a wide range of semen quality and some bucks never produce good quality semen. Some bucks are seasonal in their rutting activity and may only produce freezable quality semen for part of the year.

If fresh good quality semen is used and cervical insemination is performed, one can expect a 65% conception rate if heat detection is done carefully and does are inseminated approximately 12 hours after the first sign of estrus.

If frozen semen is to be used, the best results are obtained by synchronizing the females and inseminating them laparoscopically. A proges-terone-impregnated implant is typically placed subcutaneously or intravaginally on day 1 and removed on day 17. Most does, during the natural breeding season, will show heat on day 19. A teaser buck (see chapter on embryo transfer) is used for heat detection. Pregnant mare serum gonadotrophin (PMSG) is usually used for out of season breeding and is given when the implant is removed. A pregnancy rate of 60% may be expected with laparoscopic insemination, good quality frozen semen and properly prepared does.

Best results are obtained when does are kept in small stable groups where there is minimal intergoat aggression. New animals should not be introduced to the group during the 6 months before breeding is to take place. Kids should be weaned at least 2 months prior to insemination. Teaser bucks should be run with the does 2 weeks - so as to stimulate estrus - before putting in progesterone impregnated implants. Does should be nutritionally flushed at the start of the program and be gaining weight during the program. The flushing should continue until 40 days after insemination. Careful doe management is as important as using good quality semen.

15. EMBRYO TRANSFER

"Under more intensive management conditions, advanced reproductive technologies such as estrus synchronization, artificial insemination and embryo transfer can be applied. These techniques are suited either for the seed stock producers or when unique germplasm is to be introduced into a herd, as has been the case with the Boer goat."
- S. Wildeus, "Reproductive management for meat goat production," *Proceedings Southeast Regional Meat Production Symposium*, Tallahassee, FL, Feb. 24, 1996.

In recent years embryo transfer work has become a very successful method of propagating considerable numbers of animals relatively quickly from a few individuals. This has been made possible due to availability of top quality drugs necessary for performing this procedure as well as improved transfer techniques. Embryo transfer work has been used extensively in North America to propagate both South African Angoras and Boer goats.

Although for many persons the words "embryo transfer" conjure up visions of complex and costly surgery with questionable results, preparing goats for embryo transfer work can be performed by anyone who is good at managing and caring for livestock, careful, can read and follow instructions and give subcutaneous injections. The surgery itself should be performed by an experienced veterinarian or technician. An embryologist, who may be the veterinarian performing the surgery or another individual who specializes in examining, grading and evaluating embryos, needs to examine the embryos for viability prior to their implantation in a recipient doe.

During the normal breeding season, a goat cycles approximately every 19 to 21 days (normal range 17 to 24 days). The estrous cycle is divided into 2 phases, the follicular and the luteal phase. The follicular phase, which is only 3 to 4 days, is the period of follicular growth, during which time the follicles (the eggs and their encasing cells) on the ovaries are stimulated to grow, first by follicular stimulating hormone (FSH) and then by luteinizing hormone (LH). FSH and LH also stimulate the growing follicle to produce estrogen, which is released into the bloodstream. Low circulating levels of estrogen have an inhibitory effect on FSH secretion so that the ovaries are not excessively stimulated. When the level of estrogen in the blood becomes high enough, LH is released, causing rupture of the follicle and release of the ovum. The level of estrogen in the blood reaches a peak just before the onset of estrus. The preovulatory LH surge occurs early in estrus and, 18 to 24 hours later, ovulation occurs.

The luteal phase begins after ovulation when the ruptured follicle fills with blood. Cells in the follicle wall proliferate and form a solid mass known as the corpus luteum, which produces progesterone. Progesterone prepares the uterus for the fertilized ovum or embryo.

For embryo transfer work to be successful, the hormonal events briefly outlined above must take place, but, instead of only one ovum or a very few ova being released from the follicles, as normally occurs in ovulation, the idea is to try to stimulate multiple successful ovulations (superovulation). This is achieved not only with drugs but also with excellent management.

Flushing is a very important component of the embryo transfer program in goats and it is important that candidates for embryo transfer work be on a rising plane of nutrition for approximately a month prior to hormonal programming. Of course, the recipient animals that the embryos will be transferred to are just as important as the donors, the animals from which the embryos will be collected. If the recipients are not already in good body condition, they also need to be "flushed" during the month preceding programming. Donors and recipients must be in good health, good body condition (not too thin or too fat), and acclimated to the farm. Any processing, such as deworming, vaccinating, shearing, foot trimming or whatever, should be performed prior to programming. The goats need to be stressed as little as possible once the program begins, as in any normal breeding program. Animals should be clearly identified with ear tags that are legible from a distance. One should not need to continually catch goats to read ear tags, notches, tattoos or whatever form of identification one chooses. This just adds to the stress.

Well cared for Angora goats make some of the best recipient animals for any embryo transfer program, probably because they are less susceptible to the stress of frequent handling than some of the wilder meat-type (Spanish) goats. Recipients should be free of caprine arthritis encephalitis virus (CAEV) as well as of contagious abscesses (caseous lymphadenitis), footrot and so on. Poor quality recipients can ruin an embryo transfer program.

Teaser or vasectomized bucks*, used to detect time of onset of estrus in the recipient does, need to be made well in advance of the program so that they will have time to recover properly from the surgery. As well, they need to be semen checked several times to make sure that they are no longer fertile.

Embryo transfer programs vary as far as drug dosages and timing of administration of the drugs. However, the basis for any program is the same. As mentioned earlier, following instructions outlined by your veterinarian will ensure the best possible success. Results in any embryo transfer program are somewhat unpredictable because one is dealing with live animals.

The donor animals - those that will be providing embryos for transfer - and the recipient animals - those that the collected embryos will be transferred into - need to have their estrous cycles synchronized so that they will come into estrus at approximately the same time. This is achieved by using a progesterone-impregnated implant in each animal. High blood levels of progesterone, induced by the progesterone-containing implant, inhibit secretion of FSH and LH by the pituitary gland and follicular growth is limited. Basically, the animal's system is tricked into the luteal phase. Removal of the implant after 17 days or so leads to a new wave of follicular activity and then estrus occurs.

The teaser buck, fitted with a marking harness, is used to detect heat in the recipient animals. Grease mixed with paint may be applied to the chest of the buck daily or several times a day as necessary if a marking harness is not used. Regardless, as the does come into heat and are mounted by the vasectomized buck, a colored mark is left on the rump of the doe. As estrus is detected in the recipient does, their identification numbers are recorded and they are removed from the pen. This is so the vasectomized buck can focus on heat detection in animals that have not yet shown signs of estrus. Most of the recipient does should come into heat about 24 to 48 hours after removal of the progesterone-impregnated device.

Superovulation in the donor animals is encouraged by the administration of FSH every 12 hours for about 4 days before removal of the progesterone-impregnated device. When the progesterone-impregnated device is removed from the donors, approximately a day after removal of the devices from the recipients, donors will come into heat at the same time as the recipients, but should produce many more ova.

* See end of this chapter for preparation of teaser bucks.

It is important that the cycles of the recipients and donor are closely synchronized so that embryos will be transferred into recipients that are at the same stage of their estrus cycle as the donor. This will ensure optimum embryo survival. Embryos transferred into a doe who showed signs of estrus more than 24 hours before or 12 hours after the donor doe will have a poorer survival rate.

It also is imperative that sufficient recipient animals are prepared. Goats may have a very good response to superovulatory drugs and, on occasion, may produce well in excess of 20 or even 30 good-quality fertilized embryos. Of course, excess embryos may be frozen, but frozen embryos, when thawed, do not produce as many offspring as freshly transplanted embryos. One can expect a 10 to 20% drop (or more) in kids produced from frozen versus fresh embryos of similar quality.

Mating of donor animals can be done artificially (artificial insemination [AI]) or naturally. If the animals are to be bred artificially, good timing is essential and several inseminations will give the best results. Bucks to be used in a natural mating program should have their semen tested prior to use. A simple way to check a buck is to allow him to breed a female in heat, swab the vagina with a sterile swab, smear the swab on a slide and do a microscopic examination to evaluate sperm numbers and motility. This is not as accurate as collecting a sample into an artificial vagina either using a teaser doe or by electroejaculation, but it will give an idea of whether the buck is fertile or not. If the buck has not been used at all during the particular breeding season, he should be allowed to mate several times before one examines a sample and, as well, before breeding a donor animal.

Bucks that are heavily used in an embryo transfer program may actually refuse to breed. Best results are obtained by using a ratio of 1 buck to 1 or 2 does. Hand or pen mating is best and all matings should be observed. An obvious thrust is indicative of a successful mating. The presence of other males in the breeding area may encourage a less than enthusiastic male to breed. Once 1 or 2 positive matings have been observed, the buck and nanny should be moved to separate pens. Breeding females every 6 hours during the time that they are in heat, starting about 12 hours after they show signs of estrus, typically gives very good results.

An area that is suitable for the embryo transfer surgery should be clean and one must be able to maintain the temperature at at least 40 to 50 F. For surgical carts to move easily, a 20' by 20' room is ideal, but surgery has been performed in much smaller areas. Running water is nice but not essential. Electric outlets and adequate lighting, preferably not fluorescent light, and some counter space should be available. An embryology area or room should be warm, dust free, have minimal direct sunlight and counter space at desk height with electrical outlets available. Pens for the animals should be near the surgery area. As well, a bedded recovery area should be nearby so that animals recovering from surgery can be carefully observed. Paint and insecticides are toxic to embryos so these should not be used or stored in the surgery or embryology region.

Surgery to retrieve the embryos is performed about 6 days after mating. The donor goat is anesthetized and, after clipping, scrubbing and disinfecting the abdomen, a laparoscope - basically a light source at the end of a stalk - is introduced into the abdominal cavity and the ovaries inspected to see if there has been a response to the superovulation protocol. If the animal has responded, as evidenced by corpora lutea (hopefully many!) present on the ovaries, a portion of the uterus is exposed through an abdominal incision. A catheter is passed into the uterine horn through a tiny incision and any embryos are flushed into a Petri dish. This is repeated on the other uterine horn. The embryologist grades the embryos and discards unfertilized or very poor quality embryos.

Embryo quality varies and though the evaluation is somewhat subjective, one can expect a 70% plus conception rate from Grade 1 embryos, a 50% or so from Grade 2 embryos and a 20 to 30% conception rate from Grade 3 embryos. This will of course vary depending on the quality and care of the recipient animals that the embryos are transferred into.

Then, after checking each anesthetized recipient with the laparoscope to ensure the presence of corpora lutea on the ovaries, 2 good-quality embryos are transferred into the uterus of each recipient. Odd embryos may be transplanted as single embryos or as trios. The latter is usually preferable as reduced conception rates typically occur when single embryos are implanted.

Both the recipients and donors are treated with an injection of a broad spectrum antibiotic postsurgically and carefully observed while recovering from general anesthesia. A stress free environment postoperatively as well as good quality feed will aid in embryo survival. By 40 to 60 days after implantation of the embryos into recipient animals, ultrasounding for pregnancy diagnosis can be performed. Again, this procedure should be as low stress as possible.

A donor animal can be flushed twice or possibly 3 times, at 6 week intervals, during the normal breeding season. If the animal is to be flushed again, treatment after surgery with an abortifacient drug (a prostaglandin) is recommended. Occasionally embryos are left behind during the flushing procedure so one wants to make sure that these are removed prior to the next embryo transfer program. Otherwise, the leftover embryos may result in a pregnancy or pregnancies, making further embryo transfer work impossible during that season. If it is the last embryo flush of the season, one may elect to not interfere with any possible pregnancies. However, in rare instances, if multiple embryos are left behind, it is possible that the doe may give birth to multiple small weak kids, which of course is undesirable. So, some veterinarians may elect to use abortifacient drugs, regardless, and then have the buck breed the doe naturally.

It is advisable to time an embryo transfer program so that the donor dam still has time to be bred naturally and carry a pregnancy after the embryo transfer work has been completed. Otherwise, if the donor is simply manipulated hormonally and surgically to produce offspring, without ever going through pregnancy and lactation, she may become overconditioned. Fat animals have more reproductive difficulties and no one wants a superb animal to become lost to the gene pool because of an embryo transfer program.

TEASER MALE PREPARATION

Timid males with poor libido should NOT be used. Teaser male candidates should be aggressive sexually. A potential teaser male can be tested with several does that are showing estrous behavior to evaluate his sexual behavior. Yearling males are preferable because of their longer useful life. Teaser males should be free of any sexually transmitted diseases.

There are 2 surgical techniques for making teaser bucks:

1) Vasectomy

The usual method is to remove 4 to 5 cm (1.5 to 2 inches) of each of the two vas deferens through two surgical incisions in either side of the neck of the scrotum.

It is recommended that the 2 portions of vas deferens removed (one supplies each testicle) be submitted for histologic examination to make sure that indeed the vas deferens was removed.

Bucks should not be used for at least 6 weeks postoperatively to allow for complete clearance of live spermatozoa still present in the remaining part of the duct.

Prior to use of the vasectomized male, a semen sample should be collected and examined microscopically for the presence of spermatozoa.

2) Caudal epididectomy

The tail of the epididymis is surgically removed by pushing each testicle to the base of the scrotum and, through an incision in the bottom of the scrotum, removing the tail of the epididymis. This method is NOT felt to be as reliable as a vasectomy. Some reports have suggested that teaser males prepared using this method may become fertile 1 to 2 years postoperatively due to regeneration of the epididymis.

Bucks should not be used for 6 weeks after surgery.

Semen testing prior to buck use is recommended.

Hormonal Treatment of Wethers

Yearling or older wethers are most suitable. Wethers are treated with three doses of testosterone propionate at 150 mg subcutaneously per wether at 1 week intervals before introducing the wether to the does. This three treatment regimen will result in buck-like behavior in the treated wethers for four weeks. If the teasers need to be used for more than a month, they can be treated with 150 mg of testosterone propionate every 2 weeks. Apparently there are no adverse effects resulting from multiple treatments.

16. SHOWING MEAT GOATS

"Many a show is won or lost in the feeding program."
- Beth Mason and Becky Sauder, "You need to start with a quality goat," *Boer Breeder*, October 1999, p. 7.

Because of the incredibly varied management and environmental conditions goats have been subjected to prior to the show day and because the placings are arrived at by visual appraisal alone, it is very difficult to evaluate and compare goats in the show ring. Despite this, winning honors at a show, even in this modern day and age when the performance of a group of goats can be objectively evaluated at a test station, carries considerable prestige.

On show day, the judge(s), spectators and participants have the opportunity to examine goats from different bloodlines and farms or ranches with varying management systems. Though there are some health risks involved (after all, the goats at the show are being exposed to animals from many other farms or ranches), potential stud bucks are often selected and purchased at shows. If one's goats are well presented, showing can be terrific advertising.

Goats make excellent 4H projects. Young people can learn firsthand about proper management (control of internal and external parasites, nutrition, general care) as well as record keeping and genetic improvement. Usually evaluation and showing of goats is part of the 4H project. Good sportsmanship and fair play are part of being successful in the show ring.

For young and old alike, showing creates an opportunity to meet people with similar interests and to cultivate lifelong friendships.

Preparation for showing generally begins several years before the goats are actually displayed in the show ring. After years of improving one's flock, one may decide that one's goats are of top quality and merit show ring evaluation and competition. 4H members, on the other hand, may purchase a "show quality" animal or two and start showing immediately.

Selecting goats for show takes experience and an eye for the most appealing individual. Generally small goats, no matter how lovely, will not place well, so the emphasis should be on choosing goats of above average size. A show animal should have conformation that is as close to ideal as possible. When searching for the ideal goat, eliminate goats with any serious faults such as an over or underbite, crooked legs, deformed feet, weak pasterns, small scrotum and one or even no testicles in the scrotal sac. Show goats, apart from being conformationally correct, must have that something extra - an alert appearance with good carriage and gait. The elite animal should carry itself as if it is something special.

When a judge examines a meat goat on show day, he or she is evaluating the conformation (correct physical structure) of the goat, the general appearance, which includes size and scale and capacity, muscling as well as finish (fat cover)[1].

A good meat goat should look like a meat type animal with the appropriate finish for its size, weight and age. The animal should have straight, level top and bottom lines with a long rump, body and leg. The legs should be straight and placed squarely under the body with both fore and hind legs showing evidence of muscling. A perpendicular line originating at the pin bone should fall parallel to the leg bone from hock to pastern and touch the ground beneath the heel of the foot. Toes should be tight with a deep heel and level sole so that feet rarely, if ever, need trimming in arid conditions when the goat is on a moderate plane of nutrition. There should be adequate width between the forelegs and the head should be in proportion to the body. The hindquarters, viewed from the rear, should be muscular and long and the back, loin and rump uniform in width.

The goat should be of above average frame size and body length. The cannon bone, which is a good indication of skeletal size, should be sufficiently long from the knee to the pastern and all bones should be of adequate diameter. The goat should be slightly taller at the withers than at the hips and the rump should slope slightly from hips to the tailhead. The head should be nicely balanced with does having a feminine head and males a masculine head. The animal should move smoothly and soundly.

Muscling is evaluated by examining the loin, hindquarters, shoulders and neck. The loin eye or rib eye is the best indicator of muscling. It should be wide and symmetrically oval on either side of the backbone. The muscle should extend forward over the rib cage. The forearm circumference is the second best indicator of meatiness so the forearm muscle should be prominent and extend as far down toward the knee as possible. Muscling should increase from the withers to the point of the shoulder and the thickest muscle should be just above the chest floor. A long, deeply attached muscle, thick at the thigh and stifle, is desirable and muscle over the rump should be obvious. The neck should be long, gently sloping and should show muscling in proportion to the rest of the animal.

The finish or external fat thickness should be from 0.08 to 0.12 inches (average 0.1 inch) thick over the loin at the 13th rib[1].

This information is slanted toward market goats, though good conformation is good conformation regardless of the age and the class of the goat.

However, there are standards for the various goat breeds that include unique color markings, for example, for Boer goats. These breed standards need to be carefully studied before the show to make sure that the goat or goats that you have selected conform. Intact animals must be able to pass basic breeding soundness checks; for example, males must have adequate size testicles for their age.

As well as making sure that the goat is as near to a perfect specimen as can be found, it is important to read the show rules and regulations, including any special rules, to make sure that the animal or animals selected will be the right age and weight for the various classes. Most goats lose their kid teeth at 10 to 12 months of age so you do not want to try to enter a goat with yearling teeth in a class for kids. As well, if the class requires a finished animal, one needs to determine at what weight a goat will be correctly finished. This way the feed required can be carefully calculated so that the animal enters the show class at the appropriate weight. Frame size will help determine finished weight; a large framed goat may finish at as much as 120 pounds while a small framed goat may be finished at 80 pounds[2]. Length of head and neck, cannon bone and body all are indicators of potential frame size and growth capability.

Depending on the part of the country one is in, age groups and classes of goats showed vary. Adult, yearling and kid buck and doe classes are usual. As well, a grand champion doe and buck are selected from all the classes.

While a herd of commercial goats is typically fed for maximum profit, which may mean that the goats are fed a maintenance ration at times of the year, usually show goats are much more pampered and are fed top quality rations for months before showing begins.

Even if only a single goat is to be shown, it should be penned and fed with at least one other goat as goats are gregarious and do not do well in solitary confinement. Some people feed free choice pelleted feed; others limit feed grain with free choice roughage. Show diets are as varied as the competitors and some persons have "secret" ration formulas that they believe will give their goat(s) an added advantage on show day. Most important is that the show goat or goats receive a balanced top quality ration and that they are monitored continually. Show animals should be weighed often, even weekly, so as to monitor gain, especially if they are still growing. Young growing goats typically gain 2 to 3 pounds or more per week if well fed. Goats should not be allowed to become overfat. If the goat feels or looks too fat, remember that it is very overconditioned as goats tend to store fat internally before they deposit it externally. Young growing goats need adequate protein in their ration; between 16 and 18% should suffice. The diet must contain an adequate supply of energy (carbohydrate and fat) and calcium and phosphorus must be balanced (a 2:1 ratio or higher of calcium to phosphorus is recommended).

A top quality free choice mineral should be available at all times unless this is incorporated in the concentrate portion of the ration. Usually a coccidiostat is fed. Males receiving a substantial amount of grain should have ammonium chloride (to help prevent urinary calculi) added to the ration. Fresh clean water must be available at all times. This is essential.

Potential show goats can be started on good quality alfalfa hay with some of their pelleted ration sprinkled on top. After 3 or 4 days of this, the pelleted ration can be started at 1/3 of a pound per day and gradually increased so that 2 weeks later the goat is consuming the amount deemed necessary to keep it in peak form. Often hay is eliminated or substantially reduced towards show time so that the goat maintains a trim waistline! Right before a show, show animals should not be allowed to engorge themselves on water so that they have a enlarged abdomen. However, adequate water must be provided so that animals do not become dehydrated.

If the environment is harsh, show goats may be maintained in a shed or barn as the elements - rain, snow, wind and sun - can be hard on the coat. Bright sun may actually cause hair to change color. A "goat coat" can also be used for protection. This can be handmade or purchased from a sheep or goat supply catalog.

Feet should be trimmed regularly, every month if necessary, so that they are properly shaped.

Goats need adequate exercise. As well, they should be regularly handled, preferably by the person who will show them, so that they are calm, easily moved in the show ring and not too stressed by the show process. Show goats should be halter broken at a young age. Initially the animal should be gently haltered or collared and chained or tied to a fence.

The goat should be carefully supervised so it does not get tangled up or fight being restrained so violently that it injures itself. Just start off with a few minutes of haltering and try to make it a pleasant experience. Talking to the goat and providing some treats (food rewards) may make the goat much more enthusiastic about the whole venture. Once the goat is used to being haltered or collared and tied, then it can be taught to lead. Again, keep the sessions short and pleasant for all concerned. The goat's head needs to be kept up and the goat should be taught to walk so that its front shoulder is even with your leg. An extra person to push the goat from behind when it stops is useful in the early stages of leading. Eventually the goat can be taught to stand squarely when one stops moving. Next the goat should learn to stand calmly and quietly while being examined by another person.

During all the months of preparation for showing, basic flock health, such as internal and external parasite control, is essential.

Hooves should be trimmed a week or two prior to the show. If you do accidentally cut too deeply, the foot will have time to heal before the show. If the goat is to be dehorned, this should be done at 10 to 14 days of age. Tipping horns (removing the pointed end from the horns) should be performed 4 to 6 weeks before showing. If the goat is to be bathed, a small amount of mild soap can be used. The goat should be thoroughly rinsed and dried. Regular brushing is recommended. Rules should be read before clipping goats. If the goat is to be clipped, it should be done 7 to 10 days before the show so that the lines from the clippers are not obvious. Clippers, fitted with 20 and 23 tooth combs, should be run parallel to the length of the body. The hair on the end of the tail can be bobbed but the hair below the knees and hocks should not be tampered with. Small animal clippers can be used to trim around the eyes, ears and pasterns.

When show day arrives the exhibitor should dress neatly and should not distract attention from the goat. Once in the ring, corners should be avoided and you should leave plenty of space between your goat and the others. The exhibitor should stay out of the line of view of the judge so that the judge always has the opportunity to look at the animal, not at the exhibitor. You should make sure that the animal looks its best the entire time it is in the ring as you never know when the judge will look your way. When you stop moving, the goat should stand squarely with the body, neck and head in a straight line and the head should be up. The goat should not object to you placing a leg more correctly if that is necessary. Use both hands to show the goat; your free hand can be used to keep the goat's head and body straight. Keep your eye on the judge as much of the time as possible and be prepared when the judge reaches you. As the judge moves around your goat, make sure that you keep the goat between you and the judge. Never give up showing until you leave the ring!

Remember that the goat that wins his or her class is, in the judge's opinion, the best goat on that particular day. For example, the outstanding doe kid that won her class may develop into a mediocre yearling. This is one of the arguments against showing kids; they can change so dramatically. Another problem is that the overconditioned (by range standards) show star yearling buck may not breed any nannies his first breeding season or becomes unthrifty when put in a commercial setup.

Diseases that can be picked up at shows include respiratory infections, soremouth, pinkeye and footrot. Goats that are being showed regularly should be isolated from the main herd during show season and preferably quarantined for two months before reintroduction to the herd. The ideal would be to sell all of the goats that are showed (at the show) and not bring them, and potential disease problems, home.

Notes: Chapter 16

1. Edmundo E. Martinez, Joe C. Paschal, Frank Craddock and C. Wayne Hanselka, "Selection, Management and Judging of Meat-type Spanish Goats," Texas Agricultural Extension Service Publication No. B-5018, Texas A & M University System.

2. Frank Craddock and Ross Stultz, "4-H Meat Goat Guide," Texas Agricultural Extension Service Publication AS 3-4.060, Texas A & M University System, 10/98.

17. GUARD ANIMALS

"An [Peischel] said the guard dogs are amazing and her business would be impossible without them. 'We trust our dogs completely.'"
- Staff Reporter, *The Stockman Grass Farmer* and An Peischel, October 1998.

Dogs are the most common and useful goat guardians - although not any dog will do. Certain breeds, like the Anatolian Shepherd, Komondor or Great Pyrenees (all shown in the accompanying photographs) are among those best suited to this work. Yet even among these breeds not every animal seems to be born with the right instincts for the job. Some dogs, perhaps in play, will even maim or kill their intended charges. Training a puppy for this job starts early. At four to eight weeks of age the young animal is put in a pen or other enclosed space with a kid(s) and/or lamb(s). Gradually, as the puppy adapts to the kids and grows stronger, he or she can be put in with more of the goats he is to guard. And then, eventually, the youngster can be moved out into the pasture with the herd - preferably with some of the goats he was raised with. Most guardian dogs will be earning their keep by a year of age.

Throughout the guard dog's training he or she should not have excessive contact with human beings so that his focus will be completely on the animals he is to spend his life with. However, the owner should be able to handle the dog so that it can be vaccinated, dewormed and treated in case of an emergency. Ideally, as the dog's bond with the goats increases, he or she becomes more and more protective of them. Unless one plans on raising puppies, guard dogs should be neutered.

In regions with high coyote populations, a good guardian dog (or dogs) is essential to a range or pasture operation. With well maintained fencing, a good dog and moderate numbers of coyotes, losses to predation should be nil or, at least, minimal. However, in regions where all or most pastures are stocked with sheep and goats and coyote numbers are high, dogs are less effective. Dogs may not work harmoniously in adjacent pastures and paddocks and, typically, guard dogs pressure coyotes into another geographic region instead of killing them. When sheep and goats are concentrated in a region, the coyotes may have limited options as far as relocating.

The particular talents of canine protectors are not a recent discovery. For hundreds of years in Asia and Europe guard dogs have successfully watched over goats and sheep and scared away predators. However, their appearance and frequent use in North America is quite recent.

Guard dogs are used most in Texas and several adjoining states to protect grazing goats. Here, far from the ranch house, predators such as coyotes often attack the most vulnerable goats - particularly the kids or the does at kidding time. Good guard dogs stop these attacks almost totally.

Small wonder, most ranchers agree, that first-rate guard dogs are considered worth their weight in gold. From ranch to ranch the story is the same. Before the dogs' arrival, ranchers will tell you, goat losses to predators were significant and, in some cases, astronomic. Afterwards, with a good dog or two in each pasture, they had no losses, or only a very rare straggler.

Anatolian Shepherds can be traced back to the Asian part of Turkey - specifically to the Anatolian Mountains. Here, their owners often fitted these very strong and tough animals with dangerous-looking spiked collars. These sharp protectors gave the dogs an advantage over the wolves they sometimes had to fight when they patrolled their remote mountain pastures.

Anatolian Shepherds vary considerably from one another in color and in hair length and texture. They can be white, black or tan, or combinations of these colors, and they can be either long or short haired. In Texas and other hot and sun-drenched places the dogs with short, coarse hair are most in demand.

The endurance and stamina of Anatolians are legend. In harsh environments they are survivors. In Texas they even have to cope with poisonous snakes, which are numerous in many parts of this state. In fact, the Anatolian in the picture is just recovering from a snake bite.

In Turkey, where both animals and human beings have often had to get by on short rations, Anatolians have been known to eat anything they could scrounge. It has been said that they even survived on the same meager fare as the goats.

Today in the United States these dogs, like the goats they tend, are better fed than their Turkish ancestors. Often Anatolians eat from dry dog food dispensers which their owners set up in the pastures they patrol. But even here their traditional lack of fussiness about their food is an asset. If their dog food runs out or is eaten by other creatures such as the goats, they will not starve. They still know how to fend for themselves.

The Anatolian in the picture (on the Adams' ranch in Texas) is just recovering from being bitten by a poisonous snake.

Komondors also have ancient Turkish roots. They were brought to Hungary from Turkey in the 10th century by the Magyars. In Hungary this breed came to be known as the "king of working dogs."

Komondors are large - about the same size as Anatolian Shepherds. The males can weigh 100 pounds or more. But here the similarity ends. The Komondor's long, thick, corded coat protects him from the elements (insulating him from extreme heat or cold) and from injury from predators.

Great Pyrenees, like Anatolian Shepherds, are mountain bred. They can be traced back more than 2,000 years to the Pyrenees Mountains on the border between Spain and France. Here, they once protected herds of sheep and goats from the Pyrenean Brown bear and the Pyrenean wolf. Though extremely gentle with their charges, they are famous for their fearlessness in confronting enemies. Huge, thick-coated and square-headed dogs, they somewhat resemble Saint Bernards, to whom they are distantly related.

Besides these three well-proved breeds of guard dogs, there are others which some ranchers or farmers prefer: the Kuvasz, originally from Turkey, whose name means "protector"; the Maremma, of Italian origin; the Akbash, another Turkish breed; and the Shar Planinetz, a mountain dog originating in Macedonia in southeastern Europe.

There are also completely different species of guard animals, such as donkeys and even llamas, which some owners have tried.

Donkeys come in a variety of sizes - miniature Mediterranean or Sicilian (less than 36 inches tall), standard (36 inches to 14 hands tall) and mammoth (14 hands or more tall) - and a wide range of colors, including bay, gray, black or even spotted. Most donkeys, regardless of their physical appearance, naturally dislike dogs and their relatives, which makes them useful in protecting sheep and goats from predators. As well, donkeys prefer routine and stability so they often will make a fuss over anything that disrupts their daily schedule. For example, one of our donkeys comes racing down to the main yard, braying all the way - if she is not prevented from so doing by the electric fencing we use to make temporary paddocks - to check out any strangers who pull into the driveway. She will bray and march up and down until the "intruders" are coped with. Then she will return to her charges. Occasional stray dogs also fit into this "intruder" category. Donkeys, and guardian dogs, too, will often tolerate a dog they see on a daily basis but will attack or make a scene over an interloper.

Critics have remarked that donkeys protect their own interests first, rather than selflessly looking out for the smaller and weaker creatures in their pasture as the best guard dogs do. Like many generalizations, however, this one is open to criticisms. In regions like ours (northeastern Iowa) where coyotes are few and marauding dogs quite rare, we have used a donkey in each pasture or paddock and have never lost an animal to predators. By and large, the donkeys have bonded with their charges and appear to be a deterrent to aggressors, particularly stray dogs. However, in regions in which the coyote density is great, donkeys have been found to be less effective (or ineffective) since larger numbers of coyotes are less likely to be intimidated by a single donkey.

In acquiring a donkey the would-be buyer should remember several things. First of all, the farmer/rancher should opt for a female, a jenny: the males are more rambunctious and unpredictable, and can, on occasion, be hostile to the animals they are supposed to be guarding and may seriously injure or even kill a sheep or a goat. A bad-tempered or playful jack may actually pick a goat up by the neck and fling it over a fence. This neck biting behavior, which is normal for many jacks may, of course, result in a broken neck for an unlucky goat. Some people, however, have had good luck using castrated males as guard animals.

Donkeys prefer, if given a choice, to socialize with their own kind, so a donkey that is to be used as a guard animal is best raised in the company of the species one wants it to protect. Well cared for donkeys live for 25 to 40 years or more so that a donkey that is an effective guardian will be around for a long time. It is preferable to start off with a young, just weaned jenny or, if one is very fortunate, a jenny that has already been used as a guard animal. It is a good idea, if at all possible, to purchase a jenny with a "return or exchange" policy. So, if the donkey does not work out, she can be returned or exchanged for another animal. Unfortunately, just as with dogs, not all donkeys make good guard animals.

Whether one starts with an inexperienced or experienced jenny, the jenny should initially be placed in a small pen or pasture with a limited number of goats and/or sheep. In this restricted area, it is easy to observe the behavior of the jenny toward her future charges and, if there are any problems, they can be recognized at an early stage. It is nice to have the young donkey bond to a few animals that will be in the herd for the long term. This way, it is less traumatic for the donkey when animals are sold because at least a few of the original goats she has bonded with will remain in the group. It is also a good idea to get the donkey used to the idea of the arrival of kids and kidding season. Some donkeys will not recognize the goat youngsters as smaller versions of the species that they are supposed to be protecting and may kill or injure them. If there is any doubt as to how the guard donkey will behave at kidding time, she should be placed in an adjacent pasture, paddock or pen and only allowed to be with the does and kids when you are there to supervise.

Donkeys, although they are generally docile with humans, are extremely handy with their hooves and teeth and can be quite formidable and fast-moving when provoked. Although they will get used to herding dogs over time (if you use the same dog(s)), it is better to separate the jenny from her charges when any major sorting or processing needs to be done.

Prospective owners should be aware of the fact that the donkey they buy must be well treated - both before and after their purchase. Donkeys are extremely smart and they have long memories. Abuse a donkey once and she remembers - and is likely to pay you back in kind. Be careful not to buy a donkey which has been badly treated, and then, when you think you have your ideal animal, be patient and reasonable with her. Unlike some dogs, donkeys tend to be unforgiving.

Once the donkey appears to be functioning as part of the herd, then larger areas can be grazed and more goats added to the group. A donkey raised with sheep and goats will usually graze and rest with the group. An older donkey not brought up with small ruminants may stray farther from the group and may not necessarily graze right with her charges.

Donkeys are typically hardy and healthy, and, if your livestock overwinter outside with a windbreak for shelter, this is also adequate for the donkey. Donkeys do not require huge amounts of feed and, in fact, it is very easy to get a donkey too fat. Donkeys store their excess fat along the top of the neck, just below the mane. An overweight donkey can have a huge (fatty) neck. This is generally more of a problem when corn or top-quality alfalfa hay is fed in large quantities. If you have a mature donkey overwintering in confinement with your goats and these are on full feed, the donkey should have her feed restricted or she could even be penned adjacent to the goats and fed separately. Donkeys can eat almost anything goats and sheep do, making their care and maintenance straightforward, particularly on pasture.

One caution: if your grain contains monensin (Rumensin), which is approved for use as a coccidiostat in goats, and is also fed to ewes in late gestation to prevent toxoplasmosis, this is a major concern. Monensin is extremely toxic to horses and presumably to donkeys. If you absolutely have to feed this drug at certain times of the year, it is imperative that your donkey(s) do not have access to the feed containing the monensin. (The same warning applies to feed containing lasalocid (Bovatec), a coccidiostat approved for use in sheep.)

In humid regions and/or if the donkey is on lush feed, the hooves grow rapidly and may need to be trimmed several times a year. A farrier can do this job but, since many donkeys are calm and easy to work with, some people choose to trim their donkey's feet themselves. If you have several donkeys and you intend to trim their feet routinely, it is worth investing in some hoof trimming equipment designed for horses.

A health program for donkeys is similar to that for horses. Checking your donkey(s) on a regular basis when you check the goats should alert you to any problems before they become serious. The normal temperature is 100 to 101 F (37.5 to 38.5 C) and the average respiratory rate is 12 breaths per minute.

A minimal vaccination program should include tetanus. Other diseases that should be considered in a vaccination program in North America include Equine Encephalomyelitis (Sleeping Sickness) and rabies. If your donkeys are in contact with a fluctuating horse population or you often acquire new donkeys, vaccinating against diseases that affect the respiratory system such as influenza, Equine Rhinopneumonitis and strangles may be considered. My vaccination program is very basic: tetanus toxoid at 3 and 4 months of age and then yearly. Tetanus toxoid and antitoxin should be given if there is an injury. Equine encephalomyelitis vaccine is also given at 3 and 4 months of age and then once a year. Talk to your veterinarian about the diseases that are considered to be a problem in your geographic region.

Donkeys can host an array of gastrointestinal parasites which, if the numbers get out of control, can cause weakness, an unthrifty appearance, emaciation, rough hair coat, slow growth, colic and diarrhea. Since most of these parasites are species specific, with good pasture management, internal parasite problems in guard donkeys should be few. Deworming the donkey on arrival at the farm and keeping it in confinement for a couple of days will help prevent introduction of worm eggs onto pastures. Fecal egg counts can be used as a guide as to when to deworm your donkey. Deworming donkeys prior to turning them out onto spring pasture and again in the fall when the ground is frozen should suffice. Ivermectin and benzimidazole formulations (for horses) are effective against most gastro-intestinal parasites.

If flies are very bad, donkeys can really seem miserable. There are numerous preparations available for control of such external parasites in horses. These are available as dusts, sprays, wipe-ons, sponge-ons, collar-brow bands and pour-ons. All directions, precautions and restrictions on the labels should be observed.

Donkeys that have difficulty chewing and are dropping feed from the mouth should have their teeth checked. Over time, the molars may wear unevenly and the points that develop may need to be filed off with a float (rasp-like tool). That said, we have some very geriatric donkeys and they all seem to eat with no difficulty.

In colder regions, donkeys develop a thick furry winter coat. It seems that by the time they have finally shed the last of their coat, fall is coming and they are getting ready to grow a new one. This dense coat enables them to handle the cold winter weather easily but they do not look as beautiful (for most of the year) as their sleek-coated southern counterparts.

Donkeys should be halter broken and used to a trailer so that, if they need to be moved a long distance to a new pasture, loading them is not a major battle. Yes, they can be stubborn!

As well, it is useful when deworming, vaccinating and trimming feet to be able to control each jenny. Donkeys are easy to work with if one is patient and calm. They do not move well over ice and hate to wade through water. We have found it simpler to move them in a trailer than to try to get them to cross even a small, shallow body of water.

However, in regions where predators such as wolves, coyotes and domestic dogs run rampant, guard dogs still seem the best bet. Thus, contemporary American goat owners have generally come to the same conclusion as their European and Asian counterparts of long ago: the best custodian of endangered herds is a good guard dog.

A working Komondor, that has shed half its coat, having brunch. (Adams' Ranch, Texas)

A Great Pyrenees protecting his breakfast from the goats. (Adams' Ranch, Texas)

18. HERDING DOGS: THE BORDER COLLIE

"Everybody has differing requirements, so be prepared to wait to get the puppy which you think will suit you and which meets the various criteria you have set.... It is *essential* that you like your puppy right from the start as it is going to be with you for a long time, and if you do not like it 100 per cent you will not get the best out of it and neither you nor the dog will give each other sufficient reward to make it worthwhile to go on with training."
- H. Glyn Jones talks to Barbara C. Collins, *A Way of Life: Sheepdog Training, Handling and Trialling*, Farming Press, 1987, p. 17.

If you own more than a dozen goats and/or sheep and your focus is on grazing your stock, you should at least consider adding a border collie to your operation. This extremely intelligent, willing, focused and ept canine herder - when properly trained and bonded with you - will improve your efficiency and your state of mind, immensely.

Every cent you spend on this acquisition and every minute you devote to the dog's training will prove a most worthwhile investment. None better!

Indeed, no human being can measure up to a good border collie's accomplishments in the herding department. With incredible attention to every movement of the livestock, a well-trained dog - on your say-so - will, rapidly and with a minimum of stress on the stock, round up your animals, channel them into a pen of your choosing, back them into a corner and keep them there while you administer vaccines or deworming medication, move them from one pasture or paddock to another or load them onto your trailer. The more advanced dog can even single out individual animals or small groups of animals from the herd or flock.

Do not let the initial investment ($1,500 - $2,000 US dollars or more for a fully-trained animal, in the vicinity of $500 - $1000 for a partly-trained one and $200 - $300 for an untrained puppy) deter you. If you have chosen wisely and cope with your border collie properly, you will soon find that you are better off with her/him than with a human employee relegated to the same tasks.

Even two fit human beings cannot move a herd of goats or flock of sheep so efficiently as one border collie. You and your human employee can spend the better part of a morning or afternoon rounding up your animals, moving them to another pasture or loading them onto your trailer. Often by the time you have accomplished such jobs, you are both exhausted, your tempers frayed. But with your border collie as your partner, these tasks are accomplished in short order - and pleasantly.

Moving with amazing speed when necessary, these wonderful animals, during their most energetic exertions, almost appear to be in two places at once. Much of the time, however, the dog's movements are minimal. This is because border collies herd with their heads lowered and eye the goats, or other livestock, with an intense, almost hypnotic, stare. As the goats move, the border collie also moves, sometimes almost imperceptibly, to either block or encourage the movement of the stock. Movements of a well-trained dog are smooth and calm and do not agitate the herd. And over time, your dog's herding efforts will become easier: she/he will have "her/his" herd whipped into shape and ready to do her/his bidding. They will be "dog-broken."

Moreover, unlike a human employee, your border collie is always there when you need her/him, always willing and never asking for (or requiring) additional remuneration. The work, your sometime company and appreciation, adequate food and accommodations are her/his only requirements.

CHOOSING YOUR BORDER COLLIE

Buy your animal from a reputable breeder who also trains herding dogs, and make sure that the dog you choose is from bloodlines that are free of the genetic defects to which border collies are sometimes subject - conditions such as hip dysplasia or eye diseases such as Progressive Retinal Atrophy (PRA) and juvenile cataracts. Make sure that the breeder your dog comes from has ALL dogs' hips and eyes checked and certified free or clear of problems. Ask to see the certificates or copies of them. Eyes in the United States are certified by C.E.R.F. and hips by O.F.A. Also make certain that the animal you purchase is well-socialized and friendly. You do not want to start off with problems of someone else's making. Of course, you want to obtain a dog that is from top-notch working (herding) parents. Make certain also that all vaccinations are up to date and that the owner has records of vaccination and deworming dates.

Above all, realize the importance of acquiring an animal whose temperament is compatible with your own. Since, all going well, you and your dog will be working together frequently and over a considerable span of years, you need to like one another. Most reputable breeders will be able to help a person select a puppy that will suit their life-style and personality.

YOUR DOG'S CARE AND MAINTENANCE

It is important from the first to remember that a border collie has certain special requirements. Apart from the usual dog necessities of a well-balanced dog food to maintain strength and health and a clean, dry kennel, your border collie must have adequate exercise every day. Border collies - particularly young ones - are exceptionally energetic dogs, so that physically and psychologically they need to have a good run every day. Even a half hour vigorous run will help to keep you and your dog sane!

Although one does not need to train a border collie on a daily basis, your dog will really benefit from a 15 to 30 minute training session once or twice a day, as well as half an hour or so of vigorous exercise. I let each of my border collies out (one at a time) when I am doing chores and they get considerable exercise "helping" me. This is a good time to work on some simple commands, especially with a young pup. When the livestock are grazing, I often take both collies with me as there are usually tasks for both dogs as well as lots of walking and running.

But if you do this, it is imperative that you keep a constant eye on your dog(s). If you don't, they are apt to be off rounding something (anything) up on their own - your animals (ones you're not occupied with at the time), your neighbor's animals, or, if you are close to the road, even a passing car. A good many border collies have been killed in this last futile and hazardous occupation. So, from the beginning, watch your dog(s) carefully and call her/him back when she/he is about to abscond. Border collies are sensitive and a well-trained one is very obedient. In time, your dog will need few admonishments. Border collies tend to be most eager to please and usually are dedicated workaholics.

However, because of this species' exercise requirements, a border collie - especially a young one - is not really a suitable apartment dog; that is, unless you plan to spend most of the day exercising it. Although some owners keep a border collie in the house, I kennel mine in roomy outdoor quarters with access to cozy interior ones.

TRAINING YOUR DOG - AND YOURSELF

Ideally your border collie should be purchased from a person who trains these herding dogs as well as breeds them. Whether you are a novice or a bit more experienced, you would do well to pick this breeder-trainer's brain before starting for home with your new acquisition. If the dog is partly trained or "started", it is advantageous to know the same commands the dog does, as well as to observe how the trainer handles the dog. Learn all you can about what you should do - and how to do it. If the trainer will take time on the spot, which any reputable trainer who is selling a working dog should do, to demonstrate the basics of what you should know - and write down the necessary commands (and make an audiotape of whistle commands with an explanation of each) - you will find this hour or two invaluable when you arrive home and need to instruct your dog.

If the breeder-trainer lives near and is willing to instruct you further, this arrangement should be helpful. If, however, you find yourself far from hands-on help, buy a good book or two and/or a videotape: then study and follow the instructions set forth by the experts who have produced these works. I have found *A Way of Life: Sheepdog Training, Handling and Trialling,* H. Glyn Jones talks to Barbara C. Collins (Farming Press, Ltd. 1987), very helpful.

If you start off with a puppy, be patient. Much of the first six months will be spent getting the puppy used to his or her new home and the people associated with it, defining the pup's physical boundaries, house training, if the dog is ever to come inside, and doing basic obedience training ("come here," "lie down" and "stay" or "stay there" are essential commands). As the puppy matures a bit and shows an interest in the livestock, training can gradually be started. Although border collies are quick learners and really want to please, training a dog requires lots of patience and repetition. The end result is well worth the trouble.

Working dog housing (New Zealand).

Other useful books include:
Working Sheep Dogs: Management and Training by John Templeton and Matt Mundell, Howell Book House, Inc. 1988
The Farmer's Dog by John Holmes, Popular Dogs Pub. Co., Ltd. 1960 (revised 1984)
Herding Dogs: Progressive Training by Vergil Holland, Howell Book House 1995
The Sheepdog - Its Work and Training by Tim Longton and Edward Hart, Newton Abbot 1976
Lessons from a Stock Dog: A Training Guide by Bruce Fogt, The Working Border Collie, Inc. 1996

Good videotapes are:
Come Bye! and Away! The Early Stages of Sheepdog Training H. Glyn Jones
That'll Do! Widening the Sheepdog's Experience H. Glyn Jones
Take Time! H. Glyn Jones
Training and Working a Border Collie Rural Route Videos

Various magazines are available and include:
AMERICAN BORDER COLLIE
218 Stagecoach Lane, Crawford, Texas 76638-2911
(bi-monthly)
THE WORKING BORDER COLLIE
14933 Kirkwood Road, Sidney, Ohio 45365
(bi-monthly)
THE RANCH DOG TRAINER
P.O. Box 599, Ellendale, Tennessee 38029
(bi-monthly)
THE SHEPHERD'S DOGGE
Box 843, Ithaca, New York 14851
WORKING SHEEPDOG NEWS
Enterprise Tamar, St. Thomas Road, Launceston, Cornwall PL15 8BU, UK.
(bi-monthly)

19. HEALTHY AND DELICIOUS MEAT

"Chevon should be designated as the naturally occurring health meat." -John R. Addrizzo (M.D.), "Use of Goat Milk and Goat Meat as Therapeutic Aids in Cardiovascular Diseases," *Meat Goat Production and Marketing Handbook* (1996), p. 90. [Adapted from "Composition of Foods: Dairy and Eggs Products, *Agricultural Handbook, No. 8-1,* Agricultural Research Service, Washington, D.C., USDA.]

Statistics (see following table) support Dr. Addrizzo's claim, which he has elaborated on in the article cited above. He notes that: "The wealth of documentable evidence indicates that goat meat (chevon), regardless of age, breed, or region, will supply a high quality protein source along with a healthy fat (increased unsaturated fats/saturated fats ratio) with a minimal cholesterol intake. In addition, chevon contains comparatively higher values of iron, potassium and thiamine associated with a low sodium level.... All essential amino acids are present and a low calorie per serving value is available."[1]

COMPARISON OF GOAT MEAT TO OTHER MEAT

3 oz. cooked (roasted)	Calories	Fat (g)	Saturated Fat (g)	Protein (g)	Iron (mg)
Goat[1]	122	2.58	0.79	23	3.2
Beef[2]	245	16	6.8	23	2.9
Pork[2]	310	24	8.7	21	2.7
Lamb[2]	235	16	7.3	22	1.4
Chicken[2]	120	3.5	1.1	21	1.5

Sources:
1. USDA *Handbook* #8, 1989.
2 Nutritive Value of Foods, *Home and Garden Bulletin* Number 72, USDA. Washington, D.C. US Government Printing Office, 1981.

Ways of preparing and cooking goat meat to various consumers' ideals of perfection are legion. Some procedures and recipes are quick and easy; others take considerable time and effort.

In the following pages we have set down, for the uninitiated, a number of suggestions for using chevon. Several of these are from our own experience; others are from friends. Although the first-listed of these recipes are a dieter's delight, some of the later ones from our Greek friend, though marvellous tasting, do not qualify as lean cuisine.

Although most of our experience to date has been with chevon from Angoras - "the best chevon," according to a good many sources worldwide* - right at this moment we have a roast from a 6 month old Boer/Angora cross in the oven and strips from the same animal on trays ready to dry (some in the food dehydrator and some in the oven). The animal from which this meat was cut was a wonderful specimen and we have to agree with Fred Homeyer about the superb quality of the Boer/Angora cross - "the 'diamond' meat," as he has dubbed it.[2] This meat seems to us to be as delicious as Angora chevon - thus pretty special by our reckoning.

EASY RECIPES

Chevon roasts and chops are easily dealt with. They are cooked much as their lamb or pork counterparts. We find that, unlike older goat, chevon from a young animal generally does not need marinating in lemon juice prior to cooking since by and large it is more delicate (less strong in flavor) and tender.

Although we have cooked legs and chops from a culled doe of between 1 and 2 years old, we have never used meat from a really old animal. In North America meat from elderly goats tends to be relegated to sausages or shipped abroad. In parts of the third world, however, meat from old goats is routinely eaten. A friend, Brian McNally, who lived in Africa for 3 years, told me that where he lived "a lot of the goats available for eating were old." He found that the only way to make palatable a roast from such an animal was to sear the meat thoroughly prior to cooking it slowly. So if you suspect your chevon is not from a young animal, you might want to follow Brian's advice.

Brian's wife, Hannah, however, with her longtime experience living and cooking in Malawi, says that while most of the goats in her experience have *not* been old, she nevertheless prefers to boil goat meat whatever its

*See Chapter 3 - the section on the Angora Goat

age. When it is tender, she adds vegetables, preferably tomatoes and onions. Generous amounts of seasoning, she says, are also important for her and most other Malawians:"We like our food spicy. Curry is particularly good with goat."

Ovens, Hannah has remarked, were uncommon when she was growing up, so stove top cooking, as well as barbecuing over an open fire were usual. Goat and other meats were frequently dried. "I still prefer to dry my meat before cooking it," Hannah has told me. "But," she added - apropos of some dried chevon we had given her, "my son likes it best just dried," (essentially jerky without flavoring).

When we have a goat butchered and processed, we have the carcass divided into legs of goat (2 legs - rear legs), chops, strips and cubes. Meat can be ground instead of cubed, depending on the recipes you prefer. Of course, you can order both ground and cubed meat. Or, you may decide to do your own butchering. The chevon you will probably have most of and perhaps be most at a loss in coping with is the cubed stew meat (fresh or frozen), ground meat or dehydrated strips. Some of the recipes we use for these supposedly less choice cuts have become favorites with our family and friends. They are delectable and healthy.

MITCHAM FAMILY FAVORITES

CURRIED CHEVON

2 pounds	lean goat stew meat cut in one-inch cubes
1 1/2 cups	chopped onions
1/4 cup	olive oil
2 tablespoons	flour
1 teaspoon	brown sugar
2-3 teaspoons	curry powder
2 cups	water
2 bouillon cubes	beef (or chicken)
1/2 cup	sour milk (I sour the milk by adding 1/2 teaspoon cider vinegar and letting milk and vinegar stand for 15 minutes.)

Heat 1 tablespoon of olive oil in frying pan. Add onions. Sauté. Cook until soft, then place in casserole dish.

Place goat stew meat in frying pan. Brown meat, then add to onions in casserole dish.

Place remaining oil in frying pan and stir in flour. Add curry, sugar, bouillon cubes and water. Heat, stirring constantly, until the cubes are dissolved and the gravy thickened.

Pour into casserole dish and mix with meat and onions. Cover. Bake in oven till tender (1 1/2 hours at 325 degrees).

Stir in sour milk and serve.

CHEVON WITH HONEY AND APPLES

1 pound	lean goat stewing meat (1 inch cubes)
1 clove	garlic (optional)
3 tablespoons	olive oil
1/2 teaspoon	turmeric
1 cup	beef broth (or 2 bouillon cubes dissolved in 1 cup of water)
3/4 cup	water
4 tablespoons	liquid honey
1 cup	chopped onions
4 tablespoons	cornstarch
2 apples	(preferably cooking apples), peeled and sliced

Brown meat with turmeric (and garlic) in 2 tablespoons olive oil in frying pan. Add broth, onions, 1/2 cup water and 3 tablespoons of honey. Cover and cook in 300 degree oven for 1 1/2 hours. (We use a cast iron frying pan with lid, so that it can be transferred from stove top to oven.)

Remove pan from oven. Mix 1/4 cup water with cornstarch and blend with other ingredients over low stove top heat to thicken gravy. Return to oven for 15 minutes at 300 degrees.

In these 15 minutes, cook apples in 1 tablespoon oil and 1 tablespoon honey in a skillet on stove top until they are glazed. Top each serving of meat with a spoonful of honeyed apples.

BUTTERNUT SQUASH/CHEVON CASSEROLE

2 pounds	lean goat stewing meat (1 inch cubes)

1	butternut squash
2 tablespoons	olive oil
1	large onion (minced)
2 teaspoons	dried summer savory
1/8 teaspoon	cayenne pepper
1 tablespoon	brown sugar (optional)
2	garlic cloves (optional)
1/2 cup	grated cheddar cheese (or 1/2 cup parmesan)
1 cup	beef broth (or bouillon cubes dissolved in 1 cup of water)

Brown meat in oil with garlic, onions, summer savory and pepper.

Bake squash until tender. Cut open, remove and discard seeds. Scoop out pulp and mash with brown sugar.

Layer squash and meat in a greased casserole dish, ending with squash. Add broth. Top with cheese and bake in oven for about 1 1/2 hours at 350 degrees.

DRIED CHEVON

Goat meat dries extremely well because it is lean. (Fat in dried meat tends to lead to rancidity.)

Slice raw meat into thin slices so that it will dry quickly. (One can often get butchers who prepare deer jerky for hunters to slice up the meat in the same way.) Place slices either on cookie trays in a 150 degree oven or on the highest setting of a food dehydrator. [If you use the oven, leave the door slightly open to allow for some air movement. Most dehydrators have a fan for this purpose.]

Make sure that all moisture is removed from the meat. Then package in airtight freezer bags.

Dried meat will keep longer if you cure it first in a brine of 1 cup pickling salt to 1/2 cup sugar. However, for some constitutions this is too much salt (and sugar). (We have, by the way, had no spoilage problems with the uncured well dried chevon, despite having taken packages to warm climates like Hawaii.)

Another method of drying chevon is to roast your meat slightly prior to cutting it - in a 300 degree oven to the just done stage. (Cover the meat to prevent it forming a crust.) When just done, chill meat overnight - or place for a short time in your freezer - [not until it freezes]. Then slice as thinly as possible and dry in oven or dehydrator as described above.

The best dehydrator we have found is the American Harvest, Inc., 141 Jonathan Blvd. N, Chaska, MN 55318-9908; Telephone 1-800-288-4545.

Why you may ask, would anyone go to all the bother of drying chevon?

There are several reasons.

In drying, your 50 pounds or so of meat will shrink considerably and won't spoil for months. As well, you can reconstitute it almost anywhere when you wish. If you've dried it properly, storage is easy - whether you stay home or go on wilderness camping trips. In the latter case, you are free to travel to remote places without taking a refrigerator along. As well, dried meat makes a wonderful gift to family and friends on the opposite side of the country who like chevon but are unable to procure any where they live.

Since we also dry a large variety of fruits and vegetables, all we need to cook up a tasty and nutritious meal is fresh water and a good pot (we favor a cast iron one with lid), some favorite condiments and olive oil (which shouldn't be refrigerated anyway) - and a steady flame (from stove or campfire).

The dehydrated meat and vegetables lend themselves well to a variety of quick and easy chevon concoctions. (Just remember that dried meat and vegetables need longer cooking time than fresh meat and vegetables. Soaking both first is a good idea.) Dried chevon is excellent cooked in water with dried tomatoes, onions and squash (or any other, or additional, vegetables of your choice) and seasoned according to your taste. (Add water until you reach desired consistency and thicken gravy with flour or cornstarch as you wish or add rice.)

CROWD PLEASERS

If you have a large crowd to feed, there are two options which we find intriguing, though we must admit to not having tried either yet.

One is to roast a whole yearling goat on a spit over an open fire (as the New Zealanders do with a yearling sheep). (On a visit to New Zealand, we had a wonderful outdoor picnic from a "hogget" of lamb done this way. It fed 38 people.)

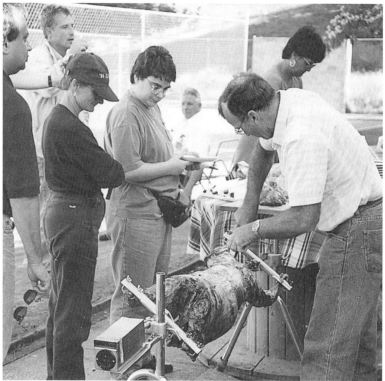

Cooking a hogget in New Zealand.

Another option entails acquiring a clean 55 gallon metal drum (or barrel) and digging a pit deep and wide enough to accommodate the drum. The drum is then installed in the pit so that the rim is flush with the ground and a fire started in the bottom. The fire must burn hotly until there is a firm bed of red coals at least 4 inches deep.

Then a grill is placed over the coals and the entire butchered goat carcass - or, if you prefer, goat pieces - deposited on the grill. If the drum does not have a lid, place an old piece of clean metal which is several inches larger than the barrel over the opening. Put a second piece of metal over the first. Cover with dirt. Then water the dirt so that it is soaked.

Leave the meat in the drum for at least 12 to 14 hours. Then, retrieve the tender and succulent chevon and serve with your favorite sauce, salads and vegetables.

In addition to the above, are the following wonderful Greek recipes which have come to us from our friend, Dr. Ted Katsigianis. These delectable dishes have been handed down in his family (originally from Greece, more recently from Long Island) from one generation to the next - and embellished slightly over the years (for instance, using tinned tomato paste instead of making the same concoction from scratch). They have been - and continue to be - favorites. In addition to Ted, the members of his family who so kindly transcribed these recipes for us are his mother, Angela Katsigianis; his aunts, Penny Zaferiou and Sapho Filou; and his cousins, Amelia Zaferiou and Barbara Filou.

When he sent these special recipes, Ted added a note which should benefit readers who decide to try the following fabulous fare: "Typically, we serve our goat meals with salad, rice and bread (baguette-type). The salad is usually lettuce, tomatoes, onions, seasoned with olive oil and vinegar. Spices are dried oregano, garlic powder, dried thyme, salt and pepper to taste."

White rice is cooked using homemade (or canned) chicken broth instead of water. (Don't use really salty broth. The rice is not the instant stuff which we think is horrible.) Top the rice with a teaspoon of plain yogurt or sour cream."

KATSIGIANIS FAMILY FAVORITES

STUFFED BABY GOAT (12-16 pounds)

Marinade
2 cups	olive oil
1 cup	lemon juice
1 cup	fresh thyme and oregano (chopped)
4 cloves	garlic (crushed)

Combine all above ingredients.

10 cloves garlic
Make slits in goat and stuff garlic clove into each slit.
Pour marinade over goat (inside and out) and marinate for several hours before stuffing.
Stuff goat and tie with butcher's twine.
Bake at 400 degrees for 0.5 hour. Turn down to 350 degrees for 2.5 hours or until goat is tender.

STUFFING FOR BABY GOAT
2 cups	red wine
3 pounds	ground goat meat
5 cups	uncooked rice
10 cups	chicken stock
2 pounds	mushrooms - large diced or quartered
2	large white or Spanish onions - diced
2	bunches Italian parsley - chopped
1 pound	butter
2 cups	pine nuts
salt and pepper to taste	

To make rice: Brown 2 sticks of butter, sauté rice until coated with butter, add chicken stock and bring to boil, turn heat off, cover rice and cook for 20 minutes. Cool.

Brown ground meat in 1/2 pound of butter, add onions and continue to brown. Add mushrooms and cook until mushrooms are soft. Add parsley and wine and simmer for 15 minutes. Let cool.

Mix rice and ground meat mixture thoroughly. Correct seasoning.

MOUSSAKA

3	large eggplants
	flour for frying eggplants
	oil for frying
2 pounds	ground (lean) goat meat
1/2	small can tomato paste
1/4 pound	butter
8 ounces	red wine
12 ounces	water
5	egg yolks

Frying Eggplants

1. Slice eggplants (approximately 1/4 inch thick).

2. Salt eggplant slices and set in a colander to drain out bitter liquid (approximately 1 hour).

3. Dust eggplant with flour.

4. Heat oil in frying pan to approximately 350 degrees.

5. Fry eggplants till golden brown on one side, then turn to brown on the other side.

6. Drain on paper towels: set aside.

Meat Sauce for Moussaka

1. Brown onions in 1 stick butter, add meat and brown.

2. Dilute tomato paste, salt and pepper in red wine and add to meat.

3. Add water and bring to a boil; lower heat and simmer for 1/2 hour - stirring occasionally.

4. Let meat mixture cool completely: beat egg yolks lightly and add to meat.

Assembling Moussaka

1. Grease large pan.

2. Layer bottom of pan with browned eggplant slices (overlapping slices).

3. Top with meat mixture.

4. Layer with remaining slices of eggplant, covering meat completely.

5. Pour cream sauce over Moussaka and bake at 350 degrees for approximately 1 hour or until top is golden brown.

<u>Cream Sauce</u> (Use for Moussaka and Pastichio)

6 1/2 cups	whole milk
6	eggs
1/4 pound	butter
1/4 cup	flour
2 tablespoons	grated Parmesan cheese

1. Using a large heavy pot, make a roux (by melting butter and adding flour and cooking till lightly browned).
2. Bring milk to a boil.
3. Ladle hot milk into roux slowly and whisk continuously so no lumps are formed.
4. Cook till slightly thickened (turn down heat).
5. Beat 5 eggs; add slowly to milk mixture and cook till thick.

PASTICHIO

2 boxes	ziti (boil *al dente* - until firm to the bite)
2 pounds	ground lean goat meat
4	onions (chopped)
1/2 small can	tomato paste
1 1/4 pounds	butter
8 ounces	red wine
12 ounces	water
5	eggs - separated
3 heaping tablespoons	grated Romano cheese

1. Brown onions in 1 stick butter; add meat and brown.
2. Dilute tomato paste, salt and pepper in red wine and add to meat.
3. Add water and bring to boil; lower heat and simmer for 1/2 hour - stirring occasionally.
4. Let meat mixture cool completely; beat egg yolks lightly and add to meat.
5. Drain ziti and rinse with cold water.
6. Melt 1 pound butter; add butter and cheese to ziti - mix well.
7. Beat egg whites till frothy and add to ziti.
8. Put 1/2 ziti in a lightly greased pan; add meat mixture; add remaining ziti.

9. Pour cream sauce into pan and sprinkle with cheese. Bake approximately 1 hour at 350 degrees.

SHISH KEBAB

3 pounds	cubed goat meat
6	onions - cubed - 1 inch square
6	peppers - cubed - 1 inch square

Marinade*

1 cup	white wine
1/2 cup	olive oil
4 cloves	garlic (crushed)
3 tablespoons each	fresh thyme and oregano
1/2 cup	lemon juice (fresh)
	salt and pepper to taste

Combine all ingredients and marinate overnight.
Skewer alternating meat and vegetables.
Barbecue or broil approximately 25-30 minutes, turning, and marinating, constantly.

* The same marinade and procedure can be used for chops.

KEFDETHES

	oil and flour for frying
2 pounds	ground goat meat
1 large	onion, chopped
1 bunch (1 1/2 cups)	fresh mint, chopped
1 bunch (1 1/2 cups)	fresh parsley, chopped
8 slices	white bread (crust removed, then soaked in water and excess water squeezed out)
1/2 cup	grated cheese
2	eggs
1 teaspoon	garlic
1 cup	red wine
1/2 tablespoon	baking powder

234

Combine the red wine and baking powder in a glass when adding to the meat mixture.

Combine all ingredients and mix well.

With a teaspoon, measure spoonfuls of meat mixture and place on flour. Roll into ball, dust flour and flatten meatballs slightly. Place in hot oil and fry until brown on both sides.

Notes: Chapter 19

1. From: "Use of Goat Meat as Therapeutic Aids in Cardiovascular Diseases," *Meat Goat Production and Marketing Handbook,* Clemson Extension, Rural Economic Development Center, Raleigh, North Carolina and Mid-Carolina Council of Governments, Fayetteville, North Carolina, 1996.

2. Fred Homeyer, "Crossing the Boer and Angora - the 'diamond' meat," *The Goat Farmer*, Volume 12, Issue 4.

APPENDIX I:
MEAT GOAT CALENDAR

*This calendar is geared towards confinement or semiconfinement-raised kids. It needs to be adjusted for kids born earlier than May and for grazing seasons starting before May 1. Portions of this may be disregarded or adjusted if goats are on pasture or range year round or if does are kidding every 8 months.

January
*Breed doe kids. (Doe kids can be bred later than adults. Kids must be at least 75% of their estimated mature weight.. If kids are bred in January, offset vaccination and management schedules accordingly.)

*Remove bucks after 2 heat cycles (42 days).

*Trim feet if necessary.

*Any processing of doe kids should be done before introduction of the buck(s).

February and March
*Adult does are put on maintenance ration - medium quality hay or pasture (if available) OR a mixture or hay and grain if grain prices are low. Don't forget to keep good quality sheep or goat mineral available at all times.

*Continue doe kids on top quality ration or pasture if they are being exposed to a buck. This ration should be continued through kidding and lactation so that the doe kid is not stunted.

late March and April
*Start improving quality and, if limit feeding, quantity, of ration so adult goats are well fed during the last 6 weeks of gestation. Rumensin/monensin can be added to the grain to help prevent Toxoplasma abortions.

*30 days before kidding give *Clostridium perfringens* type C and D and tetanus toxoid. (An 8-way clostridial vaccine can be given if necessary.)

*Deworm. a)Levamisole b)Benzimidazoles i.e. Fenbendazole (Panacur), Thiabendazole, Albendazole or c)Ivermectin. Use one anthelmintic until resistance is apparent based on fecal egg counts; then change to a product in a different family.

*Trim feet.

*Clean barn and make preparations for kidding.

May

*Kidding

-Heat lamps if necessary (A smoke detector in the barn is a good idea, especially if one is using a baby monitor to listen for newborn kids.)

-Dip navels with strong iodine.

-Make sure that all kids receive colostrum as soon as possible after birth and make sure that all kids are nursing. Give colostrum by stomach tube if necessary.

-Freeze excess colostrum in ice cube trays from heavy producers or from does that have lost kids. Once frozen, cubes can be tipped into freezer bags and thawed as needed.

-Put doe and her kid(s) in an individual kidding pen for 6 to 48 hours after kidding.

-Vitamin E and selenium injection at birth for the kids (if necessary).

-Ear tag kids and/or permanently identify kids (microchip, tattoo or notching)

-Keep barn sheet with kidding records - date of birth, birth type, dam and sire, birth weight or size, problems, good points, etc.

*Creep feed available for kids - add decoquinate.

*Separate does with twins and triplets and feed them better quality pasture/browse or hay and/or more grain - up to 2-2.5 pounds corn per head per day can be fed or free choice grain can be given. Make any ration changes gradually (over 10 days to 2 weeks). Nannies can be turned out onto pasture when available. If pasture is excellent, grain supplementation may be unnecessary.

June

*Fecal check for gastrointestinal parasite ova every 2 weeks for pastured goats (throughout grazing season depending on your climate and pasture). Deworm as necessary.

*Continue doe kids on excellent feed.

*Continue feeding older lactating nannies well.

*30 day old kids - *Clostridium perfringens* types C and D and tetanus toxoid.

July
*Fecal check for gastrointestinal parasite ova every 2 weeks for pastured goats.

*Continue doe kids on excellent feed.

*Continue feeding older lactating nannies well.

*60 day old kids - *Clostridium perfringens* types C and D and tetanus toxoid.

*Trim feet if necessary.

August
*Fecal checks for gastrointestinal parasite ova.

*Well grown kids may be weaned.

*Feed poorer quality hay or straw to does and delete grain from the ration for a week or so before weaning and for up to 2 weeks after. Pastured does may be moved to a poorer quality pasture.

*Deworm kids at weaning and move to clean good quality pasture. Continue creep feeding on pasture if kids were already on creep feed. If kids are to be moved from pasture to confinement and have been receiving no grain, introduce grain to their ration gradually.

September
*Fecal checks for gastrointestinal parasite ova.

*Mature does on maintenance ration or medium quality pasture.

*Wean kids born to doe kids.

*Continue good ration for yearling does once their milk supply has been dried up. Remember that these yearlings still have lots of growing to do and have just raised a kid.

*Restrict feed of buck kids by 40 - 60 pounds body weight if they are confined and receiving grain. They will do well on good quality hay or pasture, 1/2 pound corn per head per day and free choice good quality sheep or goat mineral. If bucks are to be fed large amounts of grain, add ammonium chloride to the ration.

*If doe kids are to be bred at 7-8 months of age, they should be on top quality feed.

October
*Trim feet if necessary.

*Deworm if necessary.

*_Chlamydia psittaci_ vaccine 30-50 days before breeding, booster 3 weeks later for young unvaccinated does, then give annually prebreeding.

*Vaccinate all goats with _Clostridium perfringens_ types C & D and tetanus toxoid.

November

*_Chlamydia_ vaccine if not given in October.

*Flush adult does so they are in good body condition - feed corn as needed up to 1.5 lb/head/day and good quality hay if in confinement. Otherwise rotate does to a good quality pasture. If goats are on a poorer quality pasture, protein should be added to the corn to give a 13-14% protein ration.

*Doe kids, particularly in a confinement setup, need to be in a separate group so they are not competing with the adult nannies. If they are to bred as doe kids they need to receive top quality feed.

*Free choice top quality sheep or goat mineral should be available at all times throughout the year.

*Feed bucks some grain also and good pasture or hay so that they are in top breeding condition by early December. Keep bucks on a separate farm if at all possible.

December

*Breed does. A marking harness can be used on the bucks. Change color of the marker every 21 days.

*Rotate bucks after 21 or so days.

*Cull late breeders.

*Use 1 buck for 25 to 50 nannies.

*Top quality registered bucks pay off even on commercial nannies.

*Continue good nutrition while breeding

APPENDIX II: NORMAL GOAT TEMPERATURE, PULSE AND RESPIRATORY RANGES AND GOAT AGING

Goat Normals

Rectal temperature = 38.6 to 40 C (101.5 to 104 F)
Heart rate = 70 to 135 beats per minute
Respiratory rate = 10 to 40 breaths per minute

Age (years) of eruption of permanent incisors

Central pair - 1
Middle pair - 1-2
Lateral pair - 2-3
Corner pair - 3-4

APPENDIX III:
MEDICATION ADMINISTRATION

Dosing

Although newborn kids can easily be treated with pills, it is quite difficult to give boluses (pills) to older goats, even with a balling gun. It is much easier to administer medication in a liquid form or by injection than to have a goat spit out a costly bolus (or parts of one) several minutes after treatment. Goats' molars are extremely sharp, even in young kids, so, if you do need to put your fingers in the mouth of a goat, be very careful not to get bitten or cut. Balling guns should be used with care - ramming the gun into the mouth or throat can damage delicate tissues.

Disposable syringes of varying sizes can be used for administering liquids orally. Do not let the goats chew on the syringe: their molars damage syringes as well as fingers! Automatic dosing guns attached to reservoir packs are useful for deworming large numbers of goats. Animals of similar weights should be processed together because automatic dosing guns deliver a preset dose based on an estimated weight. The head of a goat should be held in a level position for oral dosing.

When processing groups of goats, it is very useful to identify animals as they are vaccinated or wormed, or whatever, with a stripe of colored chalk on the nose or horn. This way if animals escape or a person runs out of vaccine, for example, one knows which animals have been processed. Paint sticks of various colors are available. If the fleece of a fiber goat is to be marked, some type of chalk that can be scoured from wool, mohair or cashmere should be used.

Large volumes of fluid can be administered by stomach tube. A foal-sized tube is useful for mature goats and a small rubber catheter for kids (see Chapter 11 on Kid Production which includes information on stomach tubing kids).

Injections

Because our goats are often processed in small pens or in a chute system, the neck is usually used for subcutaneous and intramuscular injections. Clostridial vaccines will often leave a lump at the vaccination site.

241

Tetracycline injections can be painful. One inch long 18 or 20 gauge needles and 3 or 10 ml syringes are used for most injections.

Antimicrobial and Antiinflammatory Dosages

Most drugs are *not* approved for use in goats. Thus, dosages are usually based on recommended dosages for sheep or even cattle as well as on personal experience. It is a good idea to check with one's veterinarian before administering an unfamiliar drug. As well, it is *very* important to contact your veterinarian about withdrawal times for any antibiotic or dewormer you administer. It takes time, often weeks, for antibiotics and other pharmaceutical products to be eliminated from the body. Since the main product produced by a meat goat is meat, you want to make sure that the chevon produced is as untainted as possible.

There definitely is a market for goat meat from organically raised animals. These goats are fed organically raised grains and hay and are not treated with any antibiotics and dewormers. There is a set of rules and regulations one needs to strictly adhere to when producing organically raised meat.

Drug dosages are generally given as mg per kg or mg per lb of body weight. A kg (kilogram) is equivalent to 2.2 lb. If, for example, one wants to treat a 45 kg (100 lb) goat with pneumonia with oxytetracycline and one decides to give the goat a dosage of 10 mg per kg (4.5 mg per lb) of body weight, then the goat will need to receive 450 mg (10 mg per kg X 45 kg body weight) of the antimicrobial. The label on the antimicrobial bottle will indicate how many mg are present on 1 ml (cc). If the oxytetracycline concentration is 200 mg per ml, then the goat will need to be given 2.25 ml of oxytetracycline.

ANTIMICROBIAL - SPECTRUM - ROUTE OF ADMINISTRATION - DOSAGE

Ampicillin - broad spectrum - subcutaneous injection or oral administration - 4 to 10 mg per kg (2 to 4.5 mg per lb) every 24 hours (subcutaneous); 4 to 10 mg per kg (2 to 4.5 mg per lb) every 12 or 24 hours (oral).

Benzathine Penicillin G (long acting penicillin) - Gram-positive organisms - subcutaneous injection - 10,000 to 20,000 IU (International Units) per kg (4,500 to 9,000 IU per lb) every 48 hours.

Erythromycin - Gram-positive organisms and Mycoplasma - subcutaneous injection - 4 to 8 mg per kg (2 to 4 mg per lb) every 12 to 24 hours.

Oxytetracycline - broad spectrum - subcutaneous injection - 5 to 10 mg per kg (2 to 4.5 mg per lb) every 24 hours; 20 mg per kg (9 mg per lb) every 48 to 72 hours (long acting form).

Procaine Penicillin G - Gram-positive organisms - subcutaneous injection - 10,000 to 20,000 IU per kg (4,500 to 9,000 IU per lb) every 12 or 24 hours.

ANTIINFLAMMATORY DRUGS

Aspirin - 100 mg per kg (45 mg per lb) orally every 12 hours.

Phenylbutazone - 4 mg per kg (2 mg per lb) orally every 24 hours.

APPENDIX V:
INDUCTION OF ABORTION OR PARTURITION IN THE DOE

Owners may wish to relieve a doe of the fetus(es) she is carrying for a variety of reasons including accidental mating, disease or injury. Hormonal induction of parturition is also very useful when the owner would like to predict or control the time of birthing. Careful use of hormones allows scheduling of births for daytime hours or weekends.

Prostaglandins

Prostaglandins, which lyse the corpus luteum, are currently the most commonly used hormones for ending pregnancy. In the goat, the placenta does not produce progesterone so the pregnancy is maintained by progesterone produced by corpora lutea. After day 5 of pregnancy, prostaglandins are effective. If a buck or bucks escape, 2.5 to 5 mg of prostaglandin F2-alpha (Lutalyse: Upjohn) can be administered to all does 7 to 10 days after accidental exposure to the buck(s).

If prostaglandins are to be used for parturition induction, the owner must know the exact breeding date. If the breeding date is unknown, real-time ultrasound can be used to determine the fetal age. Treatment with prostaglandin F2-alpha should not be until day 144 of pregnancy because earlier treatment may result in triplets and quads that are small and weak. The average gestation length is 150 days with a tendency for goats carrying triplets to kid a day earlier (149 days) and goats with singles to kid a day later (151 days). Prostaglandin F2-alpha given intramuscularly at 7.5 to 10 mg should result in parturition 29 to 36 hours later. The prostaglandin cloprostenol (Estrumate: Haver) at 62.5 to 150 ug is also effective.

Occasionally retained placentas and metritis (uterine infection) may occur but this is uncommon.

Corticosteroids

Corticosteroids increase placental estrogen synthesis and are not reliably effective in inducing parturition until about 141 days, at which time the fetus(es) should be old enough to survive. Younger fetuses may fail to respond to treatment with corticosteroids or parturition may be up to 6 days after treatment. Treatment with 20 to 25 mg of dexamethasone at or after day 141 of pregnancy will result in parturition in 44 to 48 hours.

APPENDIX VI:
EVALUATING THE GESTATIONAL AGE OF ABORTED GOAT FETUSES

Goat Fetal Length and Weight in Relation to Gestation Length

Days Gestation	Fetal Length (inches)	Fetal weight (lbs)
30	0.5	
60	4.5	0.2
90	8.0	1.0
120	12.0	3.5
150	16.0 - 17.0	6.5

*most fetal growth is from 90 to 150 days gestation.

*kids may weigh more than 5 to 7 pounds at birth, especially from large, well-fed nannies.

*kids weighing less than 5 pounds at birth often do not survive.

*the increase in fetal weight is geometric (like that of population growth, for example) in nature except in very late gestation where fetal growth begins to be limited by nutrition and/or uterine capacity.

*the increase in fetal length is linear.

APPENDIX VII:
TATTOING GOATS

If goats are to be permanently identified, tattooing, if performed correctly, is a good and inexpensive method. Other ways to permanently identify goats include notching the ears (Stephanie Mitcham, Allison Mitcham, Appendix 1, *The Angora Goat, its History Management and Diseases*, Second Edition, Crane Creek Publications, 1999, pg 197) or inserting a microchip under the skin (usually of an ear).

When tattooing a goat's ear, first the ear should be checked to make sure that it is clean. If the inner surface of the ear is dirty, it can be cleaned with cotton swabs dampened with rubbing alcohol.

The identification numbers and/or letters for the particular goat should be selected and inserted in the tattoo outfit. It is a good idea to try out the tattoo outfit on a piece of paper first. That way, if you have a number or letter upside down or backwards, you will be aware of the problem before it is permanently imprinted in the ear of a goat.

When the inner surface of the ear is clean and dry, tattoo ink or paste (black or green) should be rubbed inside the ear.. An old toothbrush is useful for rubbing on tattoo ink or paste. Then the tattoo outfit is clamped firmly on the ear over the inked region The tattoo outfit is then removed and the ink rubbed deeply into the ear. Again, a toothbrush is useful for this job. In several weeks, when the tattoo ink wears off the inner surface of the ear, the tattoo should be easy to see.

We use one tattoo outfit for the left ear (for our initials) and one for the right (for the goat numbers.) Then one simply needs to change the numbers for each new goat.

FECAL EXAMINATION FOR GASTROINTESTINAL PARASITES

Materials needed:
Fresh fecal material.

Fecal flotation solution (can be home made - see directions below - or purchased from your veterinarian).

Microscope - magnification of 80 - 100 low power and 344 - 430 high power are well suited to examination of fecals.

Microscope slides - standard 1 X 3 inch glass slides. These can be washed and reused.

Coverslips - 3/4 or 7/8 inch square glass or plastic coverglasses.

Forceps.

Strainer - small household tea strainer with a mesh of 12 per cm.

Test tubes - 4 inches long by 1/2 inch outside diameter with a 10 ml capacity.

Tongue depressors.

Wooden apparatus block - made by boring holes suitable for housing test tubes in a piece of wood 9 inches long, 3.5 inches wide and 1.75 inches high (these are approximate dimensions).

Paper cups (or plastic or glass cups that can be washed and reused).

To make a fecal flotation solution:
Place 355 ml (12 fl oz) of tap water in the top half of a double boiler. Add 454 gm (1 lb) sugar to the water and dissolve by stirring. The water in the bottom half of the double boiler should be close to boiling. The sugar should NOT be dissolved in the water by direct heat. Once the sugar solution is cooled to room temperature, 6 ml of 40% formaldehyde solution can be added to deter the growth of molds and yeasts in the sugar solution. The formaldehyde can be obtained from your veterinarian or possibly from your local hospital laboratory. The sugar solution can be stored in stoppered bottles and dispensed from a glass bottle or a plastic container such as an 8 oz catsup or mustard container.

You can make a much smaller batch than this, of course. If you make a very scaled down batch of this solution and use it over a short period of time, you do not need to add the formaldehyde preservative.

You may find it less hassle just to buy some commercial fecal flotation solution from your veterinarian.

Fecal examination:
If the fecal sample you have collected is not moist, add enough water to soften it. Using a tongue depressor, place 1 - 2 gm of feces in a paper cup. Add 15 ml of sugar solution and stir until the feces are suspended in the sugar solution. Pour the contents of the cup through the strainer into a second cup. Stir and gently press excess fluid from the debris remaining in the strainer. Discard the debris in the strainer and clean the strainer in hot running water. Agitate the fluid in the paper cup and immediately pour it into a test tube. (Parasite eggs may be left at the bottom of the cup if the sample is not agitated before being transferred to the test tube.) Place the test tube in the wooden apparatus block. Using forceps, gently place a glass or plastic coverslip over the top of the test tube. The fluid in the test tube MUST be touching the entire surface of the underside of the coverslip. If you do not have quite enough fluid in the test tube, a small amount of sugar solution can be added. Leave the coverslip-capped test tube undisturbed for several hours. The parasite eggs will float upward and adhere to the coverslip so it is imperative that the coverslip is handled gently. Pick up the coverslip with the forceps and lower an edge onto a glass slide. Gently lower the rest of the coverslip onto the glass slide. Air bubbles may be trapped under the coverslip if the coverslip is applied too rapidly. Do not put pressure on the coverslip because parasite eggs may be damaged.

The slide may now be placed on the microscope stage and examined for parasite eggs. Start the examination at low magnification and systematically scan the entire area that the coverslip covers. Anything resembling a parasite form may be centered and more closely examined under high power.

An excellent book that contains black and white photographs of parasite eggs of most species (including man) as they appear under the microscope is *Veterinary Clinical Parasitology* by Margaret W. Sloss, The Iowa State University Press, Ames. This book or something similar can be borrowed from your local library through the interlibrary loan program.

Fecal samples should be done before and 7-10 days after each deworming so you know whether the worm medication you used was effective or not.

APPENDIX IX:
MEAT GOAT NUTRITION AND RATION BALANCING

Dan Morrical, PhD, Sheep Extension Specialist, 337 Kildee Hall, Iowa State University, Ames, Iowa 50011-3150

In most meat goat operations, feed costs are by far and away the largest expense so it is worthwhile to examine and formulate rations carefully. A very useful book for obtaining information on goat nutrient requirements is *Nutrient Requirements of Goats: Angora, Dairy and Meat Goats in Temperate and Tropical Countries*, National Academy Press, 1981. However, it should be noted that these established nutrient requirements apply to ideal conditions. Management, diseases and environmental conditions can result in altered nutrient requirements. For a successful nutrition program in a meat goat operation - one which produces the greatest financial return - a complete and balanced management program of health, nutrition, genetics and reproduction must be developed.[1]

Specific nutrient requirements for various stages of production are listed in Tables 1 and 2. The appropriate level of feedstuffs in the daily rations of meat goats can be calculated depending on their stage of production and age. See Tables 3, 6 and 7. Extension livestock specialists or local feed resource consultants are often very helpful if one needs mathematical calculations double checked. Example rations are provided in Tables 4 and 5. These suggested portions are merely examples and not to be considered as the only or perfect goat rations.

Selenium is an extremely important micro mineral, necessary for high reproductive levels as well as kid survival. The current level of selenium in the base feedstuffs is greatly dependent upon the selenium level in the soil and producers should closely evaluate the need for additional selenium supplementation. Too much selenium can also be toxic, so it is important to calculate accurately and thoroughly mix the added selenium. The amount of selenium to add per ton of ration to increase the selenium level by 0.1 part per million (ppm) is 90 milligrams. Therefore, if the selenium premix contains 1 gram per pound, one needs to add 0.1 pound of selenium premix per ton of ration. Incorporating this minute amount of premix requires some premixing in 1 pound of feed, then mixing in 10 pounds of feed and adding it to the ton mix. The maximum allowable selenium additive, set by FDA, is 0.3 ppm.[1]

Vitamin E has a much safer threshold on toxic levels than selenium. Most complete feeds contain 15,000 international units (IU) of vitamin E. It is most difficult to improve vitamin E intake of nursing kids. Creep feed intake is minimal at very young ages and therefore the kids' vitamin E status relies solely on milk. One can drastically increase the level of vitamin E in the milk by increasing the level of this vitamin in the nannies' lactation ration. The primary source of vitamin E for the nanny is the forage or hay portion of the ration. Green pastures or browse are high in vitamin E. Hay which has been harvested in a timely manner with little rain damage and stored correctly should have adequate vitamin E. One must understand, however, that as the grain portion of the animal's ration increases, the availability of vitamin E is drastically reduced. Diets which have a high grain proportion should have additional vitamin E added. Fortunately vitamin E is a relatively inexpensive additive. Although the vitamin E levels required for high grain rations have not been studied, one can assume that the ration would be adequate with 150 IU of vitamin E intake per head per day. If nannies are receiving two pounds of grain per day, then adding 75 IU of vitamin E per pound to the grain mix would insure the 150 IU intake. This level equates to 150,000 IU per ton, and, with a 20,000 IU vitamin E premix would amount to 7.5 pounds of premix added to a ton of grain mix. Although many feed companies add both selenium and vitamin E to mineral or trace mineral sources, the levels may not be adequate for goats. An additional problem occurs with intake variation from day to day and between nannies. Therefore, to insure the most uniform intake of vitamin E and selenium, both may need to be incorporated into the grain mix.[1]

Feeding goats so that they are healthy and productive is not complicated nor is balancing rations if one takes a bit of time to understand how it is accomplished. The trick is to provide the appropriate level or density of nutrients while minimizing cost per day.

Table 1: Daily nutrient requirements for minimally active meat goat nannies (Adapted from *Nutrient Requirements of Goats: Angora, Dairy and Meat Goats in Temperate and Tropical Countries*, National Academy Press, 1981).[a]

	BW[b] lbs	DM[b] lbs	CP[b] lbs	TDN[b] lbs	Ca[b] grams	P[b] grams
Stage of Production						
Maintenance	85	1.8	0.14	0.99	2.0	1.4
and Early	110	2.1	0.17	1.17	3.0	2.1
Gestation	135	2.4	0.19	1.34	3.0	2.1
Late gestation	85	3.2	0.32	1.86	4.0	2.8
	110	3.5	0.35	2.04	5.0	3.5
	135	3.8	0.38	2.21	5.0	3.5
Lactation,	85	3.4	0.42	1.77	5.0	3.5
single	110	4.4	0.46	1.95	6.0	4.2
	135	5.4	0.50	2.12	6.0	4.2
Lactation,	85	3.8	0.53	2.26	6.8	4.8
twins	110	4.9	0.56	2.42	7.8	5.5
	135	6.0	0.59	2.58	7.8	5.5

[a] Requirements increase at least 25% for grazing goats.

[b] BW = Body weight, DM = Dry Matter, CP = Crude Protein, TDN = Total Digestible Nutrients, Ca = Calcium and P = Phosphorus

Table 2: Daily nutrient requirements for meat goat kids (Adapted from *Nutrient Requirements of Goats: Angora, Dairy and Meat Goats in Temperate and Tropical Countries*, National Academy Press, 1981).

Body Weight (lbs)	Gain[a] lbs	DM[a] lbs	CP[a] lbs	TDN[a] lbs	Ca[a] grams	P[a] grams
25	0.25	1.0	0.18	0.8	2.0	1.4
	0.35	1.2	0.22	1.0	2.5	1.8
	0.45	1.4	0.25	1.2	3.0	2.1
45	0.25	1.8	0.21	1.2	2.5	1.8
	0.35	2.0	0.26	1.5	3.0	2.1
	0.45	2.2	0.31	1.8	3.5	2.4
65	0.25	2.5	0.23	1.6	3.0	2.2
	0.35	2.7	0.28	1.9	3.5	2.5
	0.45	2.9	0.32	2.2	4.0	2.8
85	0.25	3.0	0.25	1.8	3.5	2.6
	0.35	3.2	0.30	2.2	4.0	2.9
	0.45	3.4	0.35	2.6	4.5	3.3

[a] Gain =Daily Gain, DM = Dry Matter, CP = Crude Protein, TDN = Total Digestible Nutrients, Ca = Calcium and P = Phosphorus

Table 3: Nutrient density of common feedstuffs on an as fed basis.

	DM	CP	TDN	Ca	P
Alfalfa hay	88	16.6	53.5	1.27	0.22
Brome hay*	88	14.0	52.0	0.35	0.30
Corn	88	9.30	77.0	0.02	0.31
Oats	88	11.7	67.8	0.07	0.33
Soybean Meal	88	43.9	77.4	0.26	0.61

*second cutting

Table 4. Example rations for nannies during various stages of production.

80 pound nannies

80 pound nannies	Maintenance and Early Gestation	Flushing	Late Gestation Single	Late Gestation Twin	Lactation Single	Lactation Twin
Alfalfa Hay, lbs	2.0	2.0	2.0	2.0	2.5	2.5
Brome Hay, lbs	2.2	2.2	2.2	2.2	2.5	2.5
Corn, lbs		.3	.5	1.0	.8	1.4
Oats, lbs		.4	.6	1.1	.8	1.7

110 pound nannies

Stage of Production

110 pound nannies	Maintenance and Early Gestation	Flushing	Late Gestation Single	Late Gestation Twin	Lactation Single	Lactation Twin
Alfalfa Hay, lbs	2.4	2.4	2.4	2.4	3.0	3.0
Brome Hay, lbs	2.8	2.8	2.8	2.8	3.0	3.0
Corn, lbs		.4	.7	1.2	.7	1.1
Oats, lbs		.5	.8	1.3	.9	1.5

135 pound nannies

Stage of Production

135 pound nannies	Maintenance and Early Gestation	Flushing	Late Gestation Single	Late Gestation Twin	Lactation Single	Lactation Twin
Alfalfa Hay, lbs	2.8	2.8	2.8	2.8	3.2	3.2
Brome Hay, lbs	3.4	3.2	3.2	3.2	3.2	3.2
Corn, lbs		.5	.8	1.1	.7	1.1
Oats, lbs		.6	.8	1.3	.9	1.6

*0.01 pounds of dicalcium phosphate should be added to the brome hay and oats rations for lactating nannies with twin kids.

**For nannies heavier than 135 pounds, increase requirements by 10% for every 25 pound increase in body weight.

***An 80 pound doe in early gestation can be fed 2 pounds of midbloom alfalfa hay OR 2 pounds of second cut brome hay. A lactating 80 pound doe with a single kid can be fed 2.5 pounds of midbloom alfalfa hay and 0.8 pounds of corn OR 2.5 pounds of second cut brome hay and 0.8 pounds of oats.

Table 5: Example rations for kid goats.

Goat weight (lbs)

Feed (lbs)	25-45	25-45	45-65	45-65	65+	65+
Alfalfa hay	500	500	500	500	400	100
Corn	1050	1075	1250	1300	1465	1290
Corn Cobs						300
Soybean Meal	320	125	120			
Lamb Protein Pellets		300		200		200
Molasses	100		100		100	100
Limestone	10		10		15	10
Trace Mineral Salt[a]	10		10		10	
Ammonium Sulfate	10		10		10	
% CP	18	18	14	14	11[b]	11[b]

[a]Trace Mineral salt should provide 0.3 ppm selenium to the diet.

[b]Kids born to large framed does with high mature weights have higher protein requirements.

***Rations should be fortified with 1,000,000 IU of Vitamin A, 100,000 IU of Vitamin D and from 20,000 to 30,000 IU of Vitamin E.

Figure 6: Calculating the amount to feed.

Step 1. Look up the requirements for 85 pound nannies in early gestation from the nutrient requirement table.
Requirements are DM 1.8 pounds, CP 0.14 pounds and TDN of 0.99 pounds.

Step 2. Look up the nutrient density of the hay being fed in Table 3. Alfalfa hay is 16.6 % CP and 53.5 TDN.

Step 3. Determine how much hay to feed to meet the goat's energy requirements.
1.8 pounds TDN required / 0.535 pounds TDN per pound of hay.
1.8/0.535 = 3.36 pounds of hay needed to meet requirements.

Step 4. Determine if the protein requirement is met with 3.36 pounds of alfalfa.
3.36 pounds of hay X 0.165 pounds CP per pound of alfalfa fed.
3.36 X 0.165 = 0.55 pounds of crude protein fed versus 0.14 required.

Step 5. Determine if the calcium requirement is met with 3.36 pounds of alfalfa.
3.36 pounds of alfalfa hay X 0.0127 pounds Ca per pound of alfalfa fed
3.36 X 0.0127 = 0.04 pounds of Ca provided by the hay.
0.04 X 454 grams/pound = 18.2 grams Ca versus 2 grams required.

Step 6. Determine if the phosphorus requirement is met with 3.36 pounds of alfalfa.
3.36 pounds of hay X 0.0022 pounds P per pound of alfalfa fed.
3.36 X 0.0022 = 0.0074 pounds P provided by the alfalfa hay.
0.0074 X 454 grams/pound = 3.36 grams P versus 1.4 grams required.

So, one can see that the major nutrients are met by feeding 2.25 pounds of alfalfa hay of early bloom maturity. In actuality, one is overfeeding both protein and calcium in this example.

Figure 7: Calculating the nutrients provided by a ration.

Ration fed to 110 pound goats (carrying twins) in late gestation is 2.4 pounds of alfalfa and 1.0 pound of shelled corn.

	Hay	Corn	Nutrients Provided	Nutrients Required
DM	2.4 X 0.88=2.11	1.0 X 0.88=0.88	3.0 lb[a]	3.5 lb
TDN	2.4 X 0.535=1.28	1.0 X 0.77=0.77	2.05 lb	2.04 lb
CP	2.4 X 0.165=0.40	1.0 X 0.093=0.093	0.49 lb	0.35 lb
Ca	2.4 X 0.0127=0.0305 .0305 X 454=13.8g	1.0 X 0.0002=0.0002 .0002 X 454=0.09g	13.9 g	5.0 g
P	2.4 X .0022=0.0053 .0053 X 454=2.4 g	1.0 X 0.0031=0.0031 .0031 X 454=1.4 g	3.8 g	3.5 g

[a]By comparing the nutrients provided to the nutrients required, the example ration meets all nutrient requirements with the exception of DM. However, if animals are eating at least 50% of their dry matter requirements, there is no need for concern.

As mentioned in the text, one can follow requirements exactly and still not have goats fed properly. The trained eye of the stockman is essential to determine if the goats are in the correct condition and gaining appropriately for their stage of production.

Notes: Appendix IX

1. Dan Morrical, Appendix X, Angora Goat Nutrition, *The Angora Goat, its History, Management and Diseases*, Second Edition, Crane Creek Publications, 1999.

REFERENCES

Addrizzo, John R. (MD). "Use of Goat Milk and Goat Meat as Therapeutic Aids in Cardiovascular Diseases," adapted from "Composition of Foods; Dairy and Egg Products," *Agricultural Handbook No. 8-1,* Agricultural Research Service, Washington, D.C.; USDA, 1996.

Akhtar, Abdus Salam. "Keynote address," *Goat meat production in Asia: proceedings of a workshop held in Tando Jam, Pakistan, 13-18 March 1988* (Ottawa: International Development Research Centre, 1988).

Austin, Maureen. "A Formula for Success with Livestock Guarding Dogs," *Ranch magazine,* Volume 70, Number 7, 1989.

Bhatlacharyya, N.K. and B.V. Khan. "Goat meat production in India," *Goat meat production in Asia: proceedings of a workshop held in Tando Jam, Pakistan, 13-18 March 1988,* Ottawa: International Development Research Centre, 1988.

Calhoun, Millard. "Deccox: A New Coccidiostat for Goats," *Ranch magazine,* Volume 69, Number 1, March 1987.

"Monensin Approved as Coccidiostat for Goats," *Ranch magazine,* Volume 68, Number 6, March 1987.

Campbell, Q.P. "The Boer Goat After Forty Years," Mutton Sheep and Goats Performance Testing Scheme, Bloemfontein, *Boer Goat News,* 9:42-43, 1990.

Casey, N.H. and W.A. Van Niekerk. "The Boer Goat I.: Origin, Adapability, Performance Testing, Reproduction and Milk Production," and "The Boer Goat II.: Growth, Nutrient Requirements, Carcass and Meat Quality," Department of Livestock Science, Faculty of Agriculture, University of Pretoria, Pretoria, South Africa, *Small Ruminant Research,* 1:291-302 and 355-368, respectively, 21 May 1988, http://www. boergoats.com/niekerk2.html (website).

Collier's Encyclopedia, Volume 11. New York, Toronto, Sydney: 1995.

Corbett, Jim. *Goatwalking*, New York: Viking Penguin, 1991.

Culliford, Graham. "The Genemaster Story," *AKGA Update* (Official Publication of the American Kiko Goat Association), July 1998, p. 4.

Devendra, C. "The nutritional value of goat meat," *Goat meat production in Asia, proceedings of a workshop held in Tando Jam, Pakistan, 13-18 March 1988*, Ottawa: International Development Research Centre, 1988.

Drinkwater, William, Frank Pinkerton and Terry Gipson. "Development of Grade Standards for Slaughtered Kids, Yearlings and Adult Goats," *Meat Goat Production and Marketing Handbook*, Rural Economic Development Center, Raleigh, N.C. and Mid-Carolina Council of Governments, Fayetteville, NC, 1996.

Dunbar, R. "Scapegoat for a thousand deserts," *New Scientist*, 104, 1984, 30-33.

Ellis, Merle. "Demand for Goat Meat Grows," www.boergoats.com/library/Butcher.html (website), P.O. Box 907, Tiburon, California 94920.

Gall, C. (editor). *Goat Production*, London, New York, Toronto, San Francisco, Sydney: Academic Press, 1981.

Gipson, Terry A. "Genetic Resources for Meat Goat Production," *Proceedings Southeast Regional Meat Production Symposium,* Feb. 24, 1996, Tallahassee, FL.

Gipson, Terry A. "Marketing Kids," *Proceedings of the Virginia State Dairy Goat Association,* April 1, 1995, Blacksbury, VA, pp. 13-15.

Gipson, Terry A. "Breed Capabilities and Selection for Meat Production," *Proceeding of the Meat Goat Symposium*, Dec. 7, 1996, Upper Marlboro, MD.

Goat meat production in Asia: proceedings of a workshop held in

Tando Jam, Pakistan, 13-18 March 1988, (Ottawa: International Development Research Centre, 1988).

Goatex Genetics LLC (Breeders and Developers of Genemaster Goats), "Maximizing Production by Harnessing Hybrid Vigor: Alternative Breeding Strategies for Boer and Kiko Goats," P.O. Box 34-021, Fendalton, Christchurch, New Zealand 8030, Telephone/Facsimile 64 3 3296 255, e-mail tasman@xtrta.co.nz, promotional literature.

Goatex Group LLC (Breeders and Developers of Kiko Goats), "History, Development and Characteristics of Kiko Goats - An Overview," P.O. Box 34-021, Fendalton, Christchurch, New Zealand 8030, Telephone/Facsimile 64 3 3296 255, e-mail tasman@xtra.co.nz, promotional literature.

Goats, Publication 1704, (N. A.), Information Services, Agriculture Canada, Ottawa, 1981.

Goonewardene, L.A., P.A. Day, N. Patrick and D. Patrick. "Cross Breeding with Alpine and Boer Goats - Growth and Carcass Traits," Government of Alberta (Sheep & Goats - Research Update 1996/97) , www.agric.gov.ab.ca/researchupdate/97sheep11.html (website)

Green, James T. Jr. "Potential for Producing Meat Goats in North Carolina," *Meat Goat Production and Marketing Handbook*, Rural Economic Development Center, Raleigh, N.C. and Mid-Carolina Council of Governments, Fayetteville, NC, 1996.

Harwell, Lynn. "Enterprise Analysis," *Meat Goat Production and Marketing Handbook*, Rural Economic Development Center, Raleigh, N.C. and Mid-Carolina Council of Governments, Fayetteville, NC, 1996.

Hetherington, Lois. *All About Goats*, Ipswich: Farming Books, 1988.

Homeyer, F., "Crossing the boer and angora - the 'diamond' meat," *The Goat Farmer*, Whangarei, New Zealand, www.caprine.co.nz (website).

Jaudas, Ulrich, *The New Goat Handbook*, New York, Lonon, Toronto, Sydney: Barron's, 1987.

Jones, H. Glyn and Barbara C. Collins. *A Way of Life: Sheepdog Training, Handling and Trialling,* Ipswich, United Kingdom: Farming Press Books, 1987.

Kilgour, R. and Ross D.J. "Feral goat behavior - a management guide," *New Zealand Journal of Agriculture,* 141, 1980, 15-20.

Kimberling, Cleon. *Jensen and Swift's Diseases of Sheep,* Philadelphia, Lea and Febiger, 1988.

Luginbuhl, J.-M. and M.H. Poore. "Nutrition of Meat Goats", *NCSU,* Department of Animal Science, 1998.

Meat Goat News: News Magazine of the U.S. Meat Goat Trade and Official News from the American Meat Goat Association, San Angelo: Texas 1994-1999.

Meat Goat Production and Marketing Handbook, Rural Economic Development Center, Raleigh, N.C. and Mid-Carolina Council of Governments, Fayetteville, NC, 1996

Machen, Richard V. "Great Potential in a New Industry," Texas A&M Research & Extension Center.

Mackenzie, David. *Goat Husbandry,* 4th ed., London: Faber & Faber, 1980.

Mitcham, Stephanie and Allison. *The Angora Goat: Its History, Management and Diseases,* Second Edition, Sumner, Iowa: Crane Creek Publishing, 1999.

Mowlen, Alan. *Goat Farming,* Ipswich: Farming Press, 1988.

Peischel, An. "Kiko, A New Meat Goat Breed," P.O. Box 29, Rackerby, CA 95972, Telephone 530-679-1420, Facsimile 530-679-1430, e-mail kiko@inreach.com

Pinkerton, Frank. "Recommendations for Goat Industry Development," *Meat Goat Production and Marketing Handbook,* Rural Economic

Development Center, Raleigh, N.C. and Mid-Carolina Council of Governments, Fayetteville, NC,1996.

Pinkerton, Frank. "Meat Goat Marketing in Greater New York City," A Project Report on Behalf of the Center for Agricultural Development and Entrepreneurship, State University of New York, Onconta, May 1995.

Pinkerton, Bruce and Frank Pinkerton. "Managing Forages for Meat Goats," *Meat Goat Production and Marketing Handbook,* Rural Economic Development Center, Raleigh, North Carolina and Mid-Carolina Council of Governments, Fayetteville, North Carolina, 1996.

Pinkerton, Frank. "Procurement of Foundation Stock," *Meat Goat Production and Marketing Handbook*, Rural Economic Development Center, Raleigh, North Carolina and Mid-Carolina Council of Governments, Fayetteville, North Carolina, 1996.

Pinkerton, Frank and Lynn Harwell. "Marketing Channels for Meat Goats," *Meat Goat Production and Marketing Handbook*, Rural Economic Development Center, Raleigh, NC and Mid-Carolina Council of Governments, Fayetteville, NC, 1996.

Pinkerton, Frank, Lynn Harwell, William Drinkwater, Nelson Escobar. "Consumer Demand for Goat Meat," No.M-04, April 1994, www.luresext.edu/mo4.html OR goat.clemson.edu/NC%20Handbook/demand.htm

Pirani, Dawn. "Meat: The mystery of the disappearing yields," *The Goat Farmer*, May, 1999.

Porter, Valerie. *Goats of the World*, Ipswich: Farming Press, 1996.

Shelton, Maurice. "Goat Production," *Encyclopedia of Agricultural Science, Volume 2*, San Diego, New York, Boston, London, Sydney, Tokyo, Toronto: Academic Press, 1994.

Shurley, Marvin. "Genetics: Focusing on one trait can be the fastest route to improvement," *American Meat Goat, Meat Goat News*, March 1999.

Smith, Burt. *Moving 'Em - A Guide to Low Stress Animal Handling*, The Graziers Hui, Kamuela, Hawaii, 1998.

Smith, Mary. "Symposium on Sheep and Goat Medicine," *The Veterinary Clinics of North America*, Volume 5, Number 3, W.B. Saunders Company, November 1983.

"Advances in Sheep and Goat Medicine," *The Veterinary Clinics of North America*, Volume 6, Number 3, W.B. Saunders Company, November 1990.

and David M. Sherman. *Goat Medicine*, Philadelphia, Baltimore, Hong Kong, London, Munich, Sydney, Tokyo: Lea & Febiger, 1994.

Sponenberg, D.P. "The Tennessee Goat - a forgotten resource," *The Goat Farmer*, Whangarei, New Zealand, April/May, 1998.

Sponenberg, D.P. "Meat breed must suit environment," *The Goat Farmer*, Whangarei, New Zealand, www.caprine.co.nz (website).

Sponenberg, D.P. "How to pick a strategy that works for you," [meat goats - breeding], *The Goat Farmer*, Whangarei, New Zealand, www.caprine.co.nz (website).

Sponenberg, D.P. "Healthy Goats are Happy Goats," *The Goat Farmer*, Whangarei, New Zealand, July/August, 1999.

Symposium on Health and Disease of Small Ruminants, Kerrville, Texas, June 13-15, 1991.

The, Thian Hor and Terry Gipson. "Establishing a Chevon Industry: The Boer Goat (Part 1 and Part II)," E (Kika) de la Garza Institute for Goat Research, Langston, Oklahoma.

The Goat Farmer. Whangarei, New Zealand, www.caprine.co.nz (website).

Terrill, Clair E. "Goat Meat in Our Future? The Status of Meat Goats in the United States," *Live Animal Trade & Transport Magazine*, December 1993, Volume V, No. 4, pp. 36-39

Tomlinson, Sylvia, *The Meat Goats of Caston Creek*, Edmond, OK, Redbud Publishing Co., 1999.

Tomlinson, Sylvia, "Oats and Fetlocks," *Meat Goat News*, March 1999.

Tremblay RM, Butler DG, Allen JW, Hoffman AM. Metabolic acidosis without dehydration in seven goat kids. Can Vet J 1991; 32:308-310.

Wenxiu, Huang, "Goat meat production in China," *Goat meat production in Asia: proceedings of a workshop held in Tando Jam, Pakistan, 13-18 March 1988* (Ottawa: International Development Research Centre, 1988).